D1168414

Sing
Your Heart Out,
Country Boy

Sing Your Heart Out, Country Boy

Dorothy Horstman

Sing your heart out, country boy
Sing your heart out, play your guitar
Tell about laughin', drinkin', and cryin'
Lovin' and losin', livin' and dyin'
Sing your heart out, country boy.
—James Cannon

E. P. Dutton & Co., Inc. | New York | 1975

First Edition
10 9 8 7 6 5 4 3 2 1

Published simultaneously in Canada by Clarke, Irwin & Company
Limited, Toronto and Vancouver
ISBN: 0-525-20465-2

Library of Congress Cataloging in Publication Data
Main entry under title:

Sing your heart, country boy.

Bibliography: p.
Discography: p.
1. Country music—United States—Texts.
2. Songs, American—Texts. I. Horstman, Dorothy A.
ML54.6.S56 784 75-12889

To Fred Rose, who knew

Contents

Foreword

A song is an expression of one's inner self, sometimes autobiographical, sometimes biographical, and occasionally just a flight of imagination. This basic form of communication, which transcends all generation gaps, is the common denominator among cultural, political, or geographic groups and among societies.

The question has been asked repeatedly (and seldom answered satisfactorily): why did so-and-so write such-and-such a song? Dorothy Horstman, in a labor of love and a labor of devotion to fact and detail, has provided us with the answers. But this is far more than an anthology of fact, a collection of truisms. This is the heart and soul of the product, the song itself, the single most important facet of the music business.

Dorothy, who was transplanted from Louisiana to New York some years ago, had enough of the country in herself so that the big city could never shake it loose. It was, and remains, a love of country music which led her to this needed volume and, despite some discouragements along the way, kept her pounding away until she got what she was looking for, and consequently what all of us have been looking for.

Having been blessed to read the results of her progress as it developed, I am convinced this is an exceedingly important book; not only for scholars, but for those of us just hung up on this genuine kind of music.

And it's particularly pleasurable to see one's close friend accomplish what she set out to do, against the many odds at times, and finally finish the fruits of her creativity.

Bless her heart! She has made a real contribution.

Bill Williams

Southern Editor
Billboard magazine

Author's Preface

Country music is unique. Like jazz, it is an important American art form. Unlike jazz, it has seldom been taken seriously or studied or even anthologized except in pulp magazines which have been read and reread and memorized by the people who love country music and live by it because it is their music.

We have let politics and emotions and big-city ways clutter our perceptions and obscure our opinions of a native music rich with insight not only into the lives of a certain class of rural Protestant white southern Americans, but into the lives of all of us. As Americans, we are what we have become in the last half-century, and for many of us—perhaps in some sense most of us—this music is a record of those years.

Sadder still, by ignoring or denigrating country music, by using the word "hillbilly" with a sneer instead of a smile, we have unwittingly robbed ourselves of some of the saddest, the happiest, the most touching moments in our country's literature—and we've missed out on a good time.

This book is a beginning—an attempt to disarm the cynic, to win over the uninterested, to enthrall the devotee. Perhaps it will even instill a little much-deserved pride in those who have helped to create country music and to convey its poignant messages to so many millions.

This is in no sense a scholarly book, though I have tried to adhere to scholarly principles of research. It is not a definitive collection or a sampling of the "best" or the most popular. It is a selection of what I think are some of the finest lyrics (since country music is a lyric music) and best-loved songs written over the past fifty years, plus some a good deal older than that. It is the result of several years' work spent reviewing the original lyrics of literally thousands of songs and interviewing hundreds of songwriters, artists, publishers, producers, and scholars.

It still is, at best, a compromise.

Selecting a few hundred representative and important songs from a vast and steadily growing body of literature came down in the end to a matter of personal judgment, with the advice and counsel of many others.

The annotations, which in many ways have emerged as the most important and revealing aspect of the book, came about quite by accident. They grew out of my own fascination with the creative process of songwriting and the opportunity of interviewing a number of writers for radio shows broadcast over WNYC-FM in New York City. In a sense, the annotations comprise an oral history—not only of the origin of and inspiration for these songs, but also of the emergence of this music and of the southern rural experience since the twenties. They were obtained in personal interviews or by telephone or personal correspondence. In all cases the language is that of the sources, edited only for length or clarity.

Once assembled, the material virtually organized itself into fifteen song categories which speak volumes about the "country," about the hillbilly, and about his music. From simple, unsophisticated songs of home to pointed and sometimes acid social comments, the songs tell their own story of changing attitudes and increasing urbanization—poignantly, tersely, and within the disciplines of the 78- or 45-rpm record.

Throughout the process of assembling and annotating this book, I have enjoyed the assistance, sympathy, and total cooperation of ASCAP, BMI, SESAC, The Country Music Association, The John Edwards Memorial Foundation, and the entire industry. At the risk of inadvertently missing someone who has made a major contribution, I would like to thank those who made this book possible: In addition to the songwriters and their publishers, relatives and friends who made their songs and stories available, my deepest gratitude is to Paul Ackerman, Terry Allen, Lloyd Anderson, Lee Arnold, Dick Baxter, John Benson, Jr., George Biggar, Johnny Bond, Joe Dan Boyd, June Braswell, Scoopie Bruce, Albert Brumley, Pat Bunch, Norman Cohen, Brad Cooper, Don Davis, Gertrude Dye, Jim Evans, Archie Green, Ken Griffis, Wanda Helms, Roy Horton, Bill Ivey, Bob Jennings, Paul Kapp, Elsie Kershaw, Don Jones, Arnold Joseph, John Lair, Hal Linden, Guy Logsden, Frank Mare, Dean May, Eddie Miller, Inez Morgan, William Morris, Cecil Null, Jim Oneal, Earl Owens, Wade Pepper, Don Pierce, Bob Pinson, Rick Powell, Wesley Rose, Sylvia Rosenberg, Russ Sanjec, Joyce Schwartz, Clarence Sellman, Hazel Smith, Slim Sterling, Roy Maxwell Stone, Charles Townsend, Ernest Tubb, Charlotte Tucker, Nancy Valentino, Gerald Vaughn, Gary Walker, Kent Westbury, John White, Bill Williams, Lawton Williams, Scott Wiseman, and Dave Wylie.

And special thanks to Bill C. Malone, whose additions, suggestions, and close reading of the text were invaluable; he is, indeed, a good ole country boy.

Dorothy Ann Horstman

New York City
June 3, 1974

Introduction

Country music is as American as mom's apple pie. Even those who never *listen* to it subscribe—or at least pay lip service—to its values: God, country, home, mother, good and evil, right and wrong.

Like America, it is eclectic—a musical melting pot of songs, styles, and musical elements gleaned from jazz, folk music, gospel, popular music, swing, blues, rock. And it has emerged as something distinct, something greater than the sum of these influences.

It is American, too, in its implicit celebration of capitalistic values: it is a commercial music. Its songs are properties, valuable commodities that have proven themselves worth writing, worth writing well, worth fighting for, and sometimes worth stealing.

Country music is fiercely democratic. It admits no aristocracy, permits no dynasties. Like its fans, most of its major stars have had humble beginnings. Every record and album made is subject to its own "referendum," with thousands upon thousands deciding on its popularity and longevity with dollar "votes."

As an important American phenomenon, it deserves to be understood and taken seriously by all Americans. Unfortunately, country music has suffered from its humble beginnings away from the centers of power and influence, and from its sometimes embarrassing adherence to simple virtues which many today find naive.

Until recently, when a handful of courageous scholars risked their considerable reputations on a serious study of this art form, the term "hillbilly" has invariably been used with disparagement. Unlike other popular forms (folk, jazz, rock), its songs have seldom been anthologized or given other than pulp magazine criticism. Only in the forties did magazines as divergent as *Billboard* and the *Journal of American Folklore* grudgingly acknowledge its existence after decades of neglect. Despite the fact that Vernon Dalhart's 1924 recording of "The Prisoner's Song" backed by "Wreck Of The Old 97" was the best-selling pre-electric recording of the Victor Company, that Jimmie Rodgers sold more than 20 million records during his brief career, and that country records released before World War II numbered conservatively fifty thousand individual songs, the phenomenon was largely ignored.

Contrast this with the treatment received by the southern black and the jazz and blues that he produced! From the days of the abolitionists until very recently, the Negro has been an object of interest, sympathy, and compassionate "study." Jazz has been documented, collected, and imitated since its beginnings in ragtime during the last century. It is often called the only "true" American art form.

Yet the opposite has been true of country music, despite its parallel and frequently overlapping development. One suspects that factors other than the quality of the musical form may help explain the silence that has greeted hillbilly music. Southern society itself has contributed to this process. Traditionally dominated by "better music" people, especially in ecclesiastical circles, it has ignored this rich native lore in favor of northeastern and European fashions.

Today things are slowly changing. The extraordinary ability of country music to make money has accelerated the pace of "gee whiz" articles in the popular press, which date back at least to 1908, when *The Nation* documented the enormous sales of Moody-Sankey songbooks. Musicians who traditionally have polarized in coastal cities suddenly have discovered the expert and highly commercial "Nashville sound." Furthermore, the bankruptcy of pop and rock music has driven public taste back toward the center and toward traditional American values, a position firmly in the control of country music.

It is precisely that characteristic—the innate conservatism of country music, its penchant for what once were "American" values—that has made it one of the lively arts for the past half-century and promises that it will be around in one form or another for many years to come. Actually, it always has been a "national" music, despite its origins in the white, rural South. It was northern cash and northern recording companies, reeling from the effects of the new "toy," radio, that woke up to its commercial potential in the early twenties. Dalhart, Rodgers, and others had a truly national appeal, and when in the early forties a ban on ASCAP recordings and a musicians strike in turn set back popular music, many country songs "crossed over" to the pop charts. World War II introduced many a Yankee to the country guitar, and about the same time, Bill Monroe successfully modernized "old timey" music and dubbed it bluegrass, a form that closed the college gap and made fans out of hundreds of thousands who would shiver if they thought they were listening to "country-western." Then there was the folk revival of the late fifties that brought such country regulars as Flatt and Scruggs and the Carter Family to center stage; and the same movement gave birth to a rash of newly made story songs, such as Jimmie Driftwood's "Battle of New Orleans" and Marty Robbins's "El Paso," which sold well in both pop and country markets.

Only recently has country music produced its first true superstars, and Johnny Cash, Marty Robbins, and Roy Clark have become household names all over the country. With rock sentiment split between a glittery extreme on one hand and nostalgia for the fifties on the other, with radio all but dominated by thirteen-year-old tastes, and with imitation soul the dominant pop sound even for white musicians, the sensible center was left vacant—but not for long. Country music, with conservative values and understandable lyrics, began emerging as the new American popular music.

All the more reason, then, that we should become aware of the best before we hear the worst! This book is an attempt to contribute to that awareness and understanding. It takes country music seriously and uses the term "hillbilly" as a descriptive adjective, not a term of derision. Its focus is the song lyric and the songwriter, for reasons that will become abundantly clear. Among its selections are many of the best in a large body of literature that spans more than fifty years, and some of the best American songs ever written.

What, then, is country music?

Before we attempt a working definition, it would be useful to consider some of the elements that have contributed to it in the century or more of its development. In the early twenties, a number of events occurred which were to elevate poor man's music, hillbilly music, to a new plateau of commercial potential. In 1922, station WSB in Atlanta began broadcasting with a modest five hundred watts and presented a sampling of local traditional talent including a "mountain" quartet; a group of sacred heart singers; Rev. Andrew Jenkins, a gospel singer and composer, and Fiddlin' John Carson—all of whom were "country." In 1923, OKeh Records' Ralph Peer journeyed to Atlanta quite independently of this event to record local performers at the request of a local retailer, and again Fiddlin' John was on the roster. Peer became convinced he had opened a new market when Carson's unnumbered, limited edition disc was reordered. The next year, Dalhart provided the first country million seller, confirming Peer's conviction. By 1925 the word "hillbilly" had been applied to the music, and a new commercial form was established, but as a regional, not local, music.

This was by no means the beginning of the commercialization of country music, however. Vaudeville, minstrel shows, medicine wagons, tent shows, local dances, and the sale of song lyrics provided some income to country musicians, though it was often meager or part-time. But the prospect of making a record (often at only twenty-five dollars a side) was an exciting one, one that held some promise of wider exposure and even some regularity of income.

As a result, musicians, both folk and professional, rushed to answer audition calls throughout the South, and many traveled north to recording centers in big cities. The songs they brought with them were a melange of folk, popular, and gospel, many of which they had learned in childhood and which they themselves had performed in other, more or less professional capacities. Some were traditional ballads; others the gospel songs written during the great evangelistic crusades of the late nineteenth and early twentieth centuries; and still others the professional products of Tin Pan Alley. Successful recordings were quickly "covered"—rerecorded—by other artists and sometimes by the same artist under different names. Inevitably, however, they began to run out of traditional material, and, as the insatiable appetites of radio and phonograph audiences began to exhaust the supply, new impetus was given to the commercial craft of songwriting. A majority of the songs in this book are a result of that creative process, which began in earnest during the early twenties and which dominates the industry to this day.

The songs in this book are not folksongs. Some of the selections, of course, qualify as folksongs by any current definition; others have distinct folk roots. But one of the overriding characteristics of a country song (and one that will serve in part as its definition) is its deliberate and often financially motivated creation. Frequently, throughout the book, the reason given for writing a particular song is the need for new material for a continuing radio show, to fill out a recording session, or to satisfy the demands of recording executives. Most of the songs in this book are (or once were) *property*—not of the "folk," but of individuals who either created them from scratch or modified traditional material enough so that it bears a unique personal stamp, and in many cases has thus been saved from extinction. Virtually all of the songs in this book bear a valid copyright. Some, in fact, had to be eliminated because cloudy or conflicting claims make their ownership a question of litigation and therefore outside the province of this book. The attitudes expressed in the following pages by the songwriters themselves show that, inspired or not, these songs are treated as valuable assets; they have been sold, bartered, willed to relatives and friends—even given away as one of the most precious gifts of all. I have made no conscious attempt to avoid folk-derived material, but most of it falls outside the province of this book, and most folk music (like jazz) has been documented elsewhere.

Popular music, too, has received more than its share of attention, and for the most part the songs that follow are not "popular" songs. Once again, the dividing line is far from distinct; the interaction between pop and hillbilly, as between city and country, has been constant and mutually beneficial for at least the last hundred years. Perhaps the most significant difference is that voiced by countless country performers—that country music "tells it like it is." And vague as this phrase is, it provides some useful information. Country music, assured of a large and steady audience, has not found it necessary to appeal to the lowest common denominator for wide acceptance, as popular music has, diluting its material accordingly. Country music is a more direct and personal expression of the current, the everyday, and the mundane. In the words of Loretta Lynn, it "doesn't beat around the bush." Since its audience has been fairly homogeneous, there has been general agreement as to the value structure on which hillbilly songs, until quite recently, have been based. The articulation of these values directly and simply, with few high-level abstractions, is prized as "sincerity" both in the song and in the singer, and is one of the hallmarks of commercial country success. This explains in part why popular songs of the nineteenth century, long forgotten in the cities, are cherished as "standards" in the hillbilly market today.

This reverence for tradition and Old Testament virtues explains in part the flourishing parallel field of gospel music. Although this work contains a chapter on gospel songs, and the fundamental philosophy underlying almost every song in the book is a Protestant religious one, this is not a book of religious songs. So strong were religious convictions in the rural South during the development of country music, however, and so much was religion a part of everyday life, that a "message" is clear in many of the most secular selections.

Country music, then, is a commercial music borrowing on folk, popular, and religious sources, but which is different from all of these. It is simple and direct, its lyrics easily remembered and its melodies easily sung and played. It seldom deals with abstractions, and it reflects the religious and moral values of its audience. Generally its authors are known, and its songs carry valid copyrights and are considered valuable properties.

It is a lyric music, and most of its songs tell or imply a good story within the confines of the three-minute length imposed by recording technology. This is not to imply that country music has not produced some great melodies, simply that narrative impact has been far more important to its development than a melodic line. The three-chord simplicity of early string bands and the close, straight-line harmonies of gospel music fathered musical styles that to this day are written to support the lyric content.

Finally, country music is a sad music. The social and economic factors which have characterized the lives of much of the hillbilly audience from its earliest beginnings in the frontier culture of the Appalachians to its present urban setting have produced a literature full of death, sadness, and self-pity. Even its comedy songs evoke more nostalgia than hearty laughter. And all in all, it is the music of a people who have led short, hard, severe lives. As such, the music would have a certain interest today as a social document. The fact that much of it still lives and is frequently sung and recorded argues that its importance extends beyond that; it has become a true American art form for a vast and far-ranging country audience.

Who are these people? Who makes up the audience for country music, and who creates and plays it? They are the working people of America, from the cigarette factories of Virginia, the textile mills of the Carolinas, the pencil factories of Georgia, the sugar cane mills of Louisiana, the oil refineries of Texas, ranges of the Great Plains, factories of Detroit. They are the farmers, the people who have worked the land but have seldom owned it: sharecroppers, tenant farmers, and day laborers who have grown the cotton, cane, rice, tobacco, corn, and wheat for the nation, but who have had precious little of it for themselves. They are the people who mined the coal, dug for and transported the oil, cut the lumber, worked on the railroads and rode them, sometimes for nothing. They are the people who own and patronize the bars and grills and honky tonks that are never without country music, the waitresses and bartenders who work in them, the policemen and firemen and postmen and beauticians and construction workers in small towns in every state who frequent them. They are the people who attend small country churches throughout the South and those who have walked the sawdust trail. They are the people who were among the first to be left jobless during the Depression, who suffered through the Dust Bowl of the thirties—the Arkies and Okies and Texans who went to California to look for work. They are the soldiers who have carried their guitars and their music with them through four wars. And they are the same people who gained new affluence during the fifties and sixties and sent their children off to college. And today they are the people of every class and condition of life who find in the country lyric stability in the face of uncertainty; enduring values in a godless society; simplicity and directness in a world of increasing complexity.

The songs that follow speak for themselves. They were selected not on the basis of one criterion, but of many: lyric excellence, popularity, representative content, balance, and impact. They include theme songs, answer songs, obituary songs—types which today are almost unique to country music. The list is not complete (perhaps no such list could ever be complete) but it is representative, of song types, of every generation since the Civil War, of many of the voices that to this day speak for country music.

Sing Your Heart Out, Country Boy

1 | Songs of Home

Hometown of My Heart

It is no accident that songs of "home"—of separation from family, from a place and time, from a way of life—date back at least to the post–Civil War era as a theme in southern musical expression. Nor is it circumstantial that the first recorded hillbilly song, "The Little Old Cabin In The Lane" (Fiddlin' John Carson, June 14, 1923), was a popular song from the 1870s in which a freed black slave recalls ". . . a better time for me, 'twas many years ago. . . ."

The home song is central to the appreciation of country music, because it concretely expresses the virtues of family and home life as well as the Protestant religious values that underlie virtually every other lyric in the field.

Beginning with the great upheavals of the nineteenth century—the Civil War, Reconstruction, the discovery of gold in California and the westward migration that resulted—leaving home has been an important part of the southern experience, and with leaving has come the longing to return. Long before World War I made doughboys out of plowboys, there was a steady migration away from the farms of the South, usually by young men seeking their fortunes, answering the siren call of the city, or moving on to the promise of better land and a better life. Traditionally, the country boy has been alternately attracted and repelled by the sinful city; its freedom, pleasure, and opportunities were not to be denied, but it also meant danger, separation, and loneliness.

After World War I, the economic pressures of the Depression, the consolidation of small farms, the new mobility afforded by the automobile and the availability of jobs in the industrial North maintained this emigration so that there always have been country boys and girls separated from the hometowns of their hearts. And, of course, four wars in this century have kept them separated not only from home but from each other.

With separation comes sadness, sometimes guilt—and songs of home.

The earliest and simplest of these were songs of pure yearning, expressing the sentiment of "Little Old Log Cabin," for "Kentucky" or "Alabama" or Georgia during "Peach Pickin' Time." Closely akin to this nostalgia for a place and a time where "things were better" is the conviction that the good old days were best: Times were hard and money scarce in Bill Monroe's "Uncle Pen," but if it was to do over, he would live them again; and Sam McGee didn't need much money "When The Wagon Was New." Money isn't the only root of evil, according to Mr. Sam; the fast pace of modern days precludes the friendship and neighborliness of the Old South.

"Daddy And Home" and "Uncle Pen" have special meaning and deeply reflect the lives of their composers. Jimmie Rodgers, who wrote "Daddy And Home," lost his mother when he was four and was virtually raised by his father, Aaron Rodgers. And Bill Monroe spent a number of his youthful years being raised by his Uncle Pen.

"Cabin On The Hill" and "This Ole House" are almost religious songs; so strong is the southern reverence for the home that sometimes it approaches a religious fervor. In addition to their secular popularity, both songs are often sung in a religious context, though neither is a sacred song as such.

Although we can list all the reasons southern boys might leave home, these are seldom mentioned in the songs themselves. Instead, they are far more personal. Both Carson Robison and Jimmie Rodgers, for example, cite the adolescent "need to roam," combining it almost inevitably with a sense of guilt. The guilt is sharpened in "That Silver-Haired Daddy Of Mine" and brought to an extreme in Curley Putman's song, where the narrator can return to his beloved "Green, Green Grass Of Home" only in a casket.

Why the guilt? Bill C. Malone, country music historian and author of *Country Music U.S.A.,* has one suggestion: "A person sometimes sings about 'poor old mother at home' because he's neglected her; he ran off and left his parents and went out to seek his fortune—to do his own thing—and a sense of guilt set in. The best way to assuage that guilt is to make up a song about 'poor old mother.' You don't do anything for mama in making up such a song, but you do rid yourself of the guilt."

Leaving home implied a rejection of the values of family and society which made it somehow immoral not to stay and share the common burden. And, of course, many of those who did leave actually found success and a better life than the one they left behind, but rarely one of sufficient affluence to do much about the family's poverty.

In recent years, the sentimentalized homestead of country music, where times were hard, but good and virtue reigned supreme, has given way to a far more realistic view of one's beginnings.

In "Homecoming," the guilty feeling is generalized to an entire way of life. Traditionally, following the trade of musician has been looked on with disfavor as not being "man's work," as not conforming to the Protestant ethic. There remains no longer any basis for real communication between father and son; music, too, has become a reason for alienation. This same feeling has prompted the recent creation of a number of what Frederick E. Danker, in a recent article on Johnny Cash in the *Journal of American Folklore,* calls "minstrel life" songs.

Bill Rice asks, "Wonder Could I Live There Anymore?," and Dolly Parton admits that times were bad "In The Good Old Days." Yet even John Loudermilk, who would destroy "Tobacco Road" with dynamite and a crane, still loves the place because it was home. No matter how realistic the song becomes, there still are residual pangs of guilt and loss.

From the 1960s on, there is a distinct change in point of view, though it may be the result of newfound affluence as much as a real difference in values. The new generation feels it has a choice. No longer does it have to go "back there"; no longer is it sure it wants to. In early songs of this type, the choice too often was between rural poverty and urban poverty and, bad as it was, rural poverty was familiar and comfortable. And, sometimes, it became a matter of fierce pride in home and in the rural South—the same pride Loretta Lynn expresses in "Coal Miner's Daughter."

Ironically, both the earliest and latest songs in this selection are popular numbers that have crossed over to country music and become acknowledged classics. Both of these, "The Little Old Cabin In The Lane" and "Take Me Home, Country Roads," are simple, sweet expressions of the nostalgia that is a constant theme throughout these songs.

ALABAMA

"This is our life story. Crimson red clover is the most famous thing you'll see in Alabama—hundreds of acres of it at the right time of year. They use it as a cover crop to make the land better. Cericea is a cover crop, too, a form of hay. It's a crop you would cut like soybeans or lespedeza three times a year, and it's used to feed the cows and horses. We had a sorghum mill practically all our lives. We didn't just make our own, we made it for other people and took a toll. The song talks about the 'possums and dogs barking, the highways and the loved ones waiting. It's sort of a life story of ours. They made it the Alabama state song under Governor John Paterson in 1966, right after Ira died." —Charlie Louvin

ALABAMA

by Ira and Charles Louvin

Alabama, your beautiful sunlight
Your fields of cericea, potatoes and corn
Alabama, your crimson red clover
All mingled around the old place I was born.

Alabama, your hills and your valleys
Your creeks sing with laughter as onward they flow
Alabama, so sweet in the springtime
Sweet ferns and wildflowers end winter with snow.

Alabama, so sweet to my mem'ry
You shine like a light on a beautiful hill
Alabama, in days of my childhood
I labored and toiled at the old sorghum mill.

Alabama, when red leaves are falling
I roam through your pastures with fences of rail
Alabama, when 'possums are crawling
And hound dogs are howling and wagging their tails.

Alabama, your beautiful highways
Are carved through the mountains where loved ones do wait
Alabama, your goldenrod flowers
The "welcome home" sign hanging over your gate.

Alabama, to me you are calling
My footsteps are halted, no longer to stray
Alabama, you hold all I long for
You hold all I love, so I'm coming today.

CABIN ON THE HILL

"In 1914, at the age of 18, Bolivar Lee Shook was stealing a ride on a freight train near his home in Prentiss County, Mississippi, and was thrown from the train. He injured his leg and remained a cripple for life.

His disability kept him from manual labor, and he turned to music for a livelihood. He taught piano and singing and tuned pianos until his death in March, 1964. He spent his childhood in a frame cabin on a hill located about six miles south of Booneville, Mississippi, overlooking a wide valley to the east and a wide valley to the west. In the west stands a low range of mountains. Knowing the setting of his childhood home, it is not difficult to determine the inspiration for this song. His songs were not fictional, but are a reflection of his life and experiences."

—Donald Franks, Attorney
Booneville, Mississippi

CABIN ON THE HILL
by B. L. Shook

There's a happy childhood home in the memory I can see
Standing out upon the hill 'neath the shadow of the tree
If I only had my way, it would give my heart a thrill
Just to simply wander back to the cabin on the hill.

Oh, I want to wander back to the cabin on the hill
'Neath the shadow of the tree, I would like to linger still
Just to be with those who love, joy my heart would overfill
And I want to wander back to the cabin on the hill.

But the saddest of it all, I can never more return
To that happy childhood home, matters not how much I yearn
If I only had my way, it would give my heart a thrill
Just to simply wander back to the cabin on the hill.

CARRY ME BACK TO THE MOUNTAINS

"I think this was just a product of Carson's imagination and had nothing to do with his background. His background was that of a boy raised in Cheopta, Kansas, son of the one-time champion fiddler and dance-caller of the Sunflower state. He was a railroader and a moving spirit in the colorful Oklahoma and Texas oil fields by turn. His major interest, however, continued to be that of his boyhood, singing and whistling the old time songs to his own guitar accompaniment, and his boyish attempts at songwriting. Carson later was known as the 'Granddaddy of Hillbilly

Music' as it was inelegantly called in those days. He was the forerunner of them all."

—Mrs. Catherine Robison

CARRY ME BACK TO THE MOUNTAINS

by Carson Robison

I was a wild, careless youngster
Longin' to roam from the start
So I left my home in the mountains
And broke my poor darlin's heart.

I caught a train at the crossin'
And never told her goodbye
Then someone wrote me a letter
And told me my sweetheart had died.

Carry me back to the mountains
Beneath the southern skies
Lay me to rest in the mountains
That's where my sweetheart lies
I get so lonesome and weary
No matter where I roam
Oh, carry me back to the mountains
Back to my home, sweet home.

I've roamed this whole wide world over
Livin' a life of regret
Longin' to be with my darlin'
Tryin' so hard to forget.

I pray that God will forgive me
And on that bright, peaceful shore
I'll find her waitin' in heaven
Where we will part never more.

COAL MINER'S DAUGHTER

"This is the true story of my early life in Butcher Holler, Kentucky. My daddy did work in the coal mines and my mama did wash on the scrub board. The old house is still standing, and I go back to see it every now and then."

—Loretta Lynn

COAL MINER'S DAUGHTER

by Loretta Lynn

I was born a coal miner's daughter
In a cabin on a hill in Butcher Holler
We were born poor, but we had love
That's the one thing that daddy made sure of
He shoveled coal to make a poor man's dollar.

My daddy worked all night in the Vanleer coal mine
All day long in the field a-hoein' corn
Mommie rocked the babies at night
And read the Bible by the coal oil light
And everything would start all over come break of morn.

Daddy loved and raised eight kids on a miner's pay
Mommie scrubbed our clothes on a washboard every day
I've seen her fingers bleed
To complain there was no need
She'd smile in mommie's understanding way.

In the summertime we didn't have shoes to wear
But in the wintertime we'd all get a brand new pair
From a mail order catalog
Money made from selling a hog
Daddy always managed to get the money somewhere.

I'm proud to be a coal miner's daughter
I remember well the well where I drew water
The work we done was hard
At night we'd sleep 'cause we worked hard
I never thought of ever leaving Butcher Holler.

A lot of things have changed since way back then
And it's so good to be back home again
Not much left but the floor
Nothing lives here anymore
Except the mem'ries of a coal miner's daughter.

"I accompanied my brother-in-law, Jimmie Rodgers, on a good many recording dates, as he played by ear, and I could help him there. We were on our way to such a date in New York, talking of his daddy and his early life, when I wrote the words to 'Daddy and Home.' I completed the music when we returned to his home in Washington, and we then went to Camden, New Jersey, to record this and eight more of my compositions. That session was in about 1928, I think." —Mrs. Elsie McWilliams

DADDY AND HOME

by Elsie McWilliams and Jimmie Rodgers

I am dreaming tonight of an old Southern town
And the best friend that I ever had
For I've grown so weary of roaming around
And I'm going home to my Dad.

Your hair has turned to silver
I know you're failing, too
Daddy, dear old Daddy
I'm coming home to you
You made my boyhood happy
But still I longed to roam
I've had my way, but now I'll say
I long for you and for home.

Dear old Daddy, you shared all my sorrows and joys
And you tried hard to bring me up right
I know you'll still be one of the boys
I'm starting back home tonight.

DETROIT CITY

"About three years before we wrote this, I played a little old club in Detroit—me and Annie Lou—and I saw these people that are in this song. They did go North. When I was a kid, they'd say, 'Where's John now?' 'Well, he's gone off up to De-troit.' I sat there and talked to these people. They were from Alabama, West Tennessee, Kentucky, and they'd go to Detroit and work in the car factories. Now, they had more cash money in their pockets than they'd ever seen in their lives, but they were homesick. And to keep from being so lonely, they'd go sit in a bar and drink. And when they did get home, they'd get home with no money. They wasted, literally, ten or fifteen years of their lives, and they wanted to go home all the time. They'd think they were rich, but they'd spend it. Then, eventually, they'd dovetail and catch that Southbound freight and ride back home where they came from."

—Danny Dill

DETROIT CITY

by Danny Dill and Mel Tillis

Last night I went to sleep in Detroit City
And I dreamed about the cotton fields and home
I dreamed about my mother, dear old papa, sister and brother
And I dreamed about the girl who's been waiting for so long.

I wanna go home, I wanna go home
Oh, how I wanna go home.

Home folks think I'm big in Detroit City
From the letters that I write they think I'm fine
But by day I make the cars, by night I make the bars
If only they could read between the lines.

'Cause you know I rode a freight train north to Detroit City
And after all these years I find I've just been wasting my time
So I'll just take my foolish pride and put it on the Southbound freight and ride
And go back to the loved ones, the ones that I left waiting so far behind.

EIGHT MORE MILES TO LOUISVILLE

"I wrote this song back around 1941. At that time Alton and Rabon Delmore had recorded a song entitled 'Fifteen Miles From Birmingham.' There is no similarity between the two songs, of course, but that's where I got the idea."

—Grandpa Jones

EIGHT MORE MILES TO LOUISVILLE

by Louis Marshall Jones

I've traveled o'er this country wide, seeking fortune fair
Up and down the two coast lines, I've traveled everywhere
From Portland East to Portland West and back across the line
I'm going now to the place that's best, that old home town of mine.

Eight more miles and Louisville will come into my view
Eight more miles on this old road, I'll never more be blue
I knew some day that I'd return, I knew it from the start
Eight more miles to Louisville, the home town of my heart.

There's bound to be a girl somewhere that you like best of all
Mine lives out in Louisville, she's long and she's tall
But she's the kind that you can't find a-ramblin' through the land
I'm on my way this very day to win her heart and hand.

I can picture in my mind a place that we'll call home
A humble little house for two, we never more will roam
A place that's right for that love sight is in those blue grass hills
There gently flows the Ohio by a place called Louisville.

GREEN, GREEN GRASS OF HOME

"This song has been recorded approximately 200 times, and has been my biggest hit so far. It has sold some 8–10 million records. I'll have to say this, I needed it bad. I wrote it in 1965 after I moved to Nashville. I was trying pretty hard at that time to write anything commercial. I suppose it took about two hours to finish the song when I sat down to write it. Those two hours have become two of the most profitable hours I ever spent."

—Curley Putman, Jr.

GREEN, GREEN GRASS OF HOME

by Curley Putman, Jr.

The old home town looks the same, as I step down from the train
And there to meet me is my mama and papa

Down the road I look and there runs Mary, hair of gold and lips like cherries
It's good to touch the green, green grass of home.

Yes, they'll all come to meet me, arms reaching, smiling sweetly
It's good to touch the green, green grass of home.

The old house is still standing, though the paint is cracked and dry
And there's that old oak tree that I used to play on
Down the lane I walk with my sweet Mary, hair of gold and lips like cherries
It's good to touch the green, green grass of home.

Yes, they'll all come to meet me, in the shade of that old oak tree
As they lay me 'neath the green, green grass of home.

When I awake and look around me at four grey walls that surround me
I realize that I was only dreaming
For there's a guard and there's a sad old padre, arm in arm we'll walk at day break
Again, I'll touch the green, green grass of home.

HOMECOMING

"The song was absolutely true in its sense, and I was being very honest and open. My father lived in Carter City, Kentucky, at the time, and I would go by there after I'd neglected him so much. I've always apologized for being a songwriter and an entertainer, because I think they need to. I'd be honest with him and say, 'This is what I do.' That's the way I explain what I do, by saying that's what I do. It's a confessional and an apology for being what I am, which I have no real control over, I suppose."

—Tom T. Hall

HOMECOMING
by Tom T. Hall

I guess I should have written, dad, to let you know that I was comin' home
I've been gone so many years, I didn't realize you had a phone

I saw your cattle coming in; boy, they're looking mighty fat and slick
I saw Fred at the service station, told me that his wife was awful sick.

You heard my record on the radio, oh well, it's just another song
But I've got a hit recorded, it'll be out on the market 'fore too long
I got this ring in Mexico, and no, it didn't cost me quite a bunch
When you're in the business that I'm in, people call it puttin' up a front.

I know I've lost a little weight, and I guess I am looking kinda pale
If you didn't know me better, dad, you'd think that I'd just gotten out of jail
No, we don't ever call them beer joints; night clubs are the places where I work
You meet a lot of people there, but no, there ain't no chance of gettin' hurt.

I'm sorry that I couldn't be here with you all when mama passed away
I was on the road, and when they came and told me, it was just too late
I drove by the grave to see her; boy, that really is a pretty stone
I'm glad that Fred and Jan are here; it's better than you bein' here alone.

I knew you're gonna ask me who the lady is that's sleeping in the car
That's just a girl who works for me, and man, she plays a pretty mean guitar
We worked in San Antone last night; she didn't even have the time to dress
She drove me down from Nashville and, to tell the truth, I guess she needs the rest.

Well, dad, I gotta go; we got a dance to work in Cartersville tonight
Let me take your number down; I'll call you, and I promise you I'll write
Now you be good, and don't be chasin' all those pretty women that you know
And, by the way, if you see Barbara Walker, tell her that I said hello.

"This is the way it was and the way it still is for some people back home. It's sort of like everyday living. It is true; every bit of it is true. It's a memory of how things were over in the holler in Sevierville, Tennessee."

—Dolly Parton

IN THE GOOD OLD DAYS (WHEN TIMES WERE BAD)

by Dolly Parton

We'd get up before sunup to get the work done up
We'd work in the fields till the sun had gone down
We've stood and we've cried as we helplessly watched
A hail storm a-beating our crops to the ground
We've gone to bed hungry many nights in the past
In the good old days when times were bad.

No amount of money could buy from me
Memories that I have of then
No amount of money could pay me
To go back and live through it again.

I've seen daddy's hands break open and bleed
And I've seen him work till he's stiff as a board
And I've seen mama lay and suffer in sickness
In need of a doctor we couldn't afford
Anything at all was more than we had
In the good old days when times were bad.

We've got up before and found ice on the floor
Where the wind would blow snow through the cracks in the wall
I've walked many miles to an old country school
With my lunch in the bib of my overalls
Anything at all was more than we had
In the good old days when times were bad.

KENTUCKY

"I wrote the song as a tribute to my home state. I grew up in Mount Vernon, Kentucky. About four years ago, I was made a Kentucky Colonel on the strength of having written it."

—Karl Davis

KENTUCKY
by Karl Davis

Kentucky, you are the dearest land outside of heaven to me
Kentucky, your laurel and your redbud trees
When I die, I want to rest upon a graceful mountain so high
For that is where God will look for me.

Kentucky, I miss the songs they're singing in the silvery moonlight
Kentucky, I miss the hound dogs chasing 'coons
I know that my mother, dad and sweetheart are there waiting for me
Kentucky, I'll be returning soon.

THE LITTLE OLD CABIN IN THE LANE

Written in 1871 by Will S. Hays, a native of Kentucky and contemporary of Stephen Foster, these are the original lyrics to one of the many songs he wrote for the minstrels. Recorded by Fiddlin' John Carson on June 14, 1923, it became the first commercially marketed hillbilly record. It has spawned innumerable variants including "The Little Red Caboose Behind The Train" and the cowboy ballad "The Little Old Sod Shanty On The Plain." —D. H.

THE LITTLE OLD CABIN IN THE LANE
by Will S. Hays

I'm getting old and feeble now, I cannot work no more
I've laid de rusty bladed hoe to rest
Ole massa an' ole miss's am dead, dey're sleepin' side by side
Deir spirits now are roaming wid de blest
De scene am changed about de place, de darkies am all gone
I'll nebber hear dem singing in de cane
And I'se de only one dat's left wid dis ole dog ob mine
In de little old log cabin in de lane.

De chimney's falling down, and de roof is cavin' in,
I ain't got long 'round here to remain
But de angels watches over me when I lays down to sleep
In de little old log cabin in de lane.

Dar was a happy time to me, 'twas many years ago
When de darkies used to gather round de door
When dey used to dance an' sing at night, I played de ole banjo
But, alas, I cannot play it any more
De hinges dey got rusted an' de door has tumbled down
An' de roof lets in de sunshine an' de rain
An' de only friend I've got now is dis good ole dog ob mine
In de little old log cabin in de lane.

De footpath now is covered o'er dat led us 'round de hill
An' de fences all are going to decay
An' de creek is all dried up where we used to go to mill
De time has turned its course anodder way
But I ain't got long to stay here, an' what little time I got
I'll try an' be contented to remain
Till death shall call my dog an' me to find a better home
Dan dat little old log cabin in de lane.

MOCKIN' BIRD HILL

"In 1949, my father was in the hospital in Huntingdon, Pennsylvania, and I would visit him every weekend by train from New York. I used to love to ride trains and I used to love to write songs on trains, so I would write a little bit of it each time. When I finished it, I brought a guitar to the hospital and played it for him and the nurses. That was the first public performance of 'Mockin' Bird Hill.' He predicted, 'That'll be your biggest song ever,' and sure enough, he was right. He died about a month later. Nobody would record it, so I got a band together and recorded it myself in September, 1950. Christmas week it went on the *Billboard* charts as a hillbilly record. It was recorded by Les Paul, Patti Page and Russ Morgan and soon after, I had four records in the top twenty, including number one and number two. It's one of the biggest songs of all times; it has been recorded more than 400 times and has sold over 20 million copies."

—Vaughn Horton

MOCKIN' BIRD HILL
by Vaughn Horton

When the sun in the mornin' peeps over the hill
And kisses the roses 'round my window sill
Then my heart fills with gladness when I hear the trill
Of the birds in the tree-tops on Mockin' Bird Hill.

Tra-la la twit-tle-dee dee dee, it gives me a thrill
To wake up in the mornin' to the mockin' bird's trill
Tra-la la twit-tle dee dee dee, there's peace and good will
You're welcome as the flowers on Mockin' Bird Hill.

Got a three-cornered plow and an acre to till
And a mule that I bought for a ten-dollar bill
There's a tumble-down shack and a rusty ol' mill
But it's my home sweet home up on Mockin' Bird Hill.

When it's late in the evening, I climb up the hill
And survey all my kingdom while ev'rything's still
Only me and the sky and an ol' whippoorwill
Singin' songs in the twilight on Mockin' Bird Hill.

MOM AND DAD'S WALTZ

"I was in Dallas, Texas, not working at the time. We got plenty hungry and it was only natural to think of mom and dad out in west Texas. I was thinking that I'd be glad to walk miles to see mom and dad, maybe for a good Sunday dinner or something, and it just eased out."

—Lefty Frizzell

MOM AND DAD'S WALTZ

by Lefty Frizzell

I'd walk for miles
Cry or smile
For my mama and daddy
I want them
I want them to know.

How I feel
My love is real
For my mama and daddy
I want them to know
I love them so.

In my heart for joy tears start
'Cause I'm happy

And I pray every day
For mom and pappy
And each night
I'd walk for miles
Cry or smile
For my mama and daddy
I want them to know
I love them so.

I'd fight in wars
Do all the chores
For my mama and daddy
I want them to live on
Till they're called.

I'd work and slave
And never rave
To my mama and daddy
Because I know
I owe them my all.

PEACH PICKIN' TIME IN GEORGIA

"My late husband was born in Altoona, Georgia, now covered by the Altoona Dam Project. It was natural that he write a song about Georgia. 'Pappy,' as we called him, wrote 'Peach Pickin' Time In Georgia' one night when I took our two daughters, June and Juanita, to visit my mother in Cartersville, Georgia. He always wanted us near and would never travel anywhere without us. He was so lonesome for us that night, he couldn't sleep. So he got up and sat up all night writing the song. Jimmie Rodgers and 'Pappy' were good friends. Jimmie recorded several other songs he had written."
—Mrs. Clayton McMichen

PEACH PICKIN' TIME IN GEORGIA

by Jimmie Rodgers and Clayton McMichen

When it's peach pickin' time in Georgia, apple pickin' time in
Tennessee
Cotton pickin' time in Mississippi, everybody picks on me

When it's round-up time in Texas, the cowboys make whoopee
Then down in old Alabama, it's gal pickin' time to me.

There's the blue grass down in Kentucky, Virginia's where they do
the Swing
Carolina, I'm coming to you to spend the spring
Arkansas, I hear you calling; I know I'll see you soon
There's where I'll do a little pickin', underneath the Ozark moon.

Now, when hard times overtake you, I hope they don't get me
For I've got a sweetie waiting for me down in Tennessee
I know I'm going to see her, I hope it won't be long
There's where we'll pick a little cabin and call it our mountain home.

When the pickaninnies pick the cotton, I'll pick a wedding ring
We'll go to town and pick a little gown for the wedding in the
spring
I hope the preacher knows his business, I know he can't fool me
When it's peach pickin' time in Georgia, it's gal pickin' time to me.

TAKE ME BACK TO RENFRO VALLEY

"At the time I wrote this song, I was employed as musical director of radio station WLS in Chicago. I was also writing and producing my own show with talent I had taken to Chicago from an area surrounding my old home on Renfro Creek near Mount Vernon, Kentucky. I went home on vacation and was so depressed by the changes I found that, upon my return, I put it all into this song. The more I heard it sung, the more homesick I got, and the more determined I became to go back and make it more like it had been in my boyhood. With a boy I had put on radio, Red Foley, his brother Cotton Foley, Whitey Ford and five hundred dollars borrowed money, I went home and got to work. Renfro Valley became the first community in the nation to originate and broadcast a radio program put on by the actual residents of that community. Success was instantaneous, overwhelming—and surprising—and we owed it mostly to this song. Beginning in 1942, it was the theme song of our network program for more than twelve years on CBS, and it is still used on a mixed network of 74 stations."

—John Lair

TAKE ME BACK TO RENFRO VALLEY

by John Lair

I was born in Renfro Valley
But I drifted far away
I've been back to see the old home
And my friends of other days
Gone were old familiar faces
All the friends I used to know
Things have changed in Renfro Valley
Since the days of long ago.

Others own the old plantation
I can call it home no more
Other forms are at the fireside
Other children 'round the door
Other voices sing the old songs
When the evening sun is low
Mother sang in Renfro Valley
In the days of long ago.

Take me back to Renfro Valley
When I'm free from earthly care
Lay me down by dad and mother
Let me sleep forever there
When it's springtime in the mountains
And the dogwood blossoms blow
I'll be back in Renfro Valley
As in the days of long ago.

TAKE ME HOME, COUNTRY ROADS

"We had been receiving letters from an artist friend who lived in the mountains of West Virginia reveling in the beauty of the countryside. Then, on the way to a family reunion of Taffy's relatives in Maryland, Bill started writing a song about the little, windey roads we were driving on to get there. The song hung around for awhile as the two words, 'country roads.' Later, Bill decided to write the song about our artist friend. The original second verse was:

> In the foothills, hiding from the clouds
> Pink and purple West Virginia farmhouse
> Naked ladies, men who looked like Christ
> And a dog named Pancho nibbling on the rice.

We knew before it was finished it would never get on the air, but we wrote the chorus anyway. During the last week of December, 1970, John Denver came over to our apartment after the last show at the Cellar Door in Washington, D.C., where we were both appearing. He heard the song, got excited, and we dropped the second verse and finished writing it at six o'clock in the morning. The rest is history. Someday we'll visit West Virginia."

—Bill and Taffy Danoff

TAKE ME HOME, COUNTRY ROADS

by Bill Danoff, T. Nivert Danoff, and John Denver

Almost heaven, West Virginia
Blue Ridge Mountains, Shenandoah River
Life is old there, older than the trees
Younger than the mountains, growing like the breeze.

Country roads, take me home
To the place I belong
West Virginia, mountain mama
Take me home, country roads.

All my mem'ries gather 'round her
Finest lady, stranger to blue water
Dark and dusty, painted on the sky
Misty taste of moonshine, teardrops in my eye.

I hear her voice in the morning as she calls me
The radio reminds me of my home far away
Driving down the road, I get a feeling
That I should have been home yesterday, yesterday.

" 'Silver-Haired Daddy Of Mine' was my first million-record-seller which really started me on my way to a radio and movie career. It will always have a special place in my memory. It's been such a long time ago I cannot recall how or where the idea came to me." —Gene Autry

THAT SILVER-HAIRED DADDY OF MINE
by Gene Autry and Jimmy Long

In a vine-covered shack in the mountains
Bravely fighting the battle of time
Lives a dear one who's weathered life's sorrow
'Tis that silver-haired daddy of mine.

If I could recall all the heartaches
Dear old Daddy, I caused you to bear
If I could erase those lines from your face
And bring back the gold to your hair.

If God would but grant me the power
Just to turn back the pages of time
I'd give all I own, if I could but atone
To that silver-haired daddy of mine.

I know it's too late, dear old Daddy
To repay for those sorrows and tears,
Though dear mother is waiting in heaven
Just to comfort and solace you there.

THIS OLE HOUSE

"This song was written one cold wintery day in the High Sierra mountain range when I was on a hunting trip. With a hunting companion, I had gone back into a remote section of the country. We were at least twenty miles from the nearest road when we came upon an old prospector's cabin. Although there was snow on the ground, there was no smoke coming from the chimney, but I knew the master was at home because a large hound dog was lying on the front porch. Upon entering, we found an old man dead in a back room. I can't say how long he had been dead, for he looked like he was just asleep, but because of the severe weather it might have been some time, and the old hound was nearly starved. 'This Ole House' was the old prospector's epitaph."

—Stuart Hamblen (Reprinted with permission from the book *The Birth of a Song* by Stuart Hamblen)

THIS OLE HOUSE

by Stuart Hamblen

This ole house once knew my children
This ole house once knew my wife
This ole house was home and comfort
As we fought the storms of life
This ole house once rang with laughter
This ole house heard many shouts
Now she trembles in the darkness
When the lightnin' walks about.

Ain't gonna need this house no longer
Ain't gonna need this house no more
Ain't got time to fix the shingles
Ain't got time to fix the floor
Ain't got time to oil the hinges
Nor to mend the window pane
Ain't gonna need this house no longer
I'm a-gettin' ready to meet the saints.

This ole house is a-gettin' shaky
This ole house is a-gettin' old
This ole house lets in the rain
This ole house lets in the cold
Oh my knees are gettin' chilly
But I feel no fear or pain
'Cause I see an angel peekin'
Through a broken window pane.

This ole house is afraid of thunder
This ole house is afraid of storms
This ole house just groans and trembles
When the night wind flings its arms
This ole house is a-gettin' feeble
This ole house is a-needin' paint
Just like me it's tuckered out
But I'm a-gettin' ready to meet the saints.

Now my old hound dog lies a-sleepin'
He don't know I'm gonna leave
Else he'd wake up by the fireplace
And he'd sit there and howl and grieve
But my huntin' days are over
Ain't gonna hunt the 'coon no more
Gabriel done brought in my chariot
When the wind blew down the door.

TOBACCO ROAD

"This is kind of a life story—that's the way it was. I sold out a little bit on that song, I'm sorry to say, because I said, 'Mother died and Daddy got drunk,' but Mother didn't die at childbirth, and I never saw my dad take a drink in his life. Never heard him say a cussword, either. He was a marvelous man. At the time, I was just starting out in the music business, and I was frankly hungry. I felt that was a good rhyming word—that was a catchy phrase. Now I wish I had not said that, because I seem to be giving an illusion of a father who was fairly rough and a mother who was fairly rough, and my people were very big church-going people. I grew up in the Salvation Army." —John D. Loudermilk

TOBACCO ROAD

by John D. Loudermilk

I was born in a dump
Mama died and daddy got drunk
Left me here to die or grow
In the middle of Tobacco Road.

Grew up in a rusty shack
All I owned was a-hangin' on my back
Only Lord knows how I loathe
The place called Tobacco Road.

But it's home, the only life I ever knowed
But the Lord knows I loathe Tobacco Road
But I loves you 'cause you're home.

Gonna leave, get a job
With the help and the grace of God
Save my money, get rich I know
Bring it back to Tobacco Road.

Bring dynamite and a crane
Blow it up and start over again
Build a town, be proud to show
Keep the name of Tobacco Road.

'Cause it's the only life I knowed
I despise you 'cause you're filthy, Tobacco Road
But I loves you 'cause you're home.

UNCLE PEN

"My Uncle Pen was one of Kentucky's old-time fiddlers, and he had the best shuffle with the bow that I'd ever seen, and kept the best time. That's one reason people asked him to play for the dances around Rosine, Kentucky. In his later years he was a crippled man. He had been thrown by a mule and had to use crutches the rest of his life. My last years in Kentucky were spent with him. He done the cooking for the two of us. We had fatback, sorghum molasses, and hoe cakes for breakfast, followed up with black-eyed peas with fatback, and cornbread and sorghum for dinner and supper. I can remember those days so very well. There were hard times and money was scarce, but also there were good times. If it was to do over, I'd live them again." —Bill Monroe

UNCLE PEN
by Bill Monroe

Oh, the people would come from far away
They'd dance all night till the break of day
When the caller hollered "Do-se-do"
He knew Uncle Pen was ready to go.

Late in the evenin' about sundown
High on the hill above the town

Uncle Pen played the fiddle, oh how it would ring
You can hear it talk, you can hear it sing.

He played an old piece called "Soldier's Joy"
And in the mornin' told the Folsom boy
The greatest of all was "Jenny Lind"
To me that's worse when women begin.

I'll never forget that mournful day
When Uncle Pen was called away
They hung up his fiddle, hung up his bow
They knew it was time for him to go.

WHEN IT'S PRAYER MEETIN' TIME IN THE HOLLOW

"I was 'home-grown and hand-spanked' on a farm in a country hollow in upstate New York and attended a church there, so the title came easy. My co-writer, Fleming Allan, now demised, was musical director of radio station WLS in Chicago, and I was a member of a barbershop quartet known as the Maple City Four which was the WLS staff quartet for 35 years. Fleming and I wrote many songs for various artists including Bradley Kinkaid, Gene Autry, and Louise Massey and the Westerners. This song was often done as a rhythm number without the verse."

—Al Rice

WHEN IT'S PRAYER MEETIN' TIME IN THE HOLLOW

by Al Rice and Fleming Allan

When it's prayer meetin' time in the hollow
In that vine-covered shrine 'neath the pines
Then the one that I love sends a prayer up above
Where we once pledged our love so divine.

Till the day I go back to that hollow
I will follow the old golden rule
For it taught me to pray and to live for that day
When we'll meet in the hollow back home.

A long winding pathway leads over the hill
And when all is still, I hear the whippoorwill

It calls from that woodland, my heaven to be
And tells me she waits patiently.

WHEN THE WAGON WAS NEW

"I guess it must have been back in the twenties when I wrote this song. Back in the days when I was just a kid we did a lot of that—went to church in wagons and even on horseback. Those were the horse and buggy days. I seen a lot of that during the twenties and thirties in Alabama and down through there in places that I played. In some places, especially in the hilly countries, some of that is still going on right now."

—Sam McGee

WHEN THE WAGON WAS NEW

by Sam McGee

There's an old rusty wagon that's left to rot away
It's the one the family rode in, back in the good old days
People all loved their neighbor, everybody was so free
Ridin' in the brand new wagon was something to see.

I can see my daddy sitting on a wagon seat
Mom in her old sun bonnet, she looked so nice and neat
Children all in the wagon, grandma and grandpa, too
And we used to go to church on Sunday, when the wagon was new.

Wheels were on the wagon and the body, it was green
But we were all as happy as ridin' in a limousine
People used to gather 'round from all the mountain side
Take a look at the brand new wagon, and all take a ride.

The automobiles are here now, and the wagon days are through
The airplanes are a hummin', good neighbors are so few
Everybody's in a hurry, it's the money that takes you through
We didn't need much money, when the wagon was new.

"I wrote this song on a train to Chicago from Shreveport on my way to a recording session. I was born about seventy miles from the Red River, but for several years I've had a farm located on Red River in Shreveport, Louisiana."
—Jimmie Davis

WHERE THE OLD RED RIVER FLOWS
by Jimmie Davis

The lights are bright tonight on Broadway, and the city's bright as day
On the beach at Coney Island, where the liquor makes you gay,
But I'm heading South tonight, love, on the IC when she goes
To my farm in Louisiana, where the old Red River flows.

As I sit and think of Dixie, cotton fields and whippoorwills
Where I spent my happy childhood among the rocks and among the rills
I can see my dear old mother, as around the place she goes
On my farm in Louisiana, where the old Red River flows.

Hi-lee-oh-layee, you can hear the darkies singing soft and low
And at twilight in the evening, so soft and low, so low
On my farm in Louisiana, where the old Red River flows.

WONDER COULD I LIVE THERE ANYMORE

"The song was written after a vacation trip to my hometown during the summer months of 1969."
—Bill Rice

WONDER COULD I LIVE THERE ANYMORE
by Bill Rice

Have you ever been awakened by the crowing of a rooster
While the night's dew is heavy on the ground
And the voice of Uncle Ben seems to break the morning silence
Bringing light to windows all around?
It's time to rise and shine and start another hard work day
Get the cows in and start the milking chores

It's nice to think about it, maybe even visit
But I wonder could I live there anymore?

Something 'bout the smell of cornbread cooking on a wood stove
Seems to bring a picture to my mind
Of a little three room house with mama in the kitchen
But she can't stop to talk, ain't got the time
She's fixing dad his supper, he's a-workin' overtime
Trying to pay our bill at the grocery store
It's nice to think about it, maybe even visit
But I wonder could I live there anymore?

Missus Browning was our neighbor who invited us to church
A Christian soul with Gospel words to say
When she found our denomination wasn't just the same as hers
She told us that we were bound to pay
As I think about my childhood and of my old home town
I don't really miss them like before
It's nice to think about it, maybe even visit
But I wonder could I live there anymore?

---

2 | Religious Songs

This World Is Not My Home

An anthology of country lyrics without a selection of religious songs would be as unfulfilling as a country performance without at least one sacred number to wrap it up. Indeed, the country gospel repertory predates, and probably will outlive, any other category of country songs.

These are the sentimental, emotional expressions of the southern religious experience. Simple, joyful, sincere, their promise is a better life hereafter than that available for many rural southerners, particularly during the decades of privation and suffering between the Civil War and World War II. Many of them echo the sentiment of the traditional "This World Is Not My Home":

> This world is not my home, I'm just a-passing through
> My treasures are laid up somewhere beyond the blue
> The angels beckon me from heaven's open door
> And I can't feel at home in this world anymore.

Bill Malone explains the other-worldly qualities that mark many of these songs: "By and large, the southern Protestant tradition has been Calvinistic and has taught people that life is a 'vale of tears.' Death should be sought and welcomed, because the better life lies beyond the grave; life on earth is a very short, sad, brutal existence, and the world is something to be rejected."

For the past half-century, the religious song has been an important part of the repertory of virtually every country performer. Almost everyone interviewed for this book said that gospel music played an important part in his early life. Some said it was the only music they heard as children (in many rural communities, the church provides not only salvation, but recreation as well).

Some, like the Louvin Brothers, struggled throughout their early careers to break the gospel mold and start singing a few love songs which, if less redemptive, were bound to be more lucrative. Others, like Stuart Hamblen and Country Johnny Mathis, who achieved success singing secular songs, have now turned to full-time gospel.

The demand for a popular form of church music that was less formal and more appropriate for revivals, camp meetings, and Sunday Schools goes back to the very origins of the Protestant church in America. As early as 1784, for example, this demand was a matter of controversy in the Methodist Church. Ecclesiastical hymns composed in England or in the cathedrals of the North did little to stir the hard-bitten frontier soul or win it for Jesus.

The origins of the modern-day religious song composed by professional country and gospel performers date back to the humble folk hymns of rural camp meetings which, according to George Pullen Jackson's *White Spirituals in the Southern Uplands,* got their start in July 1800, in Logan County, Kentucky. Then as now, these simple, popular songs were looked down upon by the religious and social establishment.

Around 1820, there arose a number of "missionary" hymns with simple "fasola" harmonies learned by rote or by shape notation. These songs fell on welcome ears, particularly in the South and Southwest, though they were primitive by the more sophisticated standards of the established Presbyterian, Methodist, and Baptist churches. Entire congregations flocked to "singing schools," made the songs their own, and proudly sang what they had learned at local and regional singing conventions, a custom that is preserved today and was the forerunner of our all-night gospel sings.

These hymns were written with missionary fervor, but they failed to fill the evangelistic needs of the time. As hymns, they were songs addressed to God in praise and adoration; they assumed that both singer and listener were Christians, not unbelievers or backsliders.

The Rev. Phil Kerr, writing in *Music in Evangelism,* makes clear the distinction between a hymn and a gospel song. "A hymn is a *prayer* set to music. A gospel song is a *testimony,* or *exhortation,* set to music. . . . The distinction between a *hymn* and a *gospel song* is quite important, for the determining of how the song should be sung. . . . Sing a *hymn* with the same reverence and solemnity and humility with which a prayer would be offered, and sing a *gospel song* with the same enthusiasm and earnestness and victory with which a testimony or exhortation would be delivered!"

As early as 1831, a hymnbook called *The Christian Lyre* was published, containing a number of prototypes of the gospel song. They were described by Henry Wilder Foote in *Three Centuries of American Hymnody* as including ". . . lively hymns and melodies, sometimes with 'chorusses,' on a distinctly lower literary and musical level. . . ." Despite the criticisms of the Harvard theologian, *The Christian Lyre,* written by the Rev. Joshua Leavitt expressly for the evangelical revivals of Charles Finney, went to a twenty-sixth edition by 1846 and proved enormously popular.

One other collection of the period is worthy of note. B. F. White's *Sacred Harp* (Georgia, 1844) was the predecessor of the 1911 *Original Sacred Harp* still in use at singing conventions in the South.

But the real emergence of gospel music as we know it today accompanied the religious upheavals of the last few decades of the nineteenth century, a period that saw the division of established churches (north and south) over the issues of the Civil War, the shattering introduction of Darwin's theory of evolution, the further splintering of churches as sects arose specifically to serve the poor, and the formation of a host of new churches with primitive, "perfectionist" principles.

Of the receptiveness of these churches to gospel song, Jackson, writing in *White and Negro Spirituals,* said, "A number of sects of the 'country' sort—the Nazarenes, Pentecostals, and Church of God (Holy Rollers) for example—grew up during the gospel hymn epidemic and caught the ailment. Still others, like the Disciples of Christ and the Church of Christ, though older and with a remote good-old-songs background have been too loosely organized denominationally to withstand the temptation of temporary song styles. In the cities they have therefore gone over long since to Lowell Mason [whom he calls one of the 'Better Music Boys'] and his school and, in the country, to the gospel songs."

Jackson's judgment of thirty years ago concerning "temporary song styles" was obviously faulty, at least in the case of gospel songs, but his distinction between "gospel hymns" and "gospel songs" is important. For even though the hymns were popularly written, they still were "directed upward," in praise of God; the songs, on the other hand, had all the characteristics of our contemporary gospel literature, and many have survived.

The message of "salvation through grace," the "Good News" of Gospel, inspired a long list of writers between the Civil War and the end of the century including Fanny Crosby, William Kirkpatrick, Robert Lowry, and Philip P. Bliss. Gospel song swept the nation, often spread by great revivalists like Dwight Moody and singer-composer Ira Sankey. In fact, revivalism and gospel music have had parallel histories, with great surges in evangelical spirit—Finney in the 1830s, Moody in the 1870s, Billy Sunday at the turn of the century, Billy Graham in the 1940s—prompting the creation of dozens of new songs.

One of the important new collections was that of Sankey and Bliss, who teamed up in 1875 to publish the first of six books of gospel hymns for the Moody revivals. This series, which included such classics as "Amazing Grace" and "Almost Persuaded," sold in the tens of millions.

As the evangelical fever spread, virtually every crossroads Protestant church in the South had its Sunday School, camp meetings, and other informal services, and the use of gospel song became the rule on these occasions. "All day singings and dinner on the grounds" alternated old-time religion with neighborly intercourse and provided a vital social outlet for isolated farm families.

Often the meetings were led by itinerant evangelists or "brush arbor preachers" who set up their "churches" on the local campgrounds. Vance Randolph *(Ozark Folksongs)* described a typical brush arbor:

> Inside the tabernacle are two groups of rough wooden benches, without backs or arms, separated by a broad aisle; the men are supposed to sit on one side of the aisle, and the women on the other. The pulpit is built upon a little platform at one end of the arbor, and at one side of the pulpit are two or three benches reserved for the more influential and devout Christians of the neighborhood—this place is called the 'amen corner.' Just in front of the pulpit is a long, low seat known as the mourner's bench. When the news of a camp meeting has been 'norated round,' whole families come in covered wagons, on horseback and afoot, bringing bedding and cooking utensils, with sufficient food to last several days.

These meetings, and the music that graced them, became so popular that some Protestant churches actually dropped their standard hymnals, at least temporarily, in favor of gospel songbooks. And the songs were truly ecumenical; no church—not the conventional Methodist, Baptist, or Presbyterian, nor their fundamentalist offshoots—had an exclusive right to them, and they have been traded around freely for decades.

The holiness movement of the late nineteenth century (Jackson's so-called country sects) proved a good source both of songs and of singers, and the long list of country performers raised in this tradition includes Wayne Raney, Jerry Lee Lewis, Elvis Presley, Bill Monroe, Molly O'Day, Wilma Lee and Stoney Cooper, the Bailes Brothers, and the Blue Sky Boys.

By the turn of the century, gospel music was big business, due at least in part to the enormous success of Dwight Moody and his evangelism and the foundation of a number of important gospel publishing houses. Foremost among these was J. D. Vaughn, Music Publisher (as his business was known), founded in 1902, which quickly became the largest of its kind and remains a major influence today. Vaughn is often called "the rock on which gospel music was founded."

Vaughn and his peers were enormously influential in promoting and disseminating the gospel songs we think of as classics today. These publishers included Mosie Lister ("God Put A Rainbow In The Clouds"), Albert Brumley ("I'll Fly Away"), Virgil Stamps and Jesse Baxter ("Turn

Your Radio On"), and Homer Rodeheaver ("The Old Rugged Cross" and "Beyond The Sunset"). The songbooks and sheet music that flowed from the publishing houses founded by these men made gospel music a commercial success long before the emergence of a secular country music. And, in addition to publishing, these men all played other important roles in the history of the music.

Vaughn was a pioneer in gospel radio over his station in Lawrenceburg, Tennessee, as was Rodeheaver on KDKA in Pittsburgh. Stamps and Baxter at one time had more than one hundred Stamps-Baxter quartets singing their selections on radio stations across the country. Composers Lister and Brumley have turned out gospel hit after hit.

Most of their songbooks retained the seven-note shape note system, and all were influential not only in preserving the old, but in constantly renewing gospel literature. Charlie Louvin said recently that at one time he could sing by heart every song in the Stamps-Baxter collection.

In 1911, Rodeheaver joined evangelist Billy Sunday in the first of their legendary crusades that over twenty years were to spread "the Word" to literally millions in many countries.

It was shortly thereafter that hillbilly pioneers began to spread commercial country music, incorporating a great many gospel songs in their repertories as well as the ethical and religious values on which they were based. Every true country song, religious or secular, shares common roots as well as a common appeal.

The qualities and ideas that gave life to the early revival songs are still alive in both country and gospel to this day. Musical and narrative simplicity, use of the chorus, pronounced rhythm, liveliness, sentimentality, intimacy, sincerity—in short, commercial appeal—all are common to both religious and secular country songs.

Many composers of country and gospel music share similar roots in the rural, Protestant South. Though they have followed different commercial paths, the two have interacted over the years with an easy exchange of talent, tunes, and ideas—and frequently of audiences. Together they have helped preserve the values of our southern society, its dominant religion, and its musical heritage.

Bluegrass, with its reverence for old songs and old forms, has become one of the chief repositories of older gospel in the country field. Just about every bluegrass group includes a number of these songs in their repertoire, and some groups, like the Lewis Family and the Sullivan Family, sing nothing else.

The following pages contain a selection of the best popular religious songs written since the turn of the century. They cover a broad spectrum of songs commonly sung on the country music circuit and include "The Old Rugged Cross," which is consistently named the most popular religious song in opinion surveys in both the South and the North. It is heard as often outside as inside churches.

"How Great Thou Art," introduced to this country in 1955 by George Beverly Shea of the Billy Graham Crusade, is fast joining their ranks. Others, like "Precious Memories," "Farther Along," and "Life's Railway To Heaven," are traditional country favorites that can be found in most sacred albums.

A number of the songs were made popular by country performers. These include "There'll Be Peace In The Valley For Me," "Just A Closer Walk With Thee," "Supper Time," and "Great Speckled Bird." Some, like "Dust On The Bible," "Wings Of A Dove," and "I Saw The Light," were actually written by country composers. Others, like Albert Brumley's "Turn Your Radio On" and Ira Stanphill's "Supper Time," were written by famous gospel writers with distinctly country inspiration.

Most of them are typical gospel songs, either affirming the glories of God and heaven or offering inspirational testimony to those not yet saved. One, "Keep On The Sunny Side Of Life," is a song of exhortation offering advice to the sinner. Several examples of "pure" hymns according to Kerr's definition are included: "Take My Hand, Precious Lord" and "Just A Closer Walk With Thee." And one that differs somewhat in tone from the others is "The Touch Of God's Hand." Popular with cowboy singers, it affirms the beauties of nature and the existence of God, but one that is far less personal than in most gospel songs.

BEYOND THE SUNSET

"We were guests at Rainbow Point, Winona Lake, Indiana, the home of Homer Rodeheaver, world famous song leader. . . . This guest house offers the best view of the sunset. Mrs. Brock and I watched one of these never-to-be-forgotten scenes. To us it seemed matchless in its beauty. The rapidly changing shades, deepening hues and blending colors impoverished our vocabulary in an attempt to describe it. . . . There we stood entranced, enjoying the hospitality of the householder at Rainbow Point, and watched the Householder of heaven draw down the multicolored curtains over His latticed windows. Our rapture moved to the inescapable question, 'What lies beyond the wondrous sunset? What will it be like when our work is done and the experience of heaven begun?' So amid the afterglow of the sunset, and still in the wonderland of its beauty, the poem took form and was set to music."

—Virgil Brock (As quoted in
Forty Gospel Hymn Stories
by George W. Sanville)

BEYOND THE SUNSET

by Virgil P. and Blanche Kerr Brock

Beyond the sunset, O blissful morning
When with our Saviour heav'n is begun
Earth's toiling ended, O glorious dawning
Beyond the sunset, when day is done.

Beyond the sunset no clouds will gather
No storms will threaten, no fears annoy
O day of gladness, O day unending
Beyond the sunset, eternal joy!

Beyond the sunset a hand will guide me
To God, the Father, whom I adore
His glorious presence, His words of welcome
Will be my portion on that fair shore.

Beyond the sunset, O glad reunion
With our dear loved ones who've gone before
In that fair homeland we'll know no parting
Beyond the sunset forever more!

CAN THE CIRCLE BE UNBROKEN?

The words to the chorus of this song were taken from an early gospel song written in 1907 by Ada Habershon and Charles H. Gabriel entitled "Can The Circle Be Unbroken?" It was first recorded by the Carter Family on May 6, 1935. —D. H.

CAN THE CIRCLE BE UNBROKEN?

by A. P. Carter

I was standin' by the window
On one cold and cloudy day
When I saw the hearse come rolling
For to carry my mother away.

Will the circle be unbroken, by and by, Lord, by and by?
There's a better home a-waiting in the sky, Lord, in the sky.

Lord, I told the undertaker
"Undertaker, please drive slow
For this body you are hauling
Lord, I hate to see her go!"

I followed close behind her
Tried to hold up and be brave
But I could not hide my sorrow
When they laid her in the grave.

Went back home, Lord
My home was lonesome
All my brothers, sisters crying
What a home so sad and lone.

DUST ON THE BIBLE

"I was born and raised in West Virginia in an area now considered a part of Charleston. My dad being a minister and my Christian mother led we children to believe in Christ and to go to church. It was in church while in my late teens that I found the origin for 'Dust On The Bible'. A young minister by the name of Willard Carney came there and started a church in a store basement. Since our parents had always taught us respect for all Christ-believing churches, I started attending Brother Carney's church pretty regular. In one of these services, I heard him relate this experience of going into a home to visit, which story is told in the song. I just put his story in song and bless him for it. I believe him to be a very sincere minister of Christ!"

—Walter Bailes

DUST ON THE BIBLE

by Walter and Johnny Bailes

I went into a home one day to see some friends of mine
Of all the books and magazines, not a Bible could I find
I asked them for the Bible; when they brought it, what a shame
For the dust was covered o'er it, not a fingerprint was plain.

Dust on the Bible, dust on the holy word
The words of all the prophets and the sayings of the Lord
Of all the other books you'll find, there's none salvation holds
Get that dust off the Bible and redeem your poor soul.

Oh, you can read your magazines of love and tragic things
But not one word of Bible verse, not a scripture do you know
When it is the very truth and its contents good for you
But if dust is covered o'er it, it is sure to doom your soul.

Oh, you have a friend you'd like to help along life's way
Just tell him that the Good Book shows a mortal how to pray
The best advice to give him that will make his burden light
Is to dust the family Bible, trade the wrong way for the right.

FARTHER ALONG

Written in November 1900, by W. B. Stevens of Queen City, Missouri, 'Farther Along' was composed for Mrs. Benedict, a singing evangelist. Before it was printed, Stevens himself had sung it in Fort Scott, Kansas.

—D. H.

FARTHER ALONG

by Rev. W. B. Stevens and J. R. Baxter, Jr.

Tempted and tried, we're oft made to wonder
Why it should be thus all the day long
While there are others, living about us
Never molested, though in the wrong.

Farther along, we'll know all about it
Farther along, we'll understand why
Cheer up, my brother, live in the sunshine
We'll understand it all by and by.

When death has come and taken our loved ones
It leaves our home so lonely and drear
Then do we wonder why others prosper
Living so wicked year after year.

"Faithful till death," said our loving Master
A few more days to labor and wait
Toils of the road will then seem as nothing
As we sweep through the beautiful gate.

When we see Jesus coming in glory
When He comes from His home in the sky
Then we shall meet Him in that bright mansion
We'll understand it all by and by.

GOD PUT A RAINBOW IN THE CLOUD

"This song was made by Daddy Jenkins, as we called him, after a short period of silence. It seemed like he was blue or depressed, but at times when he was thinking he seemed too quiet, and we soon learned that he was in deep thought. Going to the piano, he came up with 'God Put A Rainbow In The Cloud.' He loved the 'blue' note. I wrote it down for him and arranged the musical score. It was made one real hot summer afternoon—in August, I believe. The year: 1931. The song made a good hit with singers. Mahalia Jackson's recording made a good seller, but it had been recorded as 'not belonging to anyone.' SESAC got in touch with me, and as I had the original pencil copy, the song was verified. When I hear it on radio, it makes me so happy, for that is why Daddy made so many grand songs. He never received any remuneration for any of his work—at least not enough to be counted. He always said he could make more, and he wanted the people to sing them and love them. That was pay enough for him."
—Irene Spain Futrelle

GOD PUT A RAINBOW IN THE CLOUD

by Reverend Andrew Jenkins and Irene Spain

When God shut Noah in the grand old ark
He put a rainbow in the cloud
When thunders rolled and the sky was dark
God put a rainbow in the cloud.

God put a rainbow in the cloud
God put a rainbow in the cloud

When it looked like the sun wouldn't shine anymore
God put a rainbow in the cloud.

Away down yonder in Egypt's sand
God put a rainbow in the cloud
Just to lead his children to the promised land
God put a rainbow in the cloud.

When they put old Daniel in the Lion's den,
God put a rainbow in the cloud
Just to prove his promise to the sons of men
God put a rainbow in the cloud.

As a sign by day and a sign by night
God put a rainbow in the cloud
Just to guide his people and keep them right
God put a rainbow in the cloud.

Oh, Jordan deep and Jordan wide
God put a rainbow in the cloud
To lead his people to the other side
God put a rainbow in the cloud.

GOD WALKS THESE HILLS WITH ME

"I was walking past a Methodist Church in Nashville one day and saw a poster that read 'God Walks These Hills.' That was the inspiration for this song."
—Vic McAlpin

GOD WALKS THESE HILLS WITH ME

by Vic McAlpin and Marvin Hughes

We all have treasures we call our own
Mine are these hills I call my home
Just let me live 'til eternity
In these hills God walks with me.

Yes, he walks these hills, these beautiful hills
Where my soul is always free

What a comfort to know I'm never alone
For God walks these hills with me
Yes, God walks these hills with me.

Every day when the sun goes down
I thank God for the love I've found
For the contentment each day I see
In these hills God walks with me.

GREAT SPECKLED BIRD

"I first heard the song on radio in the 'thirties sung by a group who called themselves the Black Shirts. I took a liking to the song, picked it up and started singing it. I didn't know then who owned the song, but I later found out that Reverend Guy Smith in the Carolinas had written it [1937]. The song gave me my opportunity here in Nashville. My fiddle didn't get it. It took hold of the audience and I got a standing ovation on it, the only one that had ever been gotten at the Grand Ole Opry at that time. This was an audition at the Opry, and I opened the show with it. I came to Nashville as a fiddler and Arthur Smith was off away sick, and they called me on. I had been trying to get on for five years. You didn't get on the Opry back then for singing a song or having a hit number. They didn't ask you if you ever recorded. They didn't care. You had to be a showman. The only way you could get on was to have something to show and prove it. That night, along with my fiddling, I did the 'Great Speckled Bird,' and when I did it, the audience stood and cheered and cheered. I tried to leave but they brought me back two, three times. I went on home to Knoxville, not knowing whether I was even going to be accepted on the Opry or not. They sent me my mail, bushel baskets full of it, and it startled the WSM management. Two weeks later, they called me and asked if I would take a regular job. The song brought Roy Acuff to the Opry. I didn't bring it, it brought me." —Roy Acuff

GREAT SPECKLED BIRD
by Reverend Guy Smith

What a beautiful thought I am thinking
Concerning the great speckled bird

Remember her name is recorded
On the pages of God's Holy Word.

All the other birds are flocking 'round her
And she is despised by the squad
But the great speckled bird in the Bible
Is one with the great church of God.

All the other churches are against her
They envy her glory and fame
They hate her because she is chosen
And has not denied Jesus' name.

Desiring to lower her standard
They watch every move that she makes
They try to find fault with her teachings
But really they find no mistakes.

She is spreading her wings for a journey
She's going to leave by and by
When the trumpet shall sound in the morning
She'll rise and go up in the sky.

In the presence of all her despisers
With a song never uttered before
She will rise and be gone in a moment
Till the great tribulation is o'er.

I am glad I have learned of her meekness
I am proud that my name is on the book
For I want to be one never fearing
The face of my Savior to look.

When He cometh descending from heaven
On the cloud as is wrote in the Word
I'll be joyfully carried up to meet Him
On the wings of the great speckled bird.

Originally a Swedish hymn written by Rev. Carl Boberg, a twenty-five-year-old pastor, this song was first published as "O Store Gud" ("Oh Great God") in 1886. In 1907 it was translated into German by Manfred von Glehn and published under the title "Wie Gross Bist Du" ("How Great Thou Art"). An English missionary, Rev. Stuart K. Hine, found a Russian version in the Ukraine and began using it at evangelistic meetings. Some time later he translated the first three verses into English and upon his return home sang it at gospel meetings around the time of World War II. He added a fourth verse in 1948. In this country, it was popularized during the 1950s by the Billy Graham crusades.

—D. H.

HOW GREAT THOU ART

English lyrics by Stuart K. Hine

Oh Lord, my God, when I in awesome wonder
Consider all the worlds Thy hands have made
I see the stars, I hear the rolling thunder
Thy power throughout the universe displayed.

Then sings my soul, my Saviour God to Thee
How great Thou art, how great Thou art!
Then sings my soul, my Saviour God to Thee
How great Thou art, how great Thou art!

When through the woods and forest glades I wander
And hear the birds sing sweetly in the trees
When I look down from lofty mountain grandeur
And hear the brook and feel the gentle breeze.

And when I think that God, his Son not sparing
Sent Him to die, I scarce can take it in
That on the cross, my burden gladly bearing
He bled and died to take away my sin.

When Christ shall come with shout of acclamation
And take me home, what joy shall fill my heart!
Then I shall bow in humble adoration
And there proclaim, my God, how great Thou art!

"I first heard a version of this song from Lyman Rager, who had learned it while he was in the Elkton, Kentucky, jail. I rewrote it, rearranged it, and added to it."

—Merle Travis

I AM A PILGRIM

by Merle Travis

I am a pilgrim and a stranger
Traveling through this wearisome land
I got a home in that yonder city, oh, Lord
And it's not made by hand.

I got a mother, a sister and a brother
Who have gone to that sweet land
I'm determined to go and see them, good Lord
All over on that distant shore.

As I go down to that river of Jordan
Just to bathe my weary soul
If I could touch but the hem of His garment, good Lord
Well I believe it would make me whole.

IF I COULD HEAR MY MOTHER PRAY AGAIN

Written in 1922 by John Whitfield Vaughn and James Rowe, both of whom were prolific gospel writers of the first third of this century and were associated with the James D. Vaughn Music Company. Rowe was not a composer, but he claimed to have written more than twenty thousand "song poems" during his long association with gospel music. J. W. Vaughn was born in Alabama, and did not begin the serious study of harmony and composition until he was full grown. In 1904 he began teaching music in singing schools throughout the South, and he contributed songs to every Vaughn music publication after 1915. —D. H.

IF I COULD HEAR MY MOTHER PRAY AGAIN
by James Rowe and J. W. Vaughn

How sweet and happy seem those days of way-back dreams
When memory recalls them now and then
And with what rapture sweet my weary heart would beat
If I could hear my mother pray again.

If I could hear my mother pray again
If I could hear her tender voice, and then
So glad I'd be, 'twould mean so much to me
If I could hear my mother pray again.

She used to pray that I on Jesus would rely
And always walk the shining Gospel way
So, trusting still His love, I seek that home above
Where I shall meet my mother some glad day.

Her work on earth is done, the life crown has been won
And she is now at rest with Him above
And some glad morning she, I know, will welcome me
To that eternal home of peace and love.

I'LL FLY AWAY

"I was picking cotton on my father's farm and was humming the old ballad that went like this: 'If I had the wings of an angel, over these prison walls I would fly' [*The Prisoner's Song,* p. 263], and suddenly it dawned on me that I could use this plot for a gospel-type song. About three years later, I finally developed the plot, titled it 'I'll Fly Away,' and it was published in 1932. Those familiar with the song will note that I paraphrased one line of the old ballad to read 'Like a bird from prison bars have flown.' When I wrote it, I had no idea that it would become so universally popular." —Albert E. Brumley

I'LL FLY AWAY
by Albert E. Brumley

Some glad morning when this life is o'er
I'll fly away
To a home on God's celestial shore
I'll fly away.

I'll fly away, O glory
I'll fly away
When I die hallelujah by and by
I'll fly away.

When the shadows of this life have grown
I'll fly away
Like a bird from prison bars have flown
I'll fly away.

Just a few more weary days and then
I'll fly away
To a land where joys shall never end
I'll fly away.

I SAW THE LIGHT

"At the time Hank wrote the song, he and his band had ended a tour and were getting near Montgomery, Alabama, in a car that didn't run too well. They were afraid they wouldn't make it. Then Hank spotted the beacon light at the Montgomery airport and said, 'We're gonna make it now; I saw the light.' "

—Audrey Williams

I SAW THE LIGHT

by Hank Williams

I saw the light, I saw the light
No more darkness, no more night
Now I'm so happy, no sorrow in sight
Praise the Lord! I saw the light.

I wandered so aimless, life filled with sin
I wouldn't let my dear Saviour in
Then Jesus came like a stranger in the night
Praise the Lord! I saw the light.

Just like a blind man, I wandered alone
Worries and fears I claimed for my own

Then like a blind man that God gave back his sight
Praise the Lord! I saw the light.

IT IS NO SECRET

"I wrote 'It Is No Secret' in exactly seventeen minutes one night while waiting for my wife Suzy to get ready for bed. We had visited a movie actor. Upon parting, the actor had said, 'Hamblen, how did you break yourself from alcohol?' 'I didn't do it, fellow,' I answered. 'The Lord did it. He can do the same for anybody who'll let Him. It's no secret what God can do.' When we got home, the chimes of the grandfather clock in the hall started striking midnight. I was at my typewriter clicking away and in exactly seventeen minutes it was finished, tune and all."
—Stuart Hamblen (Reprinted with permission from the book *The Birth of a Song* by Stuart Hamblen)

IT IS NO SECRET
by Stuart Hamblen

The chimes of time ring out the news, another day is through
Someone slipped and fell; was that someone you?
You may have longed for added strength your courage to renew
Do not be disheartened, for I bring hope to you.

It is no secret what God can do
What he's done for others, he'll do for you
With arms wide open, he'll pardon you
It is no secret what God can do.

There is no night, for in His light, you'll never walk alone
Always feel at home, wherever you may roam
There is no power can conquer you while God is on your side
Take Him at His promise, don't run away and hide.

This is another example of the gospel "hymn" that addresses the Lord directly. Though it probably is of fairly recent origin and may have been composed as part of one of the evangelistic "crusades," its authorship has been lost. It became one of the first religious hits in country music when it was recorded by Red Foley in 1950. —D. H.

JUST A CLOSER WALK WITH THEE

I am weak, but Thou are strong
Jesus, keep me from all wrong
I'll be satisfied as long
As I walk, let me walk close to Thee.

Just a closer walk with Thee
Grant it, Jesus, is my plea
Daily walking close to Thee
Let it be, dear Lord, let it be.

Through this world of toil and snares
If I falter, Lord, who cares?
Who with me my burden shares?
None but Thee, dear Lord, none but Thee.

When my feeble life is o'er
Time for me will be no more
Guide me gently, safely o'er
To Thy kingdom shore, to Thy shore.

KEEP ON THE SUNNY SIDE OF LIFE

"Early in [Ada Blenkhorn's] life, she was given the task of caring for an invalid nephew who always wanted his wheel chair to be pushed 'down the sunny side of the street.' His constant repetition of this phrase inspired her to write the gospel song 'Keep On The Sunny Side Of Life.'[1899]" —Phil Kerr *(Music in Evangelism)*

"We learned this song from A. P.'s Uncle, Laish Carter, who was a music teacher. We recorded it in 1928 in Camden, New Jersey. After we recorded it and started singing it on radio, we used it as our theme song. A. P. has a gold record of this song on his tombstone."

—Mother Maybelle Carter, of the original Carter Family

KEEP ON THE SUNNY SIDE OF LIFE

by Ada Blenkhorn and J. Howard Entwisle

There's a dark and a troubled side of life
There's a bright and a sunny side, too
Though we meet with the darkness and strife
The sunny side we also may view.

Keep on the sunny side, always on the sunny side
Keep on the sunny side of life
It will help us ev'ry day, it will brighten all the way
If we keep on the sunny side of life.

Though the storm in its fury break today
Crushing hopes that we cherish so dear
Storm and cloud will in time pass away
The sun again will shine bright and clear.

Let us greet with a song of hope each day
Though the moments be cloudy or fair
Let us trust in our Savior, a way
To keep'th every one in his care.

LIFE'S RAILWAY TO HEAVEN

"Some fifty years ago [1890], here in Atlanta, an old Baptist preacher (M. E. Abbey) came to me with a poem. I took the poem to my room, placed it on the organ in front of me. The melody came quickly. We dedicated it to railroad men everywhere."

—Charles Tillman, as quoted in *Music in Evangelism* by Phil Kerr

LIFE'S RAILWAY TO HEAVEN

by M. E. Abbey and Charlie D. Tillman

Life is like a mountain railroad with an engineer that's brave
We must make the run successful from the cradle to the grave
Watch the curves, the fills, the tunnels; never falter, never quail
Keep your hand upon the throttle and your eye upon the rail.

Blessed Savior, thou will guide us, till we reach that blissful shore
Where the angels wait to join us in thy grace forever more.

You will roll up grades of trial, you will cross the bridge of strife
See that Christ is your conductor on this lightning train of life
Always mindful of obstruction, do your duty, never fail
Keep your hand upon the throttle and your eye upon the rail.

You will often find obstructions, look for storms and wind and rain
On a fill or curve or trestle they will almost ditch your train
Put your trust alone in Jesus; never falter, never fail
Keep your hand upon the throttle and your eye upon the rail.

As you roll across the trestle, spanning Jordan's swelling tide
You behold the Union Depot into which your train will glide
There you'll meet the Superintendent, God the Father, God the Son
With the hearty, joyous plaudit, "Weary pilgrim, welcome home!"

THE OLD RUGGED CROSS

"I was praying for a full understanding of the Cross and its plan in Christianity. I read and studied and prayed. I saw Christ and the Cross inseparably. The Christ of the Cross became more than a symbol . . . it was like seeing John 3:16* leave the printed page, take form and act out the meaning of redemption. While watching this scene with my mind's eye, the theme of the song came to me, and with it the melody."

—Rev. George Bennard (1873–1958), as quoted in *Forty Gospel Hymn Stories,* by George W. Sanville

"My late husband began writing this song in 1912, and he wrote it over a period of a year. During that year he went through a very severe 'life test' which inspired him to write it. He told the story in every state of the Union except two, Utah and Louisiana."

—Mrs. Hannah Bennard

THE OLD RUGGED CROSS

by Rev. George Bennard

On a hill far away stood an old rugged cross
The emblem of suff'ring and shame
And I love that old cross where the dearest and best
For a world of lost sinners was slain.

*"For God so loved the world, that He gave His only begotten Son, that whosoever believeth in Him should not perish, but have everlasting life."

So I'll cherish the old rugged cross
Till my trophies at last I lay down
I will cling to the old rugged cross
And exchange it some day for a crown.

Oh, that old rugged cross, so despised by the world
Has a wondrous attraction for me
For the dear Lamb of God left His glory above
To bear it to dark Calvary.

In the old rugged cross, stained with blood so divine
A wondrous beauty I see
For 'twas on that old cross Jesus suffered and died
To pardon and sanctify me.

To the old rugged cross I will ever be true
Its shame and reproach gladly bear
Then He'll call me some day to my home far away
Where His glory forever I'll share.

ONLY ONE STEP MORE

"In my boyhood I knew many old mountain people who led a pretty hard life and, as they neared the end of it, looked forward to that hour when they would take that one last step from earth to heaven with the hope of better things to come that helped them over the hard places. I tried to write a song for them, in their own words, expressing their philosophy of life and what lay ahead at the end of the long, long way. So far as I know this has never been published in any form except in hymnbook collections, some but not all of which were put out by Stamps-Baxter. None of their versions are exactly like the original which I was the first to get into print."

—John Lair

ONLY ONE STEP MORE

by John Lair

I have known a life of sorrow
I have borne a heavy load

And my weary feet have stumbled
On the rough and rocky road
Soon my burden will be lifted
Soon my trials will be o'er
Soon my journey will be ended
For it's only one step more.

Jesus told of many mansions
Over in that promised land
Soon I'll move from this low dwelling
To a house not built with hands
There I'll live next door to Jesus
And my friends gone on before
Soon I'll settle in that city
For it's only one step more.

Mother's long been over yonder
She'll be waiting for me, too
She'll be, O, so glad to see me
Proud to know that I've pulled through
She will be the first to greet me
When I enter heaven's door
O, I'll soon be with you, Mother
For it's only one step more.

Years ago our little darling
Journeyed to that land of love
And the flower that drooped and faded
Blossoms now in heaven above
She'll be changed, but, O, I'll know her
When I search the angels o'er
I am coming, baby, coming
And it's only one step more.

THERE'LL BE PEACE IN THE VALLEY FOR ME

"It was just before Hitler sent his war chariots into Western Europe in the late thirties. I was on a train going through Southern Indiana on the way to Cincinnati, and the country seemed to be upset about this coming war that he was about to bring on. I passed through a valley on the train. Horses, cows, sheep, they were all grazing and together in this little valley. Kind of a little brook was running through

the valley, and up the hill there I could see where the water was falling from. Everything seemed so peaceful with all the animals down there grazing together. It made me wonder what's the matter with humanity? What's the matter with mankind? Why couldn't man live in peace like the animals down there? So out of that came 'Peace In The Valley.' "
—Rev. Thomas A. Dorsey

THERE'LL BE PEACE IN THE VALLEY FOR ME

by Thomas A. Dorsey

Well, I'm tired and so weary, but I must go along
Till the Lord comes to call me away
Where the morning's so bright and the Lamb is the light
And the night, night is as fair as the day.

There will be peace in the valley for me someday
There will be peace in the valley for me, Oh Lord I pray
There'll be no sadness, no sorrow, no trouble I'll see
There will be peace in the valley for me.

Well, the bear will be gentle, and the wolf will be tame
And the lion will lay down by the lamb
And the beasts from the wild will be led by a lit'le child
I'll be changed, changed from this creature that I am.

PREACHIN', PRAYIN', SINGIN'

"My late husband was with the United States Forest Service. He started out as a surveyor in 1933 and stayed with them until his death in 1962. Music was his hobby. When he died, he was with Land and Law, traveling a great deal for them, going from court to court settling claims. On one of his trips, he was passing through McKee, Kentucky, the county seat of Laurel County, and he saw an old-time camp meeting going on at the courthouse square. They were singing and praying and hollering, and he stopped and listened a while. That was the inspiration for this song, and he came home and wrote it."
—Nora (Mrs. E. C.) McCarty

PREACHIN', PRAYIN', SINGIN'
by E. C. "Mac" McCarty

I was a stranger there, intent upon my way
But when I saw the crowd, I had the urge to stay
I heard a welcome voice bidding me come and share
Their preachin', prayin', singin', down on the public square.

Preachin', prayin', singin' everywhere
Shouting their praises of His loving care
All of God's children seem to gather there
Preachin', prayin', singin' down on the public square.

I felt so much at home amid this happy throng
That came from far and near to praise His name in song
To lay their burdens down, forget their every care
And have an old-time meetin' down on the public square.

Now as I journey on, and think back o'er the day
I am convinced within these folks have found the way
To put their hearts in song, to pray an earnest prayer
And leave the joy bells ringin', down on the public square.

PRECIOUS MEMORIES

"J. B. F. Wright, author-composer of 'Precious Memories' (originally copyrighted in 1925), was born in Tennessee, February 21, 1877. In contrast to the majority of modern day writers and composers, Mr. Wright has never taught nor does he claim a great amount of music education. He writes from inspiration, and in his own words, '. . . when words come spontaneously, flowing into place when I feel the divine urge.' Mr. Wright is a member of the Church of God, and his writing, as did his church work, began at a very early age."

—Roy Maxwell Stone *(Our Hymns and Gospel Songs)*

PRECIOUS MEMORIES

by J. B. F. Wright

Precious mem'ries, unseen angels
Sent from somewhere to my soul
How they linger, ever near me
And the sacred past unfold.

Precious mem'ries, how they linger
How they ever flood my soul
In the stillness of the midnight
Precious, sacred scenes unfold.

Precious father, loving mother
Fly across the lonely years
And old home scenes of my childhood
In fond memory appear.

In the stillness of the midnight
Echoes from the past I hear
Old-time singing, gladness bringing
From that lovely land somewhere.

I remember mother praying
Father, too, on bended knee
Sun is sinking, shadows falling
But their pray'rs still follow me.

As I travel on life's pathway
Know not what the years may hold
As I ponder, hope grows fonder
Precious mem'ries flood my soul.

SUPPER TIME

"The song was composed about 1949 in the little town of Osceola, Missouri. I was conducting a small revival meeting in a tent. I was divorced from my first wife (who later was killed in a car accident) and my small son of about five years of age was traveling with me. I suppose I was reminiscing about my own life, how pleasant it had been, and then was desiring this same happiness for my boy, who, at that time seemed to have no chance that he would ever have a real home again. While sitting on the side of the bed and watching him take a nap I wrote the words. The song is actually based upon a scripture verse in Revelation 19:9, which speaks about future hope of all Christians, which says, '. . . Blessed are they who are called to the marriage supper of the Lamb.' "

—Ira Stanphill

SUPPER TIME
by Ira Stanphill

Many years ago in days of childhood
I used to play till evening shadows come
Then winding down an old familiar pathway
I heard my mother call at set of sun.

Come home, come home, it's supper time
The shadows lengthen fast
Come home, come home, it's supper time
We're going home at last.

One day beside her bedside I was kneeling
And angel wings were winnowing the air
She heard the call for supper time in heaven
And I know she's waiting for me there.

In visions now I see her standing yonder
And her familiar voice I hear once more
The banquet table's ready up in heaven
It's supper time up on the golden shore.

TAKE MY HAND, PRECIOUS LORD

"This song is very dear to me. I left my home one morning with another fellow driving to St. Louis to sing in a revival at a Baptist church. My wife was going to become a mother in a few days. We got 24 miles outside of Chicago, and I discovered I had left my briefcase with all my music in it. I turned around, drove back to Chicago and went home. My wife was sleeping, and I didn't disturb her. When I got back in the car, the other fellow said he had changed his mind and decided not to go. As it was,

Providence was trying to tell *me* not to go away. But I went on to St. Louis, anyway. Next night, I was working in a revival, and I received a telegram: 'Your wife just died. Come home.' Some fellows volunteered to drive me to Chicago, and when I got home next day, I had the body moved. I had a bouncing boy baby. But that night, the *baby* died. That was double trouble. I felt like going back on God. He had mistreated me, I felt. About a week later, after we had put the baby and the wife away in the same casket, I was sitting with the late Theodore Fry, just drowsing. Just like water dropping from the crevice of a rock, the words dropped into the music, 'Take My Hand, Precious Lord.' " —Rev. Thomas A. Dorsey

TAKE MY HAND, PRECIOUS LORD

by Thomas A. Dorsey

Precious Lord, take my hand, lead me on, let me stand
I am tired, I am weak, I am worn
Thru the storm, thru the night, lead me on to the light
Take my hand, precious Lord, lead me home.

When my way grows drear, precious Lord, linger near
When my life is almost gone
Hear my cry, hear my call, hold my hand lest I fall
Take my hand, precious Lord, lead me home.

When the darkness appears and the night draws near
And the day is past and gone
At the river I stand, guide my feet, hold my hand
Take my hand, precious Lord, lead me home.

THE TOUCH OF GOD'S HAND

"After World War I, I came to the deserts of Arizona. The environmental change had a tremendous impact on me—from the backwoods of Canada to the deceptively barren deserts of Arizona. Actually out there on that barren land there is more to see than in a forest, on a closer look. The desert is crowded with things to see, which inspired me to write 'The Touch Of God's Hand.' " —Bob Nolan

THE TOUCH OF GOD'S HAND
by Bob Nolan

The prairie sound sends down its ray
To warm my heart through every day
The starlight beam that guides my way
Is just the touch of God's hand.

The scattered pearls of morning dew
The rainbow mist on hills of blue
The silver veil of moonbeams, too
Is just the touch of God's hand.

The desert breeze that brushed my hair
The leaf that fell from who knows where
The scent of wildflowers in the air
Is just the touch of God's hand.

The wasteland fall that fills the sky
The hum of wild wings sailing by
The warm earth bed on which I lie
Is just the touch of God's hand.

The desert yields a water pool
Where wild things meet their thirst to cool
And I'm a carefree, happy fool
I know the touch of God's hand.

The rain that falls I love so dear
And joy is mine just livin' here
I know He must be standin' near
I feel the touch of God's hand.

THE TRAMP ON THE STREET

Copyrighted in 1940, this religious song was patterned after a much earlier secular song called "Only A Tramp!," written by Dr. Addison D.

Crabtre in 1877. The two songs are similar in one verse and the chorus; Crabtre's is as follows:

> "He's somebody's darling, somebody's son
> For once he was fair, once he was young
> Someone has rocked him, a baby, to sleep
> Now only a tramp found dead on the street."

"Tramp On The Street" was popularized by Molly O'Day in the late forties.
—D. H.

THE TRAMP ON THE STREET
by Grady and Hazel Cole

Only a tramp was Laz'rus that day
It was he who lay at the rich man's gate
He begged for the crumbs from the rich man to eat
He was left there to die like a tramp on the street.

He was some mother's darling, some mother's son
Once he was fair, and once he was young
Some mother once rocked her darling to sleep
He was left there to die like a tramp on the street.

Jesus, who died on Calvary's tree
Shed His life's blood for you and for me
They pierced His side, His hands and His feet
And left Him to die like a tramp on the street.

He was King of the Jews and God's chosen Son
He was so fair, and once He was young
Mary once rocked her Darling to sleep
He was left there to die like a tramp on the street.

If Jesus should come and knock at your door
And ask you to give the crumbs from your floor
Would you welcome Him in or turn Him away?
You'll have your reward on that Judgment Day.

"I wrote 'Turn Your Radio On' in 1937, and it was published in 1938. At this time radio was relatively new to the rural people, especially Gospel music programs. I had become alert to the necessity of creating song titles, themes and plots, and frequently people would call me and say 'Turn your radio on, Albert, they're singing one of your songs on such-and-such a station.' It finally dawned on me to use their quote, 'Turn your radio on,' as a theme for a religious originated song, and this was the beginning of 'Turn Your Radio On' as we now know it."

—Albert E. Brumley

TURN YOUR RADIO ON

by Albert E. Brumley

Come and listen in to a radio station
Where the mighty hosts of heaven sing
Turn your radio on, turn your radio on
If you want to hear the songs of Zion
Coming from the land of endless spring
Get in touch with God, turn your radio on.

Turn your radio on, turn your radio on
And listen to the music in the air
Turn your radio on, heaven's glory share
Turn the lights down low
And listen to the Master's radio
Get in touch with God, turn your radio on.

Brother, listen in to the gloryland chorus
Listen to the glad hosannas roll
Turn your radio on, turn your radio on
Get a little taste of joy awaiting
Get a little heaven in your soul
Get in touch with God, turn your radio on.

Listen to the songs of the fathers and the mothers
And the many friends gone before
Turn your radio on, turn your radio on
Some eternal morning we shall meet them
Over on the hallelujah shore
Get in touch with God, turn your radio on.

"This song was written like a prayer. My father, a minister, raised me as a member of the Assembly of God church, and we believe in Christ's second coming. When you're a Christian, you want that day to come as soon as possible, because you'd like to be in heaven with the angels and have happier times than we have here on earth. Yet at the same time, you don't want Him to rush it, because there are others that might be lost because they're not saved. As a Christian, I was anxious to be in a better place, but at the same time, 'Wait a little longer—give these others I love so much a chance to become Christian, too, before the end of time.' "

—Hazel Houser

WAIT A LITTLE LONGER, PLEASE, JESUS

by Hazel Houser and Chester Smith

Here the labor is so hard, the workers are so tired
And our weary hearts are yearnin' for a rest
And we find we're getting anxious to be in that happy land
Where we'll receive such peace and happiness.

(But) wait a little longer, please, Jesus
There's so many still wand'ring out in sin
Just a little longer, please, Jesus
A few more days to get our loved ones in.

We may look into the skies, and tears will fill our eyes
For our burdened heart grows heavier with each day
First we cry "Oh Lord, please come, come and take your children home"
But then we look around us and we say:

The family's scattered here and there, but, Lord, we love them dear
And maybe we can help them find the way
Then if waiting is the cost, they may not be lost
Lord, that's the only reason why we say:

WHERE COULD I GO?

James Coats, one of the foremost gospel songwriters of the South, was born in Summerland, Mississippi, in 1901. He was a public school teacher for more than twenty years, a music teacher for most of his life, and a deacon, then a pastor, in the Baptist Church. According to "Ma" Baxter's *Gospel Song Writers Biography*, he "believed that all true music came through inspiration from God and that the true office of music is the worship of God."

—D. H.

WHERE COULD I GO?

by J. B. Coats

Living below in this old sinful world
Hardly a comfort can afford
Striving alone to face temptations sore
Where could I go but to the Lord?

Where could I go but to the Lord?
Where could I go? Oh, where could I go?
Seeking refuge for my soul
Needing a friend to save me in the end
Where could I go but to the Lord?

Neighbors are kind, I love them every one
We get along in sweet accord
But when my soul needs manna from above
Where could I go but to the Lord?

Life here is grand with friends I love so dear
Comfort I get from God's own word
Yet when I face the chilling hand of death
Where could I go but to the Lord?

WINGS OF A DOVE

"This is a personal expression of faith and joy in achieving a goal. When I wrote it, I had just completed thirteen films on wildlife, and I was elated that the job was done."

—Bob Ferguson

WINGS OF A DOVE

by Bob Ferguson

When troubles surround us, when evils come
The body grows weak, the spirit grows numb
When these things beset us, He doesn't forget us
He sends down his love on the wings of a dove.

On the wings of a snow white dove
He sends His pure, sweet love
A sign from above on the wings of a dove.

When Noah had drifted on the Flood many days
He searched for land in various ways
Troubles he had some but wasn't forgotten
He sent him His love on the wings of a dove.

When Jesus went down to the waters that day
He was baptized in the usual way
When it was done, God blessed his Son
He sent Him His love on the wings of a dove.

3 | Songs of Death and Sorrow

How Sad, How Sad the Story

Long before the Revolution, Americans had shown a distinct preference for songs of tragedy, disaster, death and sorrow. Of the English and Scottish folk ballads that accompanied the early settlers to the eastern seaboard, songs like "Black Jack David," "Fair Ellen," and "Barbara Allen"—piteous tales of tragic love, broken promises, and murder—survived the best. They were, in fact, among the earliest songs recorded by hillbilly artists in the early twenties.

An even more important source of these much-loved "weepers" (as Sigmund Spaeth called them), however, was the sentimental songs of Gussie Davis, Mitchell and Pratt, Charles K. Harris, and other early Tin Pan Alley writers whose works were retained in the country repertoire long after they had gone out of fashion in the cities of the North.

We can only speculate on the reasons for the South's penchant for the sentimental, pathetic songs that comprise this chapter and dominate several others. Perhaps they are an index of the misery experienced by the country music fan and provide an outlet for his own unhappiness, an externalization of his hardships.

Country music historian Bill C. Malone speculates that the sadness is in part a symptom of a declining culture. "Rural southerners have long been aware of being a part of a society in decline," he said, "one which is gradually, persistently losing out in the competition with an urban way of life. Not only has this music come from a rural past, it has come from a *southern* rural past—from a South traditionally defensive, beleaguered, outnumbered, which has experienced tragedy, poverty, military defeat. How can the music of such a region be anything but sad?"

Paul Hemphill, a southern journalist, also takes a straightforward stand in *The Nashville Sound: Bright Lights and Country Music:* "The music was simple and narrative, and it did what music was supposed to do: it took the mind off the miserable and lonely life these people had chosen, much as their religion did, and while they were making the music they were, in a sense, in another world."

Whether these songs are a lament for a lost and losing South or simply a way of escaping the harsh realities of rural life, they are never —to this day—taken lightly. We may sneer with Spaeth at the "School of Self-Pity" *(Weep Some More, My Lady,),* but to the country music fan, such songs are real, factual, larger than life. The excellence of a hillbilly singer and the impact of his performance are often judged on his sincerity in delivering these lyrics and his ability to make the tears flow or the chills run up and down your spine.

This curious interaction of singer, song, and audience is probably unique to country music, and is nowhere more apparent than in Ernest Tubb's "Our Baby's Book." Written after the death of his second child in a tragic accident, it remains one of his most requested songs today, more than thirty years later. Tubb says he knows of more than three hundred children named Rodger Dale in honor of his dead son. His devoted fans symbolically "gave" their children to him to help replace his loss.

Children, of course, are one of the recurring subjects in this somber chapter—abandoned children, neglected children, children dying and dead. This may simply reflect the age-old formula for commercial success, "kids and dogs," though in light of the history of the pre–World War South, where back-breaking child labor was a commonplace and childhood was cut short out of economic necessity, where the infant death rate was high enough to touch almost every family, the popularity of such songs also must be considered an expression of deep fears and guilt.

Several of the songs that follow are true or true to life; others are obvious commercial confections. Most follow the tragic pattern of so many hillbilly songs with frequent appeals to God and references to a better life hereafter. The chorus in "Willie Roy" is his "little prayer." Tubb speaks of "a new star in heaven," and the "Drunkard's Child" is assured of a "welcome on heaven's golden shore."

Children are not the only ones welcome to heaven. Mother in "Sweeter Than The Flowers," a sweetheart in "The Precious Jewel," and the whole family in "Nobody's Darling But Mine" all have taken their places "with the heavenly fold." And if dogs have a heaven, we are told, "Old Shep has a wonderful home."

The so-called event song, which Bill Malone calls "a throwback to the British broadside" and "perhaps most characteristic of the hillbilly music of the 'twenties," is a parallel form to (almost a subcategory of) these tragedy songs. Part of a long tradition of musical reportage chiefly, though not necessarily, of grisly events, they served as newspapers in preliterate and illiterate societies. Event songs were given new life in the twenties and thirties with the compositions of Carson Robison and Bob Miller which chronicled incidents like "The John T. Scopes Trial" and the deaths of "Pretty Boy Floyd" and "Outlaw John Dillinger."

Some, like "The Sinking Of The Titanic," began life as poems printed in newspapers; others, such as "The Wreck On The Highway," were composed on the spot, while others, including "Amelia Earhart's Last Flight," were inspired by newspaper and radio accounts. Many were commercial successes and have survived the years.

Perhaps the best example is Rev. Andrew ("Blind Andy") Jenkins's "The Death of Floyd Collins," which he wrote on request for $25. This song has not only remained a popular one but has been collected frequently by folklorists and has even gained an entry and identifying number in G. Malcolm Laws's *Native American Balladry*.

An ancient practice which was revived with the commercial hillbilly tradition and the recognition of a country music public was that of the "tribute" song, usually—though not necessarily—written upon the death of a hillbilly idol. The death of Jimmie Rodgers in 1933 produced a rash of songs using his name in the title. "When Jimmie Rodgers Said Goodbye" was one of the most popular and, unlike some of the songs of this type, was written and sung with real emotion. Hank Williams's untimely death, of course, inspired a number of mournful ballads, the best of which was "The Death Of Hank Williams," which rose to a position on the country music charts second only to one of Hank's own songs.

This need for hillbilly music to celebrate itself came to a logical extreme with a song called "I Dreamed Of A Hillbilly Heaven" which managed to mention virtually every big country name living and dead and which has undergone constant revision as the roster has changed. Presumably, if the song retains its popularity additional verses will be added ad infinitum.

The "good old" songs of death and tragedy have not declined in popularity, at least not for the Roy Acuffs and Ernest Tubbs who have been their greatest interpreters, for the bluegrass groups who base much of their repertoires on them, and for many other country entertainers who use them as program music. Few new ones are gaining popularity, however, perhaps because conditions have changed so in the rural South. With longer life-spans, child labor laws, and lower infant mortality rates, tragedy is no longer a day-to-day matter. Probably the last song of this type to become a major popular hit was "The Death Of Little Kathy Fiscus" in 1949, a true account of an accident that gained national headlines. Today we would expect a story of this kind to come alive on our television screens. Increasing affluence and better communications are steadily eroding another venerable hillbilly institution.

"In the early days of radio in the 1930s, each station featured live talent rather than records, and many artists would travel from time to time from one station to another. Income of the various entertainers was from selling song books, pictures, and sometimes even sponsors. While traveling from one station to another, sometimes as much as a hundred and even a thousand miles, the talent would play and sing anywhere to pick up traveling money. This included schools, night clubs, parks and churches. After the show, money was thrown on the floor or maybe a hat was passed, and the traveling troupe moved on. This was called 'busking.' 'Amelia Earhart's Last Flight' was a busking song and a sure money-getter. It was written around a campfire in New York state in 1937, shortly after we received word of Miss Earhart's disappearance."

—Red River Dave McEnery

AMELIA EARHART'S LAST FLIGHT

by Dave McEnery

Well, a ship out on the ocean
Just a speck against the sky
Amelia Earhart flying that sad day
With her partner, Captain Noonan
On the second of July
Her plane fell in the ocean far away.

There's a beautiful, beautiful field
Far away in a land that is fair
Happy landings to you, Amelia Earhart
Farewell, first lady of the air.

She radioed position
And she said that all was well
Although the fuel within the tanks was low
But they'd land on Howland Island
To refuel her monoplane
Then on the trip around the world they'd go.

Well, a half an hour later
An S.O.S. was heard
The signal weak, but still her voice was brave
Oh, in shark-infested waters
Her plane went down that night
In the blue Pacific to a watery grave.

Well, now you've heard my story
Of that awful tragedy

We pray that she might fly home safe again
Oh, in years to come when
Others blaze a trail across the sea
We'll ne'er forget Amelia and her plane.

BAGGAGE COACH AHEAD

This song was written in 1896 by Gussie L. Davis, the first successful Negro composer. Davis was a porter on the train where the incident actually occurred. In the 1920s, long after the song had become popular, newspapers carried the story of the death in Kansas City of a Mrs. Nettie Klapmeyer, who was the baby of the actual journey. Davis also wrote such country classics as "The Fatal Wedding" and "We Sat Beneath The Maple On The Hill."

—D. H.

BAGGAGE COACH AHEAD
by Gussie L. Davis

On a dark, stormy night, as the train rattled on
All the passengers had gone to bed
Except one young man with a babe in his arms
Who sat there with a bowed-down head.

The innocent one began crying just then
As though its poor heart would break
One angry man said, "Make that child stop its noise
For it's keeping all of us awake."

"Put it out," said another, "don't keep it in here
We've paid for our berths and want rest"
But never a word said the man with the child
As he fondled it close to his breast.

"Where is its mother? Go take it to her"
This a lady then softly said
"I wish I could" was the man's sad reply
"But she's dead in the coach ahead."

While the train rolled onward, a husband sat in tears
Thinking of the happiness of just a few short years
For baby's face brings pictures of a cherished hope that's dead
But baby's cries can't waken her in the baggage coach ahead.

THE DEATH OF FLOYD COLLINS

"This song was made after receiving a telegram from Mr. Polk Brockman of the James K. Polk Company in Atlanta to make one. He was in Florida. After listening to the radio so much, we knew the entire tragic horror of it, so, after getting the telegram, Daddy took his guitar out to the front steps and went to singing. I went to him, wrote it all down, made the musical score, and had it finished and in the mails in a very short time. The music was finished, but with pure simplicity. Mr. Brockman received it in a few hours from the time he sent the telegram. He then rushed it to New York, where Vernon Dalhart recorded it. We were told while in New York that this song had made several of the performers plus Mr. Brockman an awful lot of money. Well, as Daddy said many times, he wanted the people to sing them and love them, that was enough pay for him."
—Irene Spain Futrelle

THE DEATH OF FLOYD COLLINS
by Rev. Andrew Jenkins and Irene Spain

Oh, come all you young people and listen while I tell
The fate of Floyd Collins, a lad we all know well
His face was fair and handsome, his heart was true and brave
His body now lies sleeping in a lonely sandstone cave.

How sad, how sad the story, it fills our eyes with tears
Its memories, too, will linger for many, many years
A broken-hearted father, who tried his boy to save
Will now weep tears of sorrow at the door of Floyd's cave.

Oh, mother, don't you worry; dear father, don't be sad
I'll tell you all my troubles in an awful dream I had
I dreamed that I was prisoner, my life I could not save
I cried, "Oh, must I perish within this silent cave?"

"Oh, Floyd," cried his mother, "Don't go, my son, don't go
'Twould leave us broken-hearted if this should happen so"

Though Floyd did not listen, advice his mother gave
So his body now lies sleeping in a lonely sandstone cave.

His father often warned him from follies to desist
He told him of the danger and of the awful risk
But Floyd would not listen to the oft advice he gave
So his body now lies sleeping in a lonely sandstone cave.

Oh, how the news did travel! Oh, how the news did go
It traveled through the papers and over the radio
A rescue party gathered, his life they tried to save
But his body now lies sleeping in a lonely sandstone cave.

The rescue party labored, they worked both night and day
To move the mighty barrier that stood within the way
To rescue Floyd Collins, this was their battle cry
"We'll never, no, we'll never let Floyd Collins die."

But on that fatal morning, the sun rose in the sky
The workers still were busy, we'll save him by and by
But, oh how sad the ending, his life could not be saved
His body then was sleeping in a lonely sandstone cave.

Young people, oh, take warning from Floyd Collins' fate
And get right with your Maker before it is too late
It may not be a sand cave in which we find our tomb
But at the bar of judgement, we, too, must meet our doom.

The mining experts gathered, they sought to find a plan
To lift poor Floyd's body from far beneath the sand
And oh, how they did struggle with hearts brave and stout
But the cave that swallowed Collins would never let him out.

THE DEATH OF HANK WILLIAMS

"I was raised in the same country Hank came from and knew him, not intimately, but I had been on stage with him a time or two. I idolized Hank because he had done that thing I wanted to do—he had captured the feeling of the Depression, of the lonesomeness of a man who had known poverty. He had the ability to use the same words I use and express things so that people in New York could know what he was saying and feel what he was saying. The song that inspired 'The Death Of Hank Williams' was a song my brother used to sing called 'When Jimmie Rodgers Said Goodbye.' "

—Jack Cardwell

THE DEATH OF HANK WILLIAMS

by Jack Cardwell

Way up in West Virginia, between midnight and dawn
A big blue car was rolling, its wheels they hummed a song
The headlights shone out through the night to light the roads so steep
While in the back Hank Williams lay in a deep and dreamless sleep
He was heading for Ohio to play a show next day
'Cause thousands there were waiting to hear him sing and play.

The chauffeur reached into the back and shook the sleeping man
He said, "Wake up, wake up, my friend," and took him by the hand
He tried to wake him up again, then rushed him into town
But the doctor said, "Too late, too late, he's gone to a better land."

We've lost our greatest folk song star this world has ever known
But though he's gone on to his rest, his songs live on and on
He wrote songs about the Bible and songs about the hills
His songs about the lonesome blues, they gave the world a thrill
He left us songs of sadness and songs for lovers too
We'll never forget him though he's gone, Hank Williams, here's to you.

THE DEATH OF LITTLE KATHY FISCUS

"SAN MARINO, CALIF., APRIL 8—A 3-year-old girl fell down a 120-foot dry well pipe fourteen inches in diameter tonight, and rescuers and heavy digging equipment worked feverishly to reach her. Giant floodlights illuminated the vacant lot where the well was located, and police struggled to keep back crowds of onlookers. A steady stream of fresh air was pumped into the well. . . . Little Kathy Fiscus fell into the grass-covered pipe opening just before dark while playing in the lot with two companions. She slipped beyond a bend sixty feet down in the well, and so could not be seen from the top. Her faint cries were heard until about 6:30 P.M., but after that the roar of the digging equipment drowned out any possible chance of hearing her. 'She's either fallen asleep or else she's already died,' Police Sergeant T. F. Stewart said."

—*The New York Times,* April 9, 1949, p. 1

THE DEATH OF LITTLE KATHY FISCUS

by Jimmy Osborne and G. Nigh

On April the eighth, the year 'forty-nine
Death claimed a little child, so pure and so kind
Kathy, they called her, met her doom that day
I know it was God that called her away.

Playmates with Kathy were all having fun
The story was told, they all started to run
And as they looked back, she wasn't there
It's so sad to think of this tragic affair.

Just like a beast in the forest that day
The abandoned well took Kathy away
For over two days, the well was her tomb
Everyone kept praying they'd get her out soon.

Thousands were there from far and from near
Workmen, they struggled against sadness and tears
But after two days, their hopes grew so weak
They called down to Kathy, but she never did speak.

After working so hard, both day and night
Digging for hours, she came into sight
The little darling was dead; her life, it was gone
Now in San Marino, there's a heart-broken home.

I'm sure she's an angel in God's peaceful fold
Playing with children in a mansion of gold
As I stand alone, humbly I bow
I know Kathy's happy up there with God now.

Written by Hugh Cross, songwriter and performer with the Cumberland Ridge Runners on Chicago's WLS Barn Dance, this song inspired songwriter Fred Rose to comment that he never really understood country music until one night at the Grand Ole Opry when he heard Roy Acuff, with tear-filled eyes, sing "Don't Make Me Go To Bed And I'll Be Good."
—D. H.

DON'T MAKE ME GO TO BED AND I'LL BE GOOD

by Hugh Cross

A laughing baby boy, one evening in his play
Disturbed the household with his noisy glee
I warned him to be good, but he soon did disobey
For he would soon forget a word from me.

I called him to my side and said, "Son, you must go to bed
'Cause your conduct has been very, very rude"
With trembling lips and tear-filled eyes, he pleaded then with me
"Don't make me go to bed and I'll be good."

"Don't, papa, and I'll be good
Don't, papa, and I'll be good"
That's what I heard him say
And it haunts me night and day
"Don't make me go to bed and I'll be good."

Our lives had just been gladdened by his bright ascending beams
Our boy now in our hearts was very dear
I hastened to his bed and found him talking in his sleep
He didn't seem to know that we were near.

I took him in my arms and found his body racked with pain
To ease his pain, we did the best we could
It broke my heart to hear him crying loudly in his sleep
"Don't make me go to bed and I'll be good."

How sorrow fills our heart, how fears oppress our mind
When danger gathers 'round those ones we love
He lingered but a day, then his spirit passed away
To join the angel chorus up above.

All night and day we watched and prayed, we never left his side
To give him up, it seemed we never could

It broke my heart to hear him saying just before he died
"Don't make me go to bed and I'll be good."

A DRUNKARD'S CHILD

"This song was written in November, 1929, after spending the afternoon on Thanksgiving Day with Jimmie Rodgers, the famous yodeler. He and Daddy Jenkins were so jolly, and we all had such a lovely time. They sang together and talked much. Daddy promised Jimmie he would write a song just for him to record. This is the song. This was the first yodeling music I ever tried to make, but the sheet music was real pretty. We sent it to him and he immediately recorded it, and as were all his records, liked at once."

—Irene Spain Futrelle

A DRUNKARD'S CHILD

by Rev. Andrew Jenkins and Jimmie Rodgers

My father is a drunkard, my mother she is dead
And I am just an orphan child, no place to lay my head
All through this world I wander, they drive me from their door
Someday I'll find a welcome on heaven's golden shore.

Now if to me you'll listen, I'll tell a story sad
How drinking rum and the gambling hall have stole away my dad
My mother is in heaven, where God and the angels smile
And now I know she's watching her lonely orphan child.

We all were once so happy and had a happy home
Till daddy went to drinking rum and then he gambled some
He left my darling mother, she died of a broken heart
And as I tell my story, I can see your teardrops start.

Don't weep for me and mother, although I know 'tis sad
But try to get someone to cheer and save my poor lonely dad
"I'm awful cold and hungry," she closed her eyes and sighed
Then those who heard her story knew the orphan child had died.

"It was actually about a dream. When I woke up the next morning, I practically had the complete song written, because it was as if somebody laid it out for me, and all I had to do was copy it down. The song is exactly like the dream. Cowboy Copas is the only one who has passed away since recording the song. There was a very popular DJ on the west coast by the name of Squeakin' Deacon Moore, and he always talked about Bell Gardens, California, being 'Hillbilly Heaven' because there were so many country music lovers in that town, and I think that hearing him talk about it so much made me subconsciously dream about a song with that idea in mind. So I had the dream, wrote the song, Eddie Dean recorded it and it has had a profound effect on my life that I never dreamed possible when I had the dream."

—Hal Southern

I DREAMED OF A HILLBILLY HEAVEN

by Hal Southern and Eddie Dean

I dreamed I was there in Hillbilly Heaven
Stars' Hall Of Fame I had found
I heard all the stars in Hillbilly Heaven
Oh, what a beautiful sound.

Recitation:

Last night I dreamed I went to Hillbilly Heaven and
Just as I arrived, the gold curtains lifted, the stars
Were on the stage and there was Mr. Country Music himself
Mr. Hank Williams, presenting for the very first time on
The Big Show in the Sky, America's Original Soul Singer,
Mr. Red Foley.

After the applause had faded away, Hank stepped to the
mike and said, "Thank you, Red Foley, for a tremendous
performance. And now, let's welcome some friends who just
flew in today for this command showing. Four wonderful
friends of mine, Cowboy Copas, Johnny Horton, Gentleman
Jim Reeves, and the new queen of Hillbilly Heaven, Miss
Patsy Cline."

Well, after the show I got some autographs and I talked to
Patsy a while and she asked me, "Hal, are you staying over
for the next show?" Well, I just had to ask her, "Patsy,
who are the next stars booked here in Hillbilly Heaven?" She
hesitated for a moment, then said, "If you promise not to
tell, I'll whisper the names to you," and there was Marty
Robbins, Eddy Arnold, Ray Price, Eddie Dean, Tex Ritter,

Hank Snow, Johnny Cash, Roy Clark, Glen Campbell, Hal Southern . . . Hal Southern! Well that's when I woke up, and I'm sorry that I did, cause . . .

I dreamed I was there in Hillbilly Heaven
Oh, what a beautiful sound.

MOMMY PLEASE STAY HOME WITH ME

"This song is based on a true story. A woman I once knew in Nashville was always running around, going out at night and leaving her seven- or eight-year-old daughter at home alone. She did it so often, that finally the daughter started pleading with her, 'Mommy, don't go out tonight; please stay home with me.' "

—Wally Fowler

MOMMY PLEASE STAY HOME WITH ME

by Wally Fowler, Eddy Arnold, and J. Graydon Hall

A mother went out on a party
She left at home her baby son
He cried and begged her not to leave him
But she would not give up her fun
She kissed his cheek and tried to soothe him
But would not heed his childish plea
She heard him call as she was leaving
"Please, Mommy, please stay home with me."

The mother joined the merrymakers
And soon was lost in trifling joy
The mellow tunes and flitting shadows
Made her forget her baby boy
She danced and laughed and did some drinking
The world for her was full of glee
But now and then these words would haunt her
"Please, Mommy, please stay home with me."

The mother now her life would forfeit
To hear her baby's voice again
She grieves to think she rudely left him

To satisfy her wishes vain
Now mothers, don't neglect your duty
This story should a lesson be
Do not ignore your baby's pleading
"Please, Mommy, please stay home with me."

NOBODY'S DARLIN' BUT MINE

"This was a very popular song for me. It was released in the early thirties and immediately recorded by most of the country artists at that time and also by some of the top pop singers like Bing Crosby. There was an old Swedish song similar to this but not like it." —Jimmie Davis

NOBODY'S DARLIN' BUT MINE
by Jimmie Davis

Come sit by my side, little darlin'
Come lay your cool hand on my brow
Promise me that you will never
be nobody's darlin' but mine.

Nobody's darlin' but mine, love
Be honest, be faithful, be kind
Promise me that you will never
be nobody's darlin' but mine.

You're as sweet as the flowers of springtime
You're as dear as the dew from the rose
I'd rather be somebody's darlin'
Than a poor boy that nobody knows.

My mother is dead and in heaven
My daddy has gone there, I know
Sister has gone to be with them
And where I'll go, nobody knows.

Goodbye, goodbye little darlin'
I'm leaving this cold world behind

Promise me that you will never
be nobody's darlin' but mine.

OLD SHEP

"When my father was a young boy, he had a German shepherd dog named Hoover. He lived to be around 18 or 20 years old. He was poisoned by a neighbor who didn't like the dog, and Daddy found him in a field behind the house. 'Old Shep' was written about Hoover."

—Betty Foley Cummins

OLD SHEP
by Red Foley and Willis Arthur

When I was a lad and Old Shep was a pup
O'er hills and meadows we'd stray
Just a boy and his doggie, we were both full of fun
We grew up together that way.

I remember the time at the old swimming hole
When I would've drowned without doubt
But Shep was right there, to the rescue he came
He jumped in and helped pull me out.

As the years rolled on by, Old Shep, he grew old
His eyesight was fast growing dim
One day the doctor looked at him and said
"I can't do no more for him, Jim."

With a hand that was trembling, I picked up my gun
And I aimed it at Shep's faithful head
But I just couldn't do it, I wanted to run
And I wished that they'd shoot me instead.

Old Shep looked at me, his eyes were so sad
While he laid his head on my knee
Then I stroked the best pal that I ever had
Yes, I cried till I scarce couldn't see.

Old Sheppie, he knew he was going to go
For he reached out and licked at my hand
He looked up at me just as much as to say
"We're parting, but you understand."

Now Old Shep is gone where the good doggies go
And no more with Old Shep will I roam
But if dogs have a heaven, there's one thing I know
Old Shep has a wonderful home.

OUR BABY'S BOOK

"This is a true story of my second child, Rodger Dale Tubb, named after my idol Jimmie Rodgers and myself, Ernest Dale. Rodger was born July 19, 1938, at San Angelo, Texas, and died in an automobile accident near Fredricksburg, Texas, September 9, 1938. We know of more than three hundred babies who were named after our son in this song."

—Ernest Tubb

OUR BABY'S BOOK
by Ernest Tubb

There's a new star in heaven tonight
The brightest of them all up there
As we gaze at the sky we wonder why
The Lord took our baby so fair.

For he was as sweet as a rose
His eyes were so big, bright and blue
And it made me so glad, they said "He favors his dad"
And my wife said "He's the image of you."

Now you should see our baby's book
It's pink and it's bordered with gold
Though it's not complete, but on the first sheet
Our darling's life story is told.

It tells of the day that he came
To add more joy to our home

After seven short weeks our Master did speak
And now Rodger Dale is gone.

But I know that he's happy up there
I can vision each action and look
Friends, as you travel on, please remember this song
For it's written in our baby's book.

THE PRECIOUS JEWEL

"The best I can remember a long, long time ago, I was playing in Virginia, and Wilma Lee Cooper—I think she was still Wilma Lee Leary at the time —did a number called 'Hills Of Roane County,' and I liked it. I loved the tune she was singing and it stuck in my memory. A good while later, I came up with this thought that the earth has all the precious jewels such as diamonds and rubies, and when the body is placed into the grave, the soul is not placed into the grave. It must go on to a resting place. I wrote the last verse, and came up with the tune on it, and was doing it before I really realized it was the tune to 'Hills Of Roane County.' It was a number in the public domain and didn't affect anything, but that's a good thought for songwriters: they shouldn't listen to songs at all while they're writing, because they'll get off on somebody else's tune if they're not awful careful."

—Roy Acuff

THE PRECIOUS JEWEL

by Roy Acuff

Way back in the hills, when a boy I once wandered
Buried deep in her grave lies the girl that I love
She was called from this earth, a jewel for heaven
More precious than diamonds, more precious than gold.

A jewel here on earth, a jewel in heaven
She'll brighten the kingdom around God's great throne
May the angels have peace, God bless her in heaven
They've broken my heart and they left me to roam.

When a girl of sixteen, we courted each other
She promised some day to become my sweet wife

I bought her the ring to wear on her finger
But the angels, they called her to heaven one night.

This world has its wealth, its trials and troubles
Mother Earth holds her treasures of diamonds and gold
But it can't hold the soul of one precious jewel
She's resting in peace with the heavenly fold.

PUT MY LITTLE SHOES AWAY

Written by the popular songwriting team of Samuel Mitchell and Charles Pratt in 1873, this song is typical of the sentimental Victorian parlor ballads which have survived in country music long after their popularity waned. This is the original copyrighted version which, except for a few minor changes, has remained intact to this day. —D. H.

PUT MY LITTLE SHOES AWAY

by Samuel Mitchell and Charles E. Pratt

Mother dear, come bathe my forehead
For I'm growing very weak
Let one drop of water, Mother
Fall upon my burning cheek.

Tell my loving little schoolmates
That I never more will play
Give them all my toys, but, Mother
Put my little shoes away!

I am going to leave you, Mother
So remember what I say
Do it, won't you please, dear Mother?
Put my little shoes away!

Santa Claus, he gave them to me
With a lot of other things
And I think he brought an angel
With a pair of golden wings.

Then I, too, shall be an angel
By, perhaps, another day
So will you, then, dearest Mother
Put my little shoes away?

Soon the baby will grow larger
And they will fit his little feet
And he will be nice and cunning
As he walks upon the street!

I am tired now, dear Mother
So remember what I say
Do it, won't you please, dear Mother?
Put my little shoes away!

THE SINKING OF THE TITANIC

"The one that I got ahold of and made a tune to was written as a poem in an old newspaper, the *New York Clipper,* I believe. The ship was sunk April 13, 1912, and the paper came out May 23. I got ahold of this old paper—they were saving songs and poems, you know—it was about 1914 when I got ahold of it. I wasn't too old. I got to humming a tune, singing around, and my cousins all got to humming and singing, and finally I got it together. I'd play it wherever I went—at any party or anything like that —and everybody liked it. That's all I could hear, 'Play the Titanic,' 'Play the Titanic.' And I thought, well, when I got ready to go to New York to make records, I'd do that one. It sold big. Five different companies put it on."
—Ernest "Pop" Stoneman

The sinking of the *Titanic,* one of the first great media events of modern times, prompted the creation of a number of "event" songs, most of which have been long forgotten. One newspaper actually sponsored a contest which resulted in dozens of entries. Pop Stoneman's version, which he says he adapted from a newspaper poem, has driven out almost all of the other versions. While almost nothing is known about the copyright holder, Robert Brown, it is possible that he wrote the original verses of the famous Stoneman song.
—D. H.

THE SINKING OF THE TITANIC
by Robert Brown

It was on a Monday morning, just about one o'clock
That the great Titanic began to reel and rock

Then the people began to cry, saying, "Lord, I'm going to die"
It was sad when that great ship went down.

It was sad when that great ship went down
It was sad when that great ship went down
There were husbands and wives, little children lost their lives
It was sad when that great ship went down.

When they left England, they were making for the shore
The rich declared they would not ride with the poor
So they sent the poor below, they were the first that had to go
It was sad when that great ship went down.

When the boat was out sailing with men all around
God in heaven on His throne said that men should not drown
If you trust Him and obey, He will save you all today
It was sad when that great ship went down.

The people on the ship were a long ways from home
With friends all around them, didn't know their time had come
For death came riding by, sixteen hundred had to die
It was sad when that great ship went down.

When the Titanic was sinking, for decent people free
It was said they were singing, "Nearer my God to thee"
Nearer My God To Thee
When that great ship went down.

SWEETER THAN THE FLOWERS

"Carrying 'Sweeter Than The Flowers' was just like a woman carrying a baby. Now, a song is in your heart and soul just like a child. It's a load to write about your own mother, and our mother was a very sweet woman. She loved all of her children—she had fifteen head of children—and we all loved her. And when she passed away, our main remembrance of Mama was that she was more sweeter than any flower. We sang her song to hundreds of millions of people throughout our times and career in show business and we're mighty, mighty proud and happy that we had life in our bodies to do that." —Ervin T. Rouse

SWEETER THAN THE FLOWERS

by Ervin T. Rouse, Lois Mann, and Mary Burns

Just as far as I can remember
She'll remain the rose of my heart
Mama took sick along in December
February brought us broken hearts.

The reason we've not called a family reunion
We knew that she wouldn't be there
But since we've thought it all over, Mama
We know that your spirit is there.

Oh, no, I can't forget the hours
You're the onliest one, Mom, and sweeter than the flowers
Oh, no, there's no need to bother
To speak of you now would only hurt father.

Well, it looked so good to see us together
But I had to look after dad
Oh, no, Mama, when I passed by your coffin
I didn't want to remember you dead.

They all gathered 'round, I stared at their faces
All heads were bowed mighty low
But that was one time we all had to face it
Though it hurt us so bad, you know.

Oh, no, Mama, we'll never forget you
And someday we'll meet you up there.

WE SAT BENEATH THE MAPLE ON THE HILL

Written in 1880 by Gussie L. Davis, one of the few successful black songwriters on Tin Pan Alley, this song has been preserved virtually intact in country circles. Davis, a pullman porter, traveled from his native Cincinnati to New York, where he got a job sweeping the floors of the Conservatory of Music, and legend has it that it was here that he learned the elements of musical composition. It remains a great favorite of bluegrass musicians, who have shortened the title to "Maple On The Hill."

—D. H.

WE SAT BENEATH THE MAPLE ON THE HILL

by Gussie L. Davis

Near a quiet country village grows a maple on the hill
There I sat with my Jennetta long ago
When the stars were shining brightly and we heard the whippoorwill
Then we vowed to love each other ever more.

We would sing love songs together when the birds had gone to rest
And would listen to the murmurs of the rill
Then I'd fold my arms around her, lay my head upon her breast
When we sat beneath the maple on the hill.

We are getting old and feeble, yet the stars are shining bright
And we listen to the murmur of the rill
Will you always love me, darling, as you did those starry nights
When we sat beneath the maple on the hill?

Don't forget me, little darling, when they've laid me down to rest
'Tis a little wish, oh darling, grant, I crave
When you linger there in sadness, thinking, darling, of the past
Let your tears kiss the flowers on my grave.

I will soon be with the angels on that bright and peaceful shore
Even now I hear them coming o'er the rill
So goodbye, my little darling, for my time has come to go
I must leave you and the maple on the hill.

WHEN JIMMY RODGERS SAID GOODBYE

"This song was written a few days after Jimmie's death. I had always idolized Jimmie but, having been raised on a Tennessee hillside farm, never got too far away or ever had a chance to meet him. When Ralph Peer told me he was coming up to New York for a session in the spring and that he might record some of my songs, well, this was just about the most important thing I had ever had to look forward to. Lou Herscher and I had been writing songs together that year (1933) and decided to present to Jimmie, through Ralph Peer, four or five of our best numbers, 'Old Love Letters Bring Memories Of You' being among them. Jimmie arrived, but he didn't last long. I went over to the Taft Hotel several evenings and rehearsed the songs with him. He would lay on the bed and prop himself up with pillows in order to hold the guitar. The last song on his last session, he recorded our song, 'Old Love Letters.' He died that night. We wrote 'When Jimmie Rodgers Said Goodbye' a few days later. I wrote the words and Lou wrote the music. Because of our great admiration for this man, we wrote this song. Every word came straight from the heart."

—Dwight Butcher

WHEN JIMMIE RODGERS SAID GOODBYE

by Dwight Butcher and Lou Herscher

There's an old guitar that's lonely
For its master's gone away
Now he's singing to the angels
Way up in heaven today.

He left a blue song for the brakemen
And for the kids a lullaby
To all sweethearts he left a love song
When Jimmie Rodgers said goodbye.

He left a yodel for the cowboy
They'll sing it now with tear-dimmed eyes
For he left every prairie lonely
When Jimmie Rodgers said goodbye.

They'll miss him down in Alabama
In Tennessee they'll hear him sigh
And Mississippi lost their blue yodeler
When Jimmie Rodgers said goodbye.

And though the freight trains keep on running
He caught a fast one on the fly
But he left his guitar behind him
When Jimmie Rodgers said goodbye.

And I lost my pal and true friend
When Jimmie Rodgers said goodbye.

"This song was written about a true event. I visited a young nine-year-old boy in New Philadelphia, Ohio, who had two of his legs amputated in an effort to stop the growth of cancer. He was a very cheerful lad and impressed me very much. I intended to call the song just 'Willie Roy,' but after meeting him, I revised the lyrics and included 'The Crippled Boy' in the title. It has always been one of my most requested numbers, perhaps because so many of my fans are crippled or are confined to a wheel chair."
—Doc Williams

WILLIE ROY, THE CRIPPLED BOY

by Doc Williams

His age is seven years today
He don't know what it is to play
Each night, before he goes to bed
This little prayer he's always said:

"Now I lay me down to rest
Please, Mom, please give me happiness
I'm praying so my dreams come true
So I can walk and play with you."

His name, they call him Willie Roy
He's just a little crippled boy
But now the tears roll down his cheeks
I rub them off so he can sleep.

Someday I hope you can go out
And play with me and walk about
But I won't scold if you should cry
So, son, be good, my son, goodnight.

WRECK ON THE HIGHWAY

"My father wrote this song in 1936 when the '36 Fords came out with a V-8 engine and began to kill people all over the nation. The wreck took place at the Triangle Filling Station in Rockingham, North Carolina. Dad went down and seen the wreck, seen the whiskey, blood and glass on the floor of the car. One of the cars was from out of town, and the other was from Rockingham. So he knew some of the people in the crash. He named the song, 'Crash On The Highway.' Roy Acuff changed the title to 'Wreck On The Highway' when he recorded it."

—Rev. Dorsey M. Dixon, Jr.

WRECK ON THE HIGHWAY

by Dorsey Dixon

Who did you say it was, brother?
Who was it fell by the way?
When whiskey and blood ran together
Did you hear anyone pray?

I didn't hear nobody pray, dear brother
I didn't hear nobody pray
I heard the crash on the highway
But I didn't hear nobody pray.

When I heard the crash on the highway
I knew what it was from the start
I went to the scene of destruction
A picture was stamped on my heart.

The whiskey and blood ran together
Mixed up with the glass where they lay
Death lay her hand in destruction
But I didn't hear no one pray.

I wish I could change this sad story
That I am now telling you
But there is no way I can change it
Somebody's life is now through.

Their soul has been called by the Master
They died in a crash on the way
I heard the groans of the dying
But I didn't hear no one pray.

4 | Comic and Novelty Songs

Take an Old Cold Tater and Wait

Like all the other categories of songs in this book, the comedy song of the rural South grew largely out of everyday experiences. Southerners are a very humorous people, and much of what they laugh at are attitudes rather than inherently funny situations. The image of a country boy faced with an order to "Take An Old Cold Tater And Wait" until the guests have finished eating will scarcely bring forth a chuckle from anyone who has not had a similar experience. Yet this bittersweet remembrance typifies the best of country humor.

It is a private humor—a kinship humor—and much of it is aimed at pulling the group together and fending off snickers from the outside.

Actually, much country humor is a foil to urban stereotypes. It only *seems* naive. It is deliberately corny, but not because its authors are unlettered and unknowledgeable and unsophisticated. It is corny precisely because they *are* sophisticated.

This form of humor is a recognition signal, almost a separate language among country folk. Perpetuating and appreciating country humor is a mark of distinction between these "real people" and those who would laugh at them—uppity, high-hatted city people who think they are superior.

The image of the country bumpkin is a case in point. It probably originated in the cities of the North to describe in unflattering terms the rural Yankee, and was quickly applied to the southern hillbilly. Beginning with the Toby tent shows of the early 1900s, however, the bumpkin image began to change. Aimed primarily at rural and small-town audiences, these shows portrayed a different bumpkin in the person of Toby. Though he too was awkward and unschooled, he was endowed with innocence, wit, and nobility that made him an attractive character indeed. As he unfailingly outwitted both villain and scheming city slicker with his own honesty and common sense, country people took him to heart and rural comedians raised the Toby performance to a high art.

Toby's inevitable triumph is the point city people seem to miss, and it is the focus of much country humor.

Country humor has changed very little during its history, despite increasing urbanization and industrialization. In it remain ideas like chastity, sobriety, and patriotism which it has become fashionable to consider quaint and outmoded. Yet a century ago, these same values were common American values. In areas like the rural South, humor is one way of preserving them.

The fiction of southern cultural isolation has pretty much been dispelled, though so far no one has adequately documented the cross-currents of entertainment to which even the poorest and most backward rural communities must have been exposed. We do know that the South had several very successful vaudeville circuits which turned out their share of country entertainers both before and after the advent of radio and the hillbilly record: Uncle Dave Macon, Jimmie Rodgers, Cliff Carlisle, and the Weaver Brothers and Elviry, to name but a few.

Minstrels, another chiefly northern institution, contributed to hillbilly music some of the earliest novelty songs, such as "Old Dan Tucker" and "Old Zip Coon," plus a tradition of stage patter and a number of banjo styles. The tent show and the medicine wagon that traveled the byways of the South not only exposed country people to "imported" talent, but provided a showcase where hillbilly humorists and musicians could try out and perfect their talents. Zeke Clements, Rod Brasfield, Lew Childre, and Hank Williams all got their start this way.

One of the events that led directly to the recording of hillbilly artists in the early twenties was the huge commercial success of a Victor recording called "It Ain't Gonna Rain No More," which popular northern artist Wendell Hall adapted from a traditional dance tune, giving it comic lyrics like "Then how in the heck can I wash my neck if it ain't gonna rain no more?"

Fiddle tunes were among the first country songs to be recorded, and old-time fiddlers contributed to the bumpkin image in their own way. They were schooled in the carnival atmosphere of fiddling contests where "country" dress was a plus, and when radio and records opened up new opportunities, they kept their overalls and slouch hats, funny haircuts, and silly grins, even though they couldn't be seen.

Comic appearance was important too in the early string bands. Since their chief product was entertainment rather than music, humor played a major role in their acts. Almost always, one member of the band (traditionally the bass player) played the fool. He wore the outlandish clothes, was the butt of most jokes, and often got to sing, or at least start, the comedy songs. Though it has become more sophisticated, the practice persists to this day.

The fledgling Grand Ole Opry and other barn dances carefully preserved these "old time" customs, retaining not only traditional tunes and styles but "hillbilly" costumes and names. George D. Hay, the Opry's first announcer, is generally credited with having christened many of these early groups, including "The Gully Jumpers," "The Fruit Jar Drinkers," and "The 'Possum Hunters."

Early barn-dance performers took comedy and novelty materials from wherever they found them. Lew Childre, who spent many years in vaudeville, helped to popularize the adopted country song "Hang Out The Front Door Key," originally a popular song of the early 1900s, and Robert Lunn, another vaudevillian, perfected the style called "talking blues," first recorded in the twenties by Chris Bouchillon.

But though its roots reach far back into the past and even into the alien city, the self-conscious comic hillbilly song didn't really come into its own until the early recordings of the twenties. For it was then, when they were given not only a means of expression but a commercial reason for expressing themselves, that singers began translating into song what they found genuinely funny.

Typically, they borrowed humor, styling, and ideas from every source they came in contact with, then shaped these elements to their own ends. Some humor emerged as mere novelty, such as "Take Me Back To Tulsa," "Salty Dog Blues," and more recently, "May The Bird Of Paradise Fly Up Your Nose."

But many songs in their outrageous humor and exaggeration provide revealing glimpses into the everyday life of the white southern American and the problems that irritate him—poverty, of course, and tedium, advancing age, wild women and other vices, plus the loss of childhood innocence. It should be noted that some songs now accepted as comic songs originally were taken quite seriously, and vice versa.

In addition to "Take An Old Cold Tater," several of the following selections echo the home songs in harking back to a better time. Happy Wilson recalls many nights during the late twenties he spent "A-Sleepin' At The Foot Of The Bed," and Arleigh Duff remembers Grandmaw's disappointment at seeing the dinner guests leave before they've helped with the dishes. With all these discomforts, however, John Mullins conveys the real excitement they all must have felt on an isolated farm to know that "Company's Comin'."

A number of rural institutions are immortalized: the still in "Mountain Dew," the barn in "Out Behind The Barn," and the outhouse in "But I'll Go Chasin' Women" and "Ode To The Little Brown Shack Out Back." And Carson Robison pointed out the impossibility of keeping them all in repair in "Life Gits Tee-Jus, Don't It?"

To make their stage personalities more convincing, a number of comedian/musicians developed bumpkin characters that have actually taken on a life of their own with country fans. Few people, for example, know that Minnie Pearl is in real life Sarah Cannon. The song "How To Catch A Man" was written especially for Minnie Pearl and typifies her attitudes. Homer and Jethro (Henry Haynes and Kenneth Burns) developed a huge following in both the North and the South with their parodies of country and popular songs from a corny viewpoint. One of the songs they recorded, in fact, became more popular in the North than in the South—a takeoff of a lost love song, "I've Got Tears In My Ears From Lying On My Back In My Bed While I Cry Over You."

Through all these runs an image typical of country songs and a comic viewpoint that occasionally appeals as well to the city slicker, if we are to judge from the number of these selections that have crossed over to become huge popular successes. Since "Pistol Packin' Mama" dominated the hit parade of the forties for so many weeks, there have been a number of comic country songs to enrich popular music, including "Smoke, Smoke, Smoke," "Cigareetes, Whusky and Wild, Wild Women," "Too Old To Cut The Mustard," and "Jambalaya."

Today, many years after the creation of the country bumpkin, one would almost believe that the city boy has stopped laughing at him and started laughing with him—or perhaps this has always been true!

A-SLEEPIN' AT THE FOOT OF THE BED

"I lived that. I slept at the foot of the bed. For three years my family lived on a farm in Haleyville, Alabama, during the Hoover administration [1928–1932]. Those were lean days. In a farm community, people are all friends and often would drift on in and come to spend the night. You would find three or four kids sleeping in a bed and someone's got to be at the foot."

—Happy Wilson

A-SLEEPIN' AT THE FOOT OF THE BED

by Happy Wilson and Luther Patrick

Did you ever sleep at the foot of the bed
When the weather wuz whizzin' cold
When the wind wuz whistlin' around in the house
And the moon was yaller as gold?
You'd give your good warm mattress up
To Aunt Lizzie and Uncle Fred

So many kinfolks on a bad night
And you went to the foot of the bed.

I'd always wait 'till the old folks et
We'd eat the leavin's with grace
My teacher would keep me after school
I'd still have a smile on my face
I would wear the big boys' worn-out clothes
Let my sister have my sled
But it always did get my nanny goat
To sleep at the foot of the bed.

'Twas fine enough when kinfolks come
And the kids bro't brand new games
You could see how fat all the old folks wuz
And learn all the babies' names
Eat biscuits and custard and chicken pie
We all got Sunday fed
But you knowed dern well when night time come
You wuz headed for the foot of the bed.

They say some folks don't know what it is
With comp'ny all over the place
Rassle for cover on a winter night
With a big foot settin' in your face
And cold toenails a-scratchin' your back
And the footboard scrubbin' your head
I'll tell the world you ain't lost a thing
Never sleepin' at the foot of the bed.

I WON'T GO HUNTIN' WITH YOU, JAKE

"I was inspired to write this number while on a hunting trip high in the Greenhorn Mountains. 'Hardrock' Elliott and myself were lion hunting in a remote valley called Negro Rube Canyon at least 20 miles from the nearest road. We'd go hunting with my hound dogs in the morning when the dew was on the grass and rest during the afternoons. Having nothing else to do but loll around in the shade of that old log house, we quenched our thirst with alcoholic beverages (I might add this was in the late forties before I hit the sawdust trail). I was resting on an old iron bed when I saw Hardrock going into an old outhouse. He sat there, thumbing through an old catalog, when one of my hound dogs trotted by. I heard my friend remark to the indifferent hound, 'I won't go huntin' with you, Jake, but I'd sure like to go chasin' women.' Now, we'd been in that canyon about two weeks. We hadn't shaved, nor had the opportunity to do much bathing, and I said to myself, 'If we go huntin' women, we'd need the hounds to catch 'em.' "

—Stuart Hamblen (Reprinted with permission from the book *The Birth of a Song* by Stuart Hamblen)

I WON'T GO HUNTIN' WITH YOU, JAKE (BUT I'LL GO CHASIN' WOMEN)

by Stuart Hamblen

It's springtime in the mountains and I'm full of mountain dew
Can't even read my catalog like I used to do
I'm settin' in that little shed that's right behind the house
And there come Jake with all of his hounds, and he's gonna hear me shout:

I won't go huntin' with you, Jake, but I'll go chasin' women
Go put the hounds back in the pens and quit your silly grinnin'
The moon is bright, and I'm half tight; my life is just beginnin'
I won't go huntin' with you, Jake, but I'll go chasin' women.

Let's go down to the meetin' house and wait till they start home
Them gals that come from Possum Creek we'll always leave alone
We'll run them down the corn rows, them sassy little misses
We'll scare them pretty gals to death; we'll stop and throw them kisses.

Go wash your face and comb your hair, it's dang near time to start
But let me tell you 'fore we go, there's one that's got my heart
Don't chase that gal with the yaller hair and wears a dress of green
For that little gal belongs to me; I know she's past sixteen.

I was headin' for the general store, when a silly thing I seen
They make 'em in the city, and it's called a magazine

I turned to page thirty-two, and look at what I found
Them gals wear clothes that we ain't seen beneath them gingham gowns.

CIGAREETES, WHUSKY AND WILD, WILD WOMEN

"My dad wrote this song in 1947. He was with a combined rodeo-circus called the Roy Rogers Circus at the time. My mom and dad were together in a hotel in Louisville, Kentucky, and in the course of their discussions, she had been talking to him about his life at that time. My mom, being a very devout Christian woman and a churchgoer, did not feel that he was leading the type of life she wanted him to. So he wrote the song originally as a moralizing story, not as a funny song. When Red Nichols and his Five Pennies first recorded it, they did a funny version. They jazzed it up quite a bit, got kind of corny on it, and made it almost a humorous song. It was usually recorded with only two verses, and the second verse, the real moralizing one, was left out and never became popular."

—Hal Spencer

CIGAREETES, WHUSKY AND WILD, WILD WOMEN

by Tim Spencer

Once I was happy and had a good wife
I had enough money to last me for life
I met with a gal, and we went on a spree
She taught me to smoke and drink whusky.

Cigareetes and whusky and wild, wild women
They'll drive you crazy, they'll drive you insane
Cigareetes and whusky and wild, wild women
They'll drive you crazy, they'll drive you insane.

Now I am feeble and broken with age
The lines on my face make a well-written page
I'm leaving this story, how sad but how true
On women and whusky and what they can do.

Write on the cross at the head of my grave
"For women and whusky, here lies a poor slave"
Take warning, dear stranger, take warning, dear friend
Then write in big letters these words at the end.

COMPANY'S COMIN'

"I was born and raised in a log house deep in the Ozark hills of southwest Missouri. When we saw someone coming up the road, which was not often, we knew they had to be coming to our house. I remember as a small boy how excited we children were when we spotted company coming up this road. The idea came to me while I was driving a truck up a long hill years later. It reminded me of home. Many thrills of satisfaction have come to me when I would listen to some big name like Danny Kaye open his show with my song, but I think the greatest thrill of all came in a small Kansas town, where I was a stranger walking down a board sidewalk and almost got run over by a small boy on a tricycle singing to the top of his lungs: 'Company's comin', run and get the chicken; change your apron, run and get the chicken.' Not exactly how I wrote the lyrics, but I knew it had to be my song."
—John Mullins

COMPANY'S COMIN'
by John Mullins

Oh, Mama, I'm excited, I'm almost out of breath
What I saw like to make me run myself to death
I was on the mountainside when I looked down below
And, glory be, I thought I'd better come and let you know.

We've got company comin', company comin'
I saw company comin' up the road
They're down the road about a mile
They'll be here in a little while
There's company comin' up the road.

Well, Granny, change your apron, and Willie, shine your shoes
Sally, put your new dress on, we got no time to lose
I'll go find the welcome mat and spread it out with cheer
I don't know yet just who they are, can't make 'em out from here.

Oh, we've got company comin', company comin'
I saw company comin' up the road
They're comin' up the mountainside
Susie, don't you run and hide
There's company comin' up the road.

Well, run out to the henhouse and wring a neck or two
We'll have chicken and dumplin's and some yaller gravy, too
Grandpa, get your fiddle down, they might want a tune
Everybody hurry, 'cause them folks will be here soon.

Oh, we've got company comin', company comin'
We've got company comin' up the road
Land o' Goshen, I allow
They'll be here any minute now
There's company comin' up the road.

HOW TO CATCH A MAN

"Steve Sholes, head of RCA at the time, asked me to write something for Minnie Pearl who was one of his artists. The character part she played was that of the typical spinster from Grinder's Switch. Minnie was really the forerunner of women's liberation. She made no bones about how to get a man, talked about it quite a bit, and I just helped her along."

—Cy Coben

HOW TO CATCH A MAN

by Cy Coben

Now if a handsome feller smiles at you
What harm can a little flirtin' do?
And if he steals a kiss, why don't get sore
Remember honey, you've got plenty more.

Oh, how to catch a man, how to catch a man
Girls are always askin' me, how do you catch a man?
Catch him while you can with the Minnie Pearl plan

Here's a little tip on how to catch a man:
Hog tie him! (Clobber him!) (Get a bear trap!)

Tell him this and keep a straight face, hon
Tell him two can live as cheap as one
Agree with everything, 'cause you will find
That once you're married, you can change your mind.

And if you should want him for your very own
Don't let pappy talk to him alone
Tell him he's great, and give his heart a thrill
'Cause if you don't, some other female will.

If he likes blondes, and you're a dark brunette
Now there's a certain bottle that you oughta get
And if you're thin, then add some paddin' too
Football players do it, why can't you?

I'M MY OWN GRANDPAW

"Back in the early days of radio in the thirties, I had a very successful group called The Jesters performing three nights a week on NBC. Our specialty was novelty songs and bits of spoken humor. In reading a book of anecdotes and sayings by Mark Twain, I came across a paragraph wherein he proved it was possible for a man to become his own grandpa by a certain succession of events beginning with the premise that if the man married a widow with a grown-up daughter and his father married the daughter, etc. etc., he would eventually become his own grandpa. The idea seemed funny enough to repeat on the air, and sure enough, the response was very good. Later Moe Jaffe and I decided to expand the basic idea and set it as a song." —Dwight Latham

I'M MY OWN GRANDPAW

by Dwight Latham and Moe Jaffe

Many, many years ago when I was twenty-three
I was married to a widow who was pretty as could be
This widow had a grown-up daughter who had hair of red
My father fell in love with her and soon they, too, were wed.

This made my dad my son-in-law and changed my very life
For my daughter was my mother, 'cause she was my father's wife
To complicate the matter, even though it brought me joy
I soon became the father of a bouncing baby boy.

My little baby then became a brother-in-law to dad
And so became my uncle, though it made me very sad
For if he was my uncle, then that also made him brother
Of the widow's grown-up daughter, who, of course, was my
step-mother.

I'm my own grandpaw, I'm my own grandpaw
It sounds funny I know, but it really is so
Oh, I'm my own grandpaw.

Father's wife then had a son who kept them on the run
And he became my grand-child, for he was my daughter's son
My wife is now my mother's mother, and it makes me blue
Because, although she is my wife, she's my grandmother too.

Now, if my wife is my grandmother, then I'm her grandchild
And every time I think of it, it nearly drives me wild
For now I have become the strangest case you ever saw
As husband of my grandmother, I am my own grandpaw.

I'VE GOT TEARS IN MY EARS

"When my son Steven was four years old in 1949, he overslept and was still in bed at 10 o'clock on a Saturday morning. My wife Sara woke him and said, 'Steve, it's 10 o'clock, and all the other little boys are out playing!' When he heard that, he was so unhappy that tears filled his eyes and rolled down into his ears, since he was lying on his back. Sara, amused, called out, 'Look, his tears are going into his ears!' This is the only song I've written from inspiration." —Harold Barlow

I'VE GOT TEARS IN MY EARS FROM LYING ON MY BACK IN MY BED WHILE I CRY OVER YOU

by Harold Barlow

I've got tears in my ears from lying on my back
in my bed while I cry over you

And the tears in my ears, they're off the beaten track
since you said "It's goodbye, we are through"
So if I get water on the brain
you will know you are the one who is to blame
I've got tears in my ears from lying on my back
in my bed while I cry over you.

I've got tears in my ears from lying on my back
in my bed while I cry over you
I've been cryin' these tears and soakin' in my sack
since the day I found you were untrue
And if I don't get up purty soon
I'll turn into a sleepy lagoon
I've got tears in my ears from lying on my back
in my bed while I cry over you.

I've got tears in my ears from lying on my back
in my bed while I cry over you
It's been so many years, my sacroiliac
feels as though it's been soaked through and through
Oh, you lied when you said we'd take the plunge
now I know how it feels to be a sponge
I've got tears in my ears from lying on my back
in my bed while I cry over you.

JAMBALAYA

"We were in New Orleans when Hank started this song. Usually he'd start writing and finish them right then, but this is one song he just sort of fooled around with; it was some time before he finished it. We were down there, just fooling around, and we had some of those Creole dishes like jambalayas. Later on, we were in Fort Walton, Florida, and this guy had a restaurant, and he said, 'I want to fix a jambalaya dish for you because of the song.' "
—Audrey Williams

JAMBALAYA
by Hank Williams

Goodbye, Joe, me gotta go, me-oh, my-oh
Me gotta go pole the pirogue down the bayou

My Yvonne, the sweetest one, me-oh, my-oh
Son of a gun, we'll have big fun on the bayou.

Jambalaya and crawfish pie and filet gumbo
'Cause tonight I'm gonna see my ma chere amie-oh
Pick guitar, fill fruit jar and be gay-oh
Son of a gun, we'll have big fun on the bayou.

Thibadeaux, Fonteneaux, the place is buzzin'
Kinfolks come to see Yvonne by the dozen
Dress in style and go hog wild, me-oh, my-oh
Son of a gun, we'll have big fun on the bayou.

JOHNSON'S OLD GREY MULE

Though the origins of this song are obscure, it has been collected and anthologized in books of Negro folksong at least as far back as 1915 as part of the "Simon Slick" complex. Its language and construction, however, would indicate that it probably was a professionally written song—possibly of minstrel origin. Many people remember it as "Simon Slick" or as "Thompson's Old Grey Mule." The following is the version sung by Gid Tanner and the Skillet Lickers during the mid-twenties and recorded on Columbia (150–D). —D.H.

JOHNSON'S OLD GREY MULE

Johnson had an old grey mule
His name was Simon Slick
He'd wall his eyes and switch his tail
Hmmm, how that mule could kick!
He took him down to the foot of the hill
And he hitched him to his cart
He loved that mule and the mule loved him
With all his muley heart.

That mule would say:
Hee haw, hee haw, hee haw
Hee haw, hee haw, hee haw
Curried him down with a rake.

Johnson, he just hitched him up
To try him out one day
He kicked, he pawed, he brayed all night
Till he took him through the day.
He winked one eye and shook his tail
He'd greet you with a smile
Telegrammed his left hind leg
He'd send you half a mile.

That mule would say:
Hee haw, hee haw, hee haw
Hee haw, hee haw, hee haw
Turn him 'round the other way.

Johnson fed him rocks and stumps
And lumps of yellow clay
Fed him on some wooden pegs
They were his oats and hay.
That mule would chaw with all his draw
A pair of old dirty socks
Wink his eye like he had to fly
With a mouth filled full of rocks.

That mule chewed some old bed quilts
Also a wooden stool
Johnson, he concluded then
That mule, he was a fool.
Johnson thought that old grey mule
Passed through a young cyclone
You'd better bet that Johnson let
That old grey mule alone.

LIFE GITS TEE-JUS, DON'T IT?

"This song was another one of Carson's best sellers and has been consistently popular. Arthur Godfrey, Peter Lind Hayes, Walter Brennan and many others have done it on TV. Carson also wrote a sequel, 'More And More Tee-jus, Ain't It?' and his notes say this should be very good for revival later on, but with the admonition that it will have to be watched for timing, inasmuch as one line is 'The Democrats are in again.' "

—Catherine (Mrs. Carson) Robison

LIFE GITS TEE-JUS, DON'T IT?

by Carson J. Robison

The sun comes up and the sun goes down
The hands on the clock keep goin' 'roun'
I just git up and it's time to lay down
Life gits tee-jus, don't it?
My shoe's untied, but I don't care
I ain't fig'rin' on goin' nowhere
I'd have to wash and comb my hair
And that's just wasted effort.

Water in the well gettin' lower and lower
Can't take a bath for six months more
But I've heard it said and it's true, I'm sure
That too much bathin' will weaken yuh
I open the door and the flies swarm in
I shut the door and I'm sweatin' again
I move too fast and crack my shin
Just one durn thing after another.

Old brown mule, he must be sick
I jabbed him in the rump with a pin on a stick
He humped his back but he wouldn't kick
There's somethin' cock-eyed somewhere
A mouse a-chawin' on the pantry door
He's been at it fer a month er more
When he gets thru, he'll sure be sore
There ain't a durn thing in there.

Hound dog howlin' so forlorn
Laziest dog that ever was born
He's howlin' cause he's settin' on a thorn
And jist too tired to move over
The tin roof leaks and the chimney leans
There's a hole in the seat of my ol' blue jeans
And I've et the last of the pork and beans
Jist can't depend on nothin'.

Cow's gone dry and hens won't lay
Fish quit bitin' last Saturday
Troubles pile up day by day
And now I'm gittin' dandruff
Grief and misery, pains and woes
Debts and taxes and so it goes

And I think I'm gittin' a cold in the nose
Life gits tasteless, don't it?

MAY THE BIRD OF PARADISE FLY UP YOUR NOSE

"I was in El Paso, Texas, working at KHEY Radio at the time. I was home one night watching Johnny Carson on television. Johnny said something like, 'May the bird of paradise lay a golden egg in Skitch Henderson's beard.' I thought, 'What an idea for a song.' So I sat down, picked up a guitar, had a couple of beers and in about 20 minutes it was finished."
—Neal Merritt

MAY THE BIRD OF PARADISE FLY UP YOUR NOSE
by Neal Merritt

One day as I was walking down the street
Spied a beggar man with rags upon his feet
Took a penny from my pocket, in his tin can I did drop it
And I heard him say as I made my retreat:

May the bird of paradise fly up your nose
May an elephant caress you with its toes
May your wife be plagued with runners in her hose
May the bird of paradise fly up your nose.

My laundry man is really on his toes
Found a hundred dollar bill among my clothes
When he called me I came running, gave him back his dime for phoning
And I heard him saying as I turned to go:

I was way behind one day to catch a train
The taxi driver said we'll make it just the same
A speed cop made it with us, and as he wrote out the ticket
I stood by politely waiting for my change.

"The original 'Mountain Dew' was made up by Bascom Lunsford, who has directed a mountain folk festival in Asheville, North Carolina, for almost 30 years. After I returned to Chicago, I remembered the melody and composed a new set of verses for it. Lulu Belle and I cut a Vocalion record of it in 1939 in Chicago. Roy Acuff and other Nashville singers learned it from our record and started singing it. Station WLS, where we sang for 25 years, would never allow any mention of giggle water or tobacco in those days, so we were never allowed to sing it on the National Barn Dance. Mr. Lunsford came to Chicago after our version of the song became well-known and was elated with what we had done with it. He, John Lair of Renfro Valley and I sat in a Chicago hotel one evening discussing old songs. Mr. Lunsford said, 'I believe I know how to pay my bus fare back to Asheville; I'll just sell Scotty my interest in "Mountain Dew" for $25.' I wrote a brief agreement on hotel stationery and closed the deal. After we retired, he came to visit us. I called the publisher and BMI and gave them instructions to pay him 50 per cent of all royalties on the song during his lifetime. He is almost 90 now."

—Scott Wiseman

MOUNTAIN DEW

by Bascom L. Lunsford, Lulu Belle and Scotty Wiseman

There's a big hollow tree
Down the road here from me
Where you lay down a dollar or two
Then you go around the bend
When you come back again
There's a jugful of mountain dew.

Oh, they call it that good old mountain dew
And them that refuse it are few
Oh, I'll shut up my mug
If you'll fill up my jug
With that good old mountain dew.

Well, there's my old Aunt Jane
Bought some brand new perfume
It had such a sweet smellin' phew
But to her surprise, when she had it analyzed
It was nothing but good old mountain dew.

And there's Uncle Mort
He's sawed off and short
He's just five feet and one inch or two
But he thinks he's a giant

When he gets him a pint
Of that good old mountain dew.

Now, there's Uncle Bill
Got a still on the hill
Where he runs off a gallon or two
And the buzzards in the sky
Get so dizzy they can't fly
Just from smelling that mountain dew.

ODE TO THE LITLE BROWN SHACK OUT BACK

" 'Shack' was written after two direct stimuli were fed into my songwriter's net (Roger Miller once said a songwriter is like a man with a butterfly net; he's always got it out waiting to catch something). One was a comment by Judy Stammer of Berea, Kentucky, about some city's passing an ordinance prohibiting outhouses. Another was reading an article in the *West Virginia Hillbilly,* a weekly newspaper written by wit Jim Comstock, in which reference was made to that faded edifice. I wrote the song, and was right pleased with it, and the following summer I sang it at the Mountain State Arts and Crafts Fair at Ripley, West Virginia. It went over great. That's all I can say about 'Shack' except that sixteen years of my life went into the research for it."

—Billy Edd Wheeler

ODE TO THE LITTLE BROWN SHACK OUT BACK
by Billy Edd Wheeler

They passed an ordinance in the town
They said we'd have to tear it down
That little old shack out back, so dear to me
Though the health department said its day was over and dead
It will stand forever in my memory.

Don't let 'em tear that little brown building down
Don't let 'em tear that precious building down
Don't let 'em tear that dear old building down
For there's not another like it in the country or the town.

It was not so long ago
That I went tripping through the snow

Out to that house behind my old hound dog
Where I'd sit me down to rest
Like a snowbird on his nest
And read the Sears and Roebuck catalog.

I would hum a happy tune
A-peepin' through the quarter moon
As my daddy's kin had done before
It was in that quiet spot
Daily cares would be forgot
It gave the same relief to rich and poor.

It was not a castle fair
But I could dream my future there
And build my castles to the yellow jacket's drone
I could orbit 'round the sun
Fight with Gen'ral Washington
Or be a king upon a golden throne.

It wasn't fancy built at all
We had newspapers on the wall
It was air-conditioned in the winter time
It was just a humble hut
But its door was never shut
And a man could get inside without a dime.

ORIGINAL TALKING BLUES

Robert Lunn was one of the many performers who brought the songs and stylings of vaudeville to the country music stage. During his twenty years on the Grand Ole Opry (1938–1958), he specialized in novelty numbers like "Original Talking Blues," to which there were countless verses.

—D.H.

ORIGINAL TALKING BLUES

by Robert Lunn and William York

Now, if you want to get to heaven, let me tell you how to do it
Grease your feet with a little old mud and suet

Every night over in the promised land
Skip right over in the devil's hand
Go easy . . . make it easy . . . go greasy.

I was standing in the corner by the mantelpiece
I looked over my head and a bucket of grease
Greased my feet with a little axle grease
Slippin' up and down that mantelpiece
Hunting matches . . . cigarette butts . . . chewing tobacco.

Now, out in the wildwood, sittin' on a tree
I sat down on a bumblebee
Thought it was a snake or a bug, you see
On second thought, I knew it was a bee
'Cause it kept stinging . . . achin', too . . . no relief.

Now, it ain't no use of me workin' so hard
I gotta woman in the rich folks' yard
When you kill a chicken, gotta save the head
Think I'm workin', but I'm layin' in bed
Sleepin' . . . havin' a good time . . . dreaming about her.

Now, behind the hen house on my knees
Thought I heard that chicken sneeze
'Twas only a rooster sayin' his prayers
Givin' out the hymns for the hens upstairs
Just preachin' . . . hens a-singin' . . . roosters prayin'
Takin' up collections . . . payin' off in eggs . . . stuff like that.

OUT BEHIND THE BARN

"I didn't grow up on a farm, but I was raised on the rural outskirts of Moultrie, a small town in South Georgia. Although my father was a lawyer, he still remembered life on the farm, and as a young boy I learned how to milk cows and plant turnips on the farms of my relatives. 'Out Behind The Barn' is typical of a rural upbringing."

—Boudleaux Bryant

OUT BEHIND THE BARN

by Boudleaux Bryant

My pappy used to tan my hide out behind the barn
He taught me to be dignified out behind the barn
When he took his strap to me and turned me down across his knee
He sure did hurt my dignity out behind the barn.

I got my education out behind the barn
I ain't foolin', no siree
Passed each examination out behind the barn
And it almost made a wreck out of me.

I smoked my first cigarette out behind the barn
Now that's the day I won't forget out behind the barn
I got sick, you shoulda seen how that tobacco turned me green
I almost died from nicotine out behind the barn.

I met a pretty girl one day out behind the barn
She wanted me to stay and play out behind the barn
She taught me to kiss and pet, that's the game I won't forget
We still play the same game yet out behind the barn.

I sure would like to go again out behind the barn
And do some things that I did then out behind the barn
You might think it ain't no fun to be a poor old farmer's son
You just don't know what all I've done out behind the barn.

PISTOL PACKIN' MAMA

"I once owned a tavern in Turnertown, Texas. A fellow came in one night with a beautiful girl named Jo Ann and asked me to give her a job. I put her to work, but then found out the guy was married to another woman. His wife came looking for Jo Ann and said she was going to kill her. When I asked Jo Ann why she didn't find a nice single man, she said, 'Dex, I love that little cross-eyed man.' About a year later, after I sold the tavern, I was sitting in a honky tonk, and Jo Ann came in all scratched up. She had been chased through a barbed wire fence, and said that same man's old lady was after her with a gun. I began wondering, 'How do you talk to a lady with a gun?,' and I thought, 'Lay that pistol down, babe, lay that pistol down.' "

—Al Dexter

PISTOL PACKIN' MAMA

by Al Dexter

Drinking beer in a cabaret
And was I having fun
Until one night she caught me right
And now I'm on the run.

Lay that pistol down, babe
Lay that pistol down
Pistol packin' mama
Lay that pistol down.

Well, she kicked out my windshield
She hit me o'er the head
She cursed and cried and said I'd lied
And wished that I was dead.

Drinking beer in a cabaret
And dancing with a blonde
Until one night, she shot out the lights
Bang! that blonde was gone.

I'll see you every night, babe
I'll woo you every day
I'll be your regular daddy
If you'll put that gun away.

Now there was old Al Dexter
He always had his fun
But with some lead, she shot him dead
His honkin' days are done.

"At the time my brother wrote this song, he had been going to the horse races at Turf Paradise in Phoenix, Arizona. Being the genius that he was, it was just a matter of converting a horse race into a song."

—Rosemary Rollins Smartt

THE RACE IS ON

by Don Rollins

I feel tears wellin' up cold and deep inside
Like my heart's sprung a big break
And a stab of loneliness sharp and painful
That I may never shake
Now, you might say that I was taking it hard
Since you wrote me off with a call
But don't you wager that I'll hide my sorrow
When I may break right down and bawl?

Now the race is on and here comes Pride up the back-stretch
Heartaches are going to the inside
My Tears are holding back
They're trying not to fall
My Heart's out of the running
True Love's scratched for another's sake
The race is on and it looks like Heartaches
And the winner loses all.

One day I ventured in love, never once suspectin'
What the final result would be
How I lived in fear of waking up each morning
And finding that you're gone from me
There's ache and pain in my heart
For today was the one that I hated to face
Somebody new came up to win her
And I came out in second place.

SMOKE, SMOKE, SMOKE (THAT CIGARETTE)

"My dad was a non-smoker, and he worked at the coal mines. He always said, 'If I was a foreman at the mines, and I was going to hire a fellow,

I'd never hire one that smoked.' Every time you'd ask him to do something he'd say, 'Wait till I roll a cigarette.' That's where the idea came from. Tex Williams needed a song to record and asked me to write him one. He had done such a good job on 'The Dark Town Poker Club,' I more or less copied that and wrote down these verses."

—Merle Travis

SMOKE, SMOKE, SMOKE (THAT CIGARETTE)

by Merle Travis and Tex Williams

Now, I'm a feller with a heart of gold
And the ways of a gentleman, I've been told
The kind of a guy that wouldn't even harm a flea
But if me and a certain character met
The guy that invented the cigarette
I'd murder that son of a gun in the first degree.

Not 'cause I don't smoke myself
I don't reckon they'll harm your health
I've smoked them all my life and I ain't dead yet
But nicotine slaves are all the same
At a pettin' party or a poker game
Everything must stop while they smoke that cigarette.

Smoke, smoke, smoke that cigarette
Puff, puff, puff, and if you smoke yourself to death
Tell St. Peter at the Golden Gate
That you hate to make him wait
But you just got to have another cigarette.

In a game of chance the other night
Old Dame Fortune was a-doin' me right
The kings and queens just kept on comin' round
I played 'em hard and I bet 'em high
But my bluff didn't work on a certain guy
He kept on raisin' and layin' the money down.

He'd raise me and I'd raise him
I sweated blood, gotta sink or swim
He finally called and didn't raise the bet
I said, "Aces full, Pal, how 'bout you?"
He said, "I'll tell you in a minute or two
Right now, I've just got to have a cigarette."

The other night I had a date
With the cutest little girl in the forty-eight states
A highbred, uptown fancy little dame
She said she loved me and it seemed to me
That things were about like they oughta be
So hand-in-hand, we strolled down lovers' lane.

She was, oh, so far from a cake of ice
Our smoochin' party was a-goin' nice
So help me, Hannah, I think I'd a-been there yet
But I gave her a kiss and a little squeeze
And she said, "Tex, excuse me, please
I've just gotta have another cigarette."

TAKE AN OLD COLD TATER (AND WAIT)

"My father, E. M. Bartlett, Sr., wrote this song in the early twenties. It was considered then a comic quartet number along with other titles he wrote such as 'You Can't Keep A Good Man Down,' 'The Old Razor Strap' and 'The Men Will Wear Kimonos By And By.' It was not written with country music in mind, but Little Jimmy Dickens picked it up and made it a popular country song." —Gene Bartlett, Jr.

TAKE AN OLD COLD TATER (AND WAIT)

by E. M. Bartlett

When I was a little boy around the table at home
I remember very well when company would come
I would have to be right still until the whole crowd ate
My mama always said to me, "Just take a tater and wait."

Taters never did taste good with chicken on a plate
But I had to eat 'em just the same
That is why I look so bad and have these puny ways
Because I always had to take an old cold tater and wait.

And then the preachers, they would come to stay awhile with us
I would have to slip around and raise but little fuss

In fear that I would spill the beans or break a china plate
My mama always said to me, "Just take a tater and wait."

Well, I thought that I'd starve to death before my time would come
All that chicken they would eat and just leave me the bun
The feet and neck were all that's left upon the china plate
It makes you pretty darn weak to take an old cold tater and wait.

TAKE ME BACK TO TULSA

"The tune 'Take Me Back To Tulsa' was part of an old folk tune handed down from my grandfather. It had many verses and several different names. Like my father and grandfather, I added my own verse and called the tune 'Take Me Back To Tulsa.' It was also used in my first motion picture, *Take Me Back To Oklahoma.*" —Bob Wills

TAKE ME BACK TO TULSA

by Bob Wills and Tommy Duncan

Where's that gal with the red dress on?
Some folks call her Dinah
Stole her heart away from me
Way down in Louisiana.

Take me back to Tulsa
I'm too young to marry
Take me back to Tulsa
I'm too young to marry.

Little bee sucks the blossom
The big bee gets the honey
The darkey raises cotton
The white man gets the money.

I went to the railroad
Laid my head down on the track
I thought about that gal of mine
And I gradually eased it back.

We always wear a great big smile
We never do look sour
Travel all over the country
Playing by the hour.

TOO OLD TO CUT THE MUSTARD

"There was a saying up there in Kentucky where I was born that if you couldn't do a job, you 'couldn't cut the mustard.' Well, I used to do a comedy character on the radio in Knoxville, Tennessee, called 'Hotshot Elmer,' and I would tell the old story about the mule the old farmer had who got too old to work. One night he was listening to his master and his master's wife talking, and the farmer said, 'We're just gonna have to send him to the glue factory, because he's too old to work anymore,' and so the mule ran off. He ran into an old hound dog laying by the side of the road who was too old to hunt 'possum and 'coon and several other old, useless animals, and they all got together and made their own home in the wilderness. Now that's an old story I got from a first grade reader, and I named it. I tied it in with that old saying and called it 'Too Old To Cut The Mustard.' Finally, I wrote the song with that title."

—Bill Carlisle

TOO OLD TO CUT THE MUSTARD

by Bill Carlisle

When I was young, I had lots of pep
I could get around, I didn't need no help
But since I'm old and a-gettin' gray
The people look at me and say:

Too old, too old
He's too old to cut the mustard anymore
He's a-gettin' too old, he's done got too old
He's too old to cut the mustard anymore.

I used to could jump just like a deer
But now I need a new landing gear

I used to could jump a picket fence
But now I'm lucky if I jump an inch.

When I was young, I had an automobile
I'd scoot myself right under that wheel
I had to fight the gals off with a stick
But now they say, "Oh, he makes me sick."

Y'ALL COME

"I was coaching basketball and staying with my Grandma. One Sunday afternoon, this old lady came to visit in a flat bed truck. I was lying in the porch swing listening to their conversation. (Picture this old house that was never painted. Dogs on the porch.) As the old lady started to leave, before she finally crawled into that flat bed truck, she said 'Y'all come' seventeen times. I just knew there had to be a song there somewheres. I accidentally wrote it, accidentally recorded it, and it turned out to be a standard."

—Arleigh Duff

Y'ALL COME
by Arleigh Duff

When you live in the country, everybody is your neighbor
On this one thing you can rely
They'll all come to see you and never, ever leave you
Say "You all come to see us bye and bye."

Y'all come! Y'all come!
You all come to see us now and then
Y'all come! Y'all come!
You all come to see us when you can.

Kinfolks a-comin', they're comin' by the dozen
Eatin' everything from soup to hay
And right after dinner, they ain't lookin' any thinner
And here's what you hear them say:

Grandmaw's a-wishin' they'd come to the kitchen
And help do the dishes right away
But they all start a-leavin', even though she's grievin'
You can still hear Grandmaw say:

5 | Winning Love Songs

I Love You Because

Songwriters have always found it practically impossible to avoid the subject of love, and hillbilly composers are no different, despite the fact that "pure" love songs seldom have become either hits or standards in country music.

Though many love songs have been written and recorded, few seem to have had the lasting qualities of songs written about unhappy or unrequited love affairs. The reasons are not complex or difficult to understand. The fifty years which saw the rise of country music have been hard ones in the South. The struggle for economic survival left precious little time for romantic thoughts. Courtship was brief and to the point; marriage was long and filled with hardship.

As for the songs themselves, few pure love songs have the conflict and tension so important to the craft of song. Unless they also contain an element of tragedy and sadness, they have little chance of becoming country standards.

The songs that follow are the exceptions. Sensitive, thoughtful, often naive, they have become classics in the tradition of the sentimental Victorian song "Molly Darling."

Like "Molly Darling," all are written in the first person and are usually addressed directly to the object of affection. All except one ("We Could") were written by men and reflect the sentiment of the line, "I'm no good without you, anyhow," in Scotty Wiseman's "Have I Told You Lately That I Love You?"

For the most part, these are songs of courtship—declarations of abiding love despite temptation, loss, or separation—with the threat of one's love not being returned creating a certain amount of tension. "I'm so afraid to go to bed at night, afraid of losing you" complains Floyd

Tillman in his song "I Love You So Much It Hurts," and Johnny Cash is careful to "Walk The Line."

The earlier songs—those written before about 1947—are somewhat more nostalgic. The Carter Family's famous "You Are My Flower" tells a simple tale of mountain love. "My Mary" wanders down "memory lane." And constant love in the face of separation is the theme of both "Shenandoah Waltz" and "I'll Hold You In My Heart."

In "Before I Met You," the joy of discovering a woman proves fatal to a man's rambling ways, while in "I Really Don't Want To Know," the past will be forgotten as long as it's not talked about.

With few exceptions the songs of the forties and fifties (the heyday of the pure love song) are songs of supplication. One that suggests a more mature and settled love is Leon Payne's "I Love You Because," which he wrote for his wife. He loves her, it says, simply "'cause you're you," and it goes on to describe her faithfulness and support in spite of hardships and obstacles. Both Leon and his wife were blinded at very early ages. It remains one of country music's best-loved songs and has been recorded many, many times since it was written in 1950.

By the late sixties, a new realism was becoming apparent in the country love song. Harlan Howard wrote what he calls a "wedding prayer" entitled "Yours/Love" that ends with the touching line, "May the last fingertips that touch these two lips/As life from me slips be yours love."

And Marty Robbins's "My Woman, My Woman, My Wife" is a tender ode to "a saint in a dress made of gingham." Its description of her strength and constancy is in the tradition of "I Love You Because."

Finally, John Hartford's "Gentle On My Mind" hints at the South's changing morality. Hartford, born in 1937 and raised in Missouri, reflects the relaxation of the old morality and the emergence of more casual love relationships so characteristic of today's youth in all parts of the country. It marks, too, the return of the "rambling man" to hillbilly love songs after fifty years, and as such is reminiscent of the Jimmie Rodgers "blue yodels."

Perhaps the song about country love is coming full circle.

ALL THE TIME

"At the time Mel Tillis and I wrote the song, we were in our office at Cedarwood Publishing, just trying to see if we could come up with something. The way we got the melody is I was singing another song and Mel sang the harmony. It just happened that the harmony notes made a beautiful melody for a new song. That's what started the melody and the rest just came. At the time, we were just writing all we could and trying to make as much money as we could. There's no romantic story behind this song."

—Wayne P. Walker

ALL THE TIME

by Wayne P. Walker and Mel Tillis

All the time,
Yes, darling, all the time
Tenderly, constantly
I'll love you.

Every day
I'll prove it every day
In happiness or loneliness
I'll love you.

Other arms may tempt me
Don't let it worry you
For even when they tempt me
I'll never be untrue.

All the time
Yes, darling, all the time
Through the years, through smiles or tears
I'll love you.

BEFORE I MET YOU

"I wrote this song shortly after I started going with my wife, Lucille. She was the inspiration for it."

—Charles L. Seitz

BEFORE I MET YOU

by Charles L. Seitz, Joe "Cannonball" Lewis, and Elmer Rader

I thought I had seen pretty girls in my time
But that was before I met you
I never saw one that I wanted for mine
But that was before I met you.

I thought I was swingin' the world by the tail
I thought I could never be blue
I thought I'd been kissed and I thought I'd been loved
But that was before I met you.

I wanted to ramble and always be free
But that was before I met you
I said that no woman could ever hold me
But that was before I met you.

They tell me I must reap just what I have sown
But, darling, I hope it's not true
For once I made plans about livin' alone
But that was before I met you.

GENTLE ON MY MIND

"Jim Glaser and I and both our wives at the time all went to the movies to see *Dr. Zhivago* one night, and when I came home I was really turned on. I sat down and wrote it and that's how it came out. It has a lot of other scenes in it in addition to that movie, but the movie had a long traveling sensation that I liked. Some of the images in it I had thought might work sometime, and I'm sure the song built up in my subconscious over a long period, but when I finally sat down, I just wrote it. I have never really understood commercial music like I've wanted to, and I have no idea, except for the message in that song, why it was a hit."

—John Hartford

GENTLE ON MY MIND
by John Hartford

It's knowing that your door is always open and your path is free to walk
That makes me tend to leave my sleeping bag rolled up and stashed behind your couch
And it's knowing I'm not shackled by forgotten words and bonds and the ink stains that have dried upon some line
That keeps you in the back roads, by the rivers of my mem'ry that keeps you ever gentle on my mind.

It's not clinging to the rocks and ivy planted on their columns
now that bind me
Or something that somebody said because they thought we fit
together walkin'
It's just knowing that the world will not be cursing or forgiving
When I walk along some railroad track and find
That you're moving on the back roads, by the rivers of my mem'ry
And for hours, you're just gentle on my mind.

Though the wheat fields and the clothes lines and the junkyards
and the highways come between us
And some other woman's crying to her mother 'cause she turned and
I was gone
I still run in silence, tears of joy might stain my face
And summer sun might burn me 'til I'm blind
But not to where I cannot see you walkin' on the back roads
By the rivers flowing gentle on my mind.

I dip my cup of soup back from the gurglin' cracklin' caldron in
some train yard
My beard a roughening coal pile and a dirty hat pulled low across
my face
Through cupped hands 'round a tin can
I pretend I hold you to my breast and find
That you're waving from the back roads, by the rivers of my mem'ry
Ever smilin', ever gentle on my mind.

HAVE I TOLD YOU LATELY THAT I LOVE YOU?

"I was a patient in Wesley Memorial Hospital in Chicago for several weeks in 1944. My wife, Lulu Belle, was visiting me one afternoon and whispered to me before she left, 'Have I told you lately that I love you?' As I lay there thinking tender thoughts about her, it occurred to me that this would be a good title for a song. I got paper and pencil and wrote the first verse and chorus down that afternoon. When Lu came the next day, I sang it to her. She said, 'That's pretty good.' A friend of mine took a copy to Gene Autry in Hollywood. He made the first recording. Lu and

I still get a thrill when we hear it done by so many fine artists, and it paid for our retirement home in the hills of North Carolina. It has sold approximately 10 million records here and abroad."

—Scott Wiseman

HAVE I TOLD YOU LATELY THAT I LOVE YOU?

by Scott Wiseman

Have I told you lately that I love you?
Could I tell you once again, somehow?
Have I told you with all my heart and soul how I adore you?
Well, darling, I'm telling you now.

This heart would break in two if you refuse me
I'm no good without you, anyhow
Dear, have I told you lately that I love you?
Well, darling, I'm telling you now.

Have I told you lately how I miss you
When the stars are shining in the sky?
Have I told you why the nights are long when you're not with me?
Well, darling, I'm telling you now.

Have I told you lately when I'm sleeping
Every dream I dream is you, somehow?
Have I told you who I'd like to share my love forever?
Well, darling, I'm telling you now.

I'LL HOLD YOU IN MY HEART

"I recorded this in 1947, and it was a very successful song. I used to get letters from mamas and sweethearts. It was a universal kind of song, because it said something everybody could identify with. A mama could say it about her own son away from home, 'I'll hold you in my heart till I can hold you in my arms,' or lovers could use the same expression. I wish I could find another one like that."

—Eddy Arnold

I'LL HOLD YOU IN MY HEART
by Eddy Arnold, Hal Horton, and Tommy Dilbeck

I'll hold you in my heart till I can hold you in my arms
Like you've never been held before
I'll think of you each day, and then I'll dream the night away
Till you are in my arms once more.

The stars up in the sky know the reason why
I feel so blue when I'm away from you
I'll hold you in my heart till I can hold you in my arms
So, darling, please wait for me.

I LOVE YOU BECAUSE

"Leon said he wrote this song for me."

—Myrtie (Mrs. Leon) Payne

I LOVE YOU BECAUSE
by Leon Payne

I love you because you understand, dear
Every single thing I try to do
You're always there to lend a helping hand, dear
I love you most of all because you're you.

No matter what the world may say about me
I know your love will always see me through
I love you for the way you never doubt me
But most of all I love you 'cause you're you.

I love you because my heart is lighter
Every time I'm walking by your side
I love you because the future's brighter
The door to happiness you open wide.

No matter what may be the style or season
I know your heart will always be true

I love you for a hundred thousand reasons
But most of all I love you 'cause you're you.

I LOVE YOU SO MUCH IT HURTS

"It was right after World War II. I was fooling around with my guitar, alone, but happy to be free. My fingers lay flat across the last four strings. I strummed and the first four notes just said 'I love you so . . .' and then I improvised almost unconsciously 'much it hurts me.' I suppose if any song ever came to me like automatic writing this one did."

—Floyd Tillman

I LOVE YOU SO MUCH IT HURTS
by Floyd Tillman

I love you so much it hurts me
Darlin', that's why I'm so blue
I'm so afraid to go to bed at night
Afraid of losing you
I love you so much it hurts me
And there's nothing I can do
I want to hold you, my dear
For ever and ever
I love you so much it hurts me so.

(REMEMBER ME) I'M THE ONE WHO LOVES YOU

"I was short a song for a recording session one time, and told my wife, so as I was leaving the house she said, 'Why not write a song about me? Remember me? I'm the one who loves you.' Going into the studio this song came to me. We didn't even have time to make an orchestration, but the song turned out to be a big hit. That was about ten years ago. My Susy

is just like the wording of the lyrics, and perhaps there are millions of girls just like her when it comes to really loving some 'hunk of man.'"
—Stuart Hamblen (Reprinted with permission from the book *The Birth of a Song* by Stuart Hamblen)

(REMEMBER ME) I'M THE ONE WHO LOVES YOU

by Stuart Hamblen

When you're all alone and blue,
No one to tell your troubles to
Remember me, I'm the one who loves you.

When this old world turns you down
Not a true friend can be found
Remember me, I'm the one who loves you.

And through all kinds of weather
You'll find I'll never change
Through the sunshine and the shadows
I'll always be the same.

We're together right or wrong
Where you go, I'll tag along
Remember me, I'm the one who loves you.

I REALLY DON'T WANT TO KNOW

"I wrote the lyric in 1949. The thought that inspired me to write the lyric was—'How few persons seem to find the right or perfect lover for them, at least until they have been held and kissed by many?' Hence, the opening phrase: 'How many arms have held you?'"

—Howard Lee Barnes

I REALLY DON'T WANT TO KNOW

by Howard Barnes and Don Robertson

How many arms have held you
and hated to let you go?

How many, how many, I wonder?
But I really don't want to know.

How many lips have kissed you
and set your soul a-glow?
How many, how many, I wonder?
But I really don't want to know.

So always make me wonder, always make me guess
And even if I ask you, darling, don't confess
Just let it remain your secret, but, darling, I love you so
No wonder, no wonder, I wonder, though I really don't want to know.

I WALK THE LINE

"I wrote the song backstage one night in 1956 in Gladewater, Texas. I was newly married at the time, and I suppose I was laying out my pledge of devotion."
—Johnny Cash

I WALK THE LINE

by John R. Cash

I keep a close watch on this heart of mine
I keep my eyes wide open all the time
I keep the ends out for the tie that binds
Because you're mine, I walk the line.

I find it very, very easy to be true
I find myself alone when each day is through
Yes, I'll admit that I'm a fool for you
Because you're mine, I walk the line.

As sure as night is dark and day is light
I keep you on my mind both day and night
And happiness I've known proves that it's right
Because you're mine, I walk the line.

You've got a way to keep me on your side
You give me cause for love that I can't hide

For you I know I'd even try to turn the tide
Because you're mine, I walk the line.

I keep a close watch on this heart of mine
I keep my eyes wide open all the time
I keep the ends out for the tie that binds
Because you're mine, I walk the line.

MOLLY DARLING

"I don't remember who I first heard singing the song, but I learned it from an old song folio that I found, which had other old songs in it like 'When You And I Were Young, Maggie.' 'Molly Darling' is sort of like 'September Song.' It was never a fantastic hit, but it's a song everybody loves. I sang it everywhere I went, on radio and personal appearances. It's a great old song."
—Eddy Arnold

(Written by Civil War composer Will S. Hays [1837–1907], this is his most celebrated song.)
—D. H.

MOLLY DARLING
by Will Hays

Won't you tell me, Molly darling
That you love none else but me
For I love you, Molly darling
You are all the world to me
Oh, tell me darling that you love me
Put your little hand in mine
Take my heart, sweet Molly darling
Say that you will give me thine.

Molly fairest, sweetest, dearest
Look up darling, tell me this
Do you love me, Molly darling
Let your answer be a kiss.

Stars are smiling, Molly darling
Through the mystic veil of night

They seem laughing, Molly darling
While fair Luna hides her light
Oh, no one listens but the flowers
While they hang their heads in shame
They are modest, Molly darling
When they hear me call your name.

MY MARY

"This number was written about my first real sweetheart. Her real name was Mary. When I left Texas and came out to California, all I could ever do was to dream of this Texas beauty that I'd left behind. I couldn't see then how I could ever go on through life without her, but fortunately she married an old friend of mine. I never saw Mary, nor her husband, for about twenty five years, but one time they came out to California and looked me up. Mary had sure put on weight. She would have tipped the scales at, at least two hundred pounds, and had acquired a very 'bossy' attitude towards men. Her husband had tried repeatedly to converse with me, but she'd glare at him and he'd clam up. The four of us spent an entire evening visiting with Mary, and to be quite truthful about the whole matter, I breathed a sigh of relief when those two tourists left to go back to their Texas home. There's a verse of scripture in the Bible that reads, 'The Lord giveth and the Lord taketh away.' Mary was my first sweetheart. The Lord giveth her to me. But, thank God, he taketh her away and gave her to my friend. Through all my life God has been so good to me."
—Stuart Hamblen (Reprinted with permission from the book *The Birth of a Song,* by Stuart Hamblen)

MY MARY
by Stuart Hamblen and Jimmie Davis

I take a trip in the evening, journey down memory lane
Strolling along those familiar paths, living those days again
I can always see my sweetheart, dressed as she used to be
Waiting for someone by the garden gate, and I know that someone is me.

Big brown eyes and curly hair
Now can't you tell that's Mary?
Rosy cheeks and ruby lips
Oh, can't you tell that's Mary?

Ofttimes in the evening we'd go strolling
Hand in hand together beneath the pepper tree
And I can feel her hand in mine as I sit alone tonight
Just a-dreaming of the hours I spent with Mary.

Recitation:

Oh gee, wouldn't it be wonderful to open up the doors of the past and live again as in yesterday? But you know, no matter where I wander, no matter where I roam, there'll always be a place in my heart, boys, for a girl 'way back, for a girl I used to call Mary.

MY WOMAN, MY WOMAN, MY WIFE

"I wrote this song for my wife, Marizona, because I felt that these were things a man would want to say to his wife. She's everything that I said in the song."
—Marty Robbins

MY WOMAN, MY WOMAN, MY WIFE
by Marty Robbins

Hands that are strong but wrinkled
Doing work that never gets done
Hair that's lost some of the beauty
By too many hours in the sun
Eyes that show some disappointment
And there's been quite a lot in her life
She's the foundation I lean on
My woman, my woman, my wife.

Every day has been uphill
We climb but we can't reach the top
I'm weak and I'm easily discouraged
She just smiles when I want to stop
Lips that are weary but tender
With love that strengthens my life
A saint in a dress made of gingham
My woman, my woman, my wife.

Two little babies were born in the spring
But died when the winter was new
I lost control of my mind and my soul
But my woman's faith carried us through.

When she reaches that river, Lord
You know what she's worth
Give her that mansion up yonder
'Cause she's been through hell here on earth
Lord, give her my share of heaven
If I've earned any here in this life
'Cause, God, I believe she deserves it
My woman, my woman, my wife.

SHENANDOAH WALTZ

"Chubby Wise and I wrote this song one day while drinking coffee in my kitchen. Chubby wrote the music and I wrote the words. I had gone through the Shenandoah Valley of Virginia, playing dates there. I think it's one of the most beautiful spots there is. I did then and I still do. I said to Chubby, 'There's never been a song that I know of about the Shenandoah Valley of Virginia.' The very first time I performed the song on the Grand Ole Opry, I received an encore. It was a success then and has become a standard waltz tune in country music. At the time the song became a hit I was given the name of 'Hillbilly Waltz King Of The World.' The title was later changed to 'Country And Western Waltz King Of The World.' I've also written and recorded several other waltzes which were successful." —Clyde Moody

SHENANDOAH WALTZ
by Clyde Moody and Chubby Wise

In the Shenandoah Valley of Virginia
Lives a girl who is waiting just for me
Oh, how many times we've waltzed in the moonlight
And in her lovely arms I long to be.

I miss her smile in the moonlight
I know she misses me, too

In the Shenandoah Valley of Virginia
I know that her love for me is true.

SPARKLING BROWN EYES (SPARKLING BLUE EYES)

"I was told about Billy Cox by Clark Kessinger, who's a great old-time fiddler. When I found him, Billy was living in an old converted chicken house in a holler in West Virginia. Although Billy had released over 150 records for Columbia, Gennett and Decca, he was on welfare and wasn't getting any money from any of his songs. He didn't have any relatives he cared about or that cared anything about him. We became good friends and I helped Billy. We got together and did an album on Kanawah Records, and I got this song copyrighted for him. It was fifty-fifty on that, and when he died in 1968, he willed his portion of it to me. Billy was kind of appreciative of the fact that somebody was caring a little bit about what he did."

—Ken Davidson, Kanawah Records

SPARKLING BROWN EYES (SPARKLING BLUE EYES)

by Billy Cox

There's a ram-shackle shack down in old Caroline
That's calling me back to that gal of mine
Those dear blue eyes I long to see
The girl of my dreams she will always be.

Those dear blue eyes that sparkle with love
Sent down to me from heaven above
If I had wings like a beautiful dove
I'd fly to the arms of the one I love.

When the whippoorwills call from the hills far away
I would sing love songs and she would say
"My love for you will never die
But I bid farewell with a sad goodbye."

When it's harvest time down in old Caroline
I'll be drifting back to that gal of mine

I'll spend my days with the girl I love
By the help of One up in heaven above.

WE COULD

"It was a birthday present to my husband, Boudleaux. We were working in the basement house. He was laying on the couch; he likes to lay on the couch when he's working. I was sitting in the chair directly across from him and he fell asleep. I kept looking at him and thinking 'How precious,' and I thought, 'If anybody could make this old world whistle, we could, we could.' If you want to talk about inspirational tunes, that song came so fast it was all I could do to write it down. My name's on it, but it was there so fast, I don't even feel like I wrote it." —Felice Bryant

WE COULD
by Felice Bryant

If anyone could find the joy
That true love brings a girl and boy
We could, we could, you and I.

If anyone could ever say
That their true love was here to stay
We could, we could, you and I.

When you're in my arms I know
You're happy to be there
And just as long as I'm with you
I'm happy anywhere.

If anyone could pray each night
To thank the Lord 'cause all is right
We could, we could, you and I.

"I got the idea for this song one day when Lonnie Glossen's little daughter Mary got on her father's lap and said, 'Daddy, why don't you haul off and give me some lovin'?' It was one of the easiest songs I've ever written. My recording of the song sold over a million copies, and it has been recorded twenty-one times or more since."
—Wayne Raney

WHY DON'T YOU HAUL OFF AND LOVE ME?

by Wayne Raney and Lonnie Glossen

They say the love bug will get you at the age of twenty-three
Well, I'm not telling my age, but something's got a-hold of me
I'm just cravin' some lovin' in the old fashioned way
Honey, lend an ear and listen to all I have to say.

Why don't you haul off and love me one more time?
Why don't you squeeze me until I'm a-turning blind?
If you don't cuddle up and love me like I want you to do
I'm a-gonna haul off and die over you.

I can feel your warm lips near me, hear you breathe so soft and fine
I can feel the matrimony crawlin' up and down my spine
I don't believe this love will hurt you 'cause it feels so nice and fine
It seems mighty close to heaven when your love is on the line.

YOU ARE MY FLOWER

"I wrote the music to this song myself. Sara Carter and I found some words in a pamphlet with the words, 'you are my flower.' We changed some of the words and fixed a tune to it. It was a good song for us."
—Mother Maybelle Carter, of the original Carter Family

YOU ARE MY FLOWER

A. P. Carter

When summertime is gone and snow begins to fall
You can sing this song and say to one and all
You are my flower that's blooming in the mountain so high
You are my flower that's blooming there for me.

So wear a happy smile and life will be worthwhile
Forget the tears and don't forget to smile
You are my flower that's blooming in the mountain so high
You are my flower that's blooming there for me.

YOURS LOVE

"This song was written for my wife, Donna Gail, when we were preparing to get married. About four years ago, about a week before we got married, I had written a poem. It was called 'My Wedding Prayer.' In this poem I put all the things I really felt, hoped and wished for her. After I got the poem done, I looked at it, and every line it seemed ended up saying 'yours love.' My commercial songwriter's mind took over, and I said, 'Man, this might be a good song.' So then I changed the title, put a melody to it, and instead of handing her a poem, I sang her a song."
—Harlan Howard

YOURS LOVE
by Harlan Howard

May the fruit of my toil be yours love
May the food from my soil be yours love
And from this moment on may a love that is strong
And lives on and on be yours love.

May the sons that I raise be yours love
May the comforts I praise be yours love
If I ever get weak may the love words I speak
And the arms that I seek be yours love.

May the Lord's shining grace be yours love
May the happiest face be yours love
May the last fingertips that touch these two lips
As life from me slips be yours love.

---

6 | Songs of Lost and Unrequited Love

And Now I'm Losing You

If there is a "typical" country song, it probably tells a tale of lost and unrequited love.

From the antique "Wildwood Flower" to the ultramodern "She Thinks I Still Care," the frailty of human relationships is a constantly recurring theme in country music. Both the "pure" love song and the lost love song usually are written in the first person and express a one-sided emotion; where they differ is in the confidence (or at least hopefulness) that one's love will be accepted and returned.

Yet that simple change in point of view often spells the difference between a hit and an also-ran. A tragic love affair is either so much more interesting or so much more believable that (in hillbilly music, at least) it will outsell a winning love song by a huge ratio. Estimates of the proportion of country songs describing unfulfilled love range from more than half to almost two-thirds, an impressive majority which is reflected only to a degree in this book.

The songs in this chapter have proven to be the most valuable copyrights, and most of them have been recorded again and again.

Webb Pierce, who has recorded well over sixty hit songs, many of them lost love songs, explained why: "It's different things that make a song a hit. One of the things is you sing about the things they think about most, but don't talk about. That becomes an emotional outlet for the people, and they feel they have a friend in the song. They like it, they buy it, they play it, they sing it, because it's something that seems to fit their purpose."

The popularity of the unhappy love song in the rural South predates the period of recorded commercial hillbilly music, probably by centuries. Of the rich folk heritage available to them from English and Scotch-Irish balladry, the southern frontiersman seemed to select the saddest and most tragic songs, such as "Knoxville Girl" and "Pretty Polly," to pass along to their children. Popular songs of the Victorian era like "The Fatal Wedding" and "The Little Rosewood Casket" stayed in the country music repertory long after they had been forgotten in the cities. All these songs can still be heard in the South today.

And so it was that when the first hillbilly recordings were made in the early twenties and thirties, a rich store of tragic and unrequited love songs was available and was quickly put to use. Recordings and radio provided a new commercial incentive for original compositions, and before long the first country songwriters were consciously creating for the new style that was developing. The bulk of these songs followed the popular themes of nostalgia—particularly for Dixie—and innocent love, or they told sad tales of disasters or of repentant prisoners. But some of the most popular dealt with unhappy love affairs, particularly with "the wrong woman." Jimmie Rodgers's first blue yodel, "T For Texas," tells of Thelma who was stolen by a "rounder" and who made "a wreck" out of him; and Bob Miller's "Seven Years With The Wrong Woman" contains the warning, "Don't marry the wrong woman; it's worse than living in hell."

These early songs, which usually carry a note of retribution, are quite different in tone from the self-pitying songs that developed in the late thirties, peaked during the forties, and became frequent national popular hits in the fifties when they were introduced by Hank Williams and crossed over to the pop field.

Two songs in 1939, "It Makes No Difference Now" and "The Last Letter," began an important new trend in country music which is still apparent today. Both were huge commercial successes, and their influence can be traced in more recent hits like "There Goes My Everything" and "Don't You Ever Get Tired Of Hurting Me?" The fact that this type of song became popular at the same time the honky tonk was emerging as a major institution in the South is not coincidental, as Ted Daffan pointed out in annotating "Worried Mind": "This song was an attempt to catch the mood of the people who haunted the little taverns where juke boxes were the only source of entertainment."

"Worried Mind," published in 1941, was followed in 1943 by two major hits, "Born To Lose" and "Walking The Floor Over You," which remained on jukeboxes literally for years. World War II, while it relieved some of the economic hardships of the Depression, introduced two new elements into this style of song: physical separation and working (and therefore more independent) women. This was the era which marked the beginning of the "Dear John letter," and songs of self-pity struck an especially responsive chord with homesick soldiers and displaced war workers.

"The Tennessee Waltz," a simple, straightforward tale of lost love released as a hillbilly record in 1948, proved to be a commercial watershed in country music when it was recorded by Patti Page in 1950 and became a smash popular hit. Still one of the largest-selling songs in any category, it began a period of commercialization which culminated in the career of Hank Williams. Williams and songwriter-publisher Fred Rose together and separately produced some of the biggest country songs ever from 1948 to 1953, most of which were hits for Williams and many of which crossed over to popular music.

"A Mansion On The Hill," one of Williams's first hits, was co-written with Rose, and the expert hand of Rose is apparent in Williams's songs like "Your Cheatin' Heart," "I'm So Lonesome I Could Cry," and "Cold, Cold Heart." Williams remains to this day the most sympathetic and successful figure in the musical expression of unrequited love.

During the fifties, a new note of realism entered the unhappy love song. "Take These Chains From My Heart," released shortly before Williams's death in 1953, hinted at divorce in a serious song. It was quickly followed by "Release Me" in 1954, which introduced the possibility that the *singer's* love could cool, and that under the circumstances "to live together is a sin." "Blackboard Of My Heart" and "Crazy Arms," both written in 1956, admit that a broken heart is not a terminal condition and that another love is possible.

Songs of unrequited love of the sixties ranged from the traditional "There Goes My Everything" to the ironic "She Thinks I Still Care" and included such extreme points of view as Willie Nelson's "I Just Can't Let You Say Goodbye," in which the singer can prevent his mate from leaving only by strangling her.

Why do songs burdened with negative emotions—self-pity, guilt, retribution—fit the purpose of great numbers of the country music public?

Wayne Walker, a Nashville songwriter, suggested that "men cry just like women. They don't always do it out in public, so maybe they're just letting out what they really feel inside. Everybody's had some sadness in their love lives at one time or another; there wouldn't be so many divorces if they didn't. And maybe it's just easier for a man to write a love song when he's sad."

Chances are, however, that this preference for tragic love affairs goes much deeper and much further back. Certainly one contributing factor was the Calvinistic teaching, so prevalent in the rural South, that man is unworthy and life is a "vale of tears." This conviction still persists today. Songwriter Ted Harris, for example, explained the preference for sad songs this way: "People who adhere to the 'Bible truths' know that the Bible doesn't paint a glorious, rewarding picture of life. Life itself is basically very sad, and I adhere to the philosophy that you should celebrate a funeral and cry at a birth. This life is a hard row to hoe, and 'hard-row-to-hoe' songs are going to be the most popular. While we make a little progress once in a while, or somebody hits a good lick and we're all happy, we just don't seem to overcome it, and the Bible says we won't overcome it."

By this fundamentalist philosophy, man must live with a sense of shame and guilt, and love (especially sexual love), along with life, was bound to be unhappy.

Probably a more important factor was the South's extreme economic privation that began with the Civil War and lasted well into the present century. The farmers and laborers who made up the original market for country music were for the most part dirt-poor, bypassed by the American dream and the means of achieving it. Burdened with poor land, a poor economy, and hostile natural forces beyond their control, many felt they were, indeed, "born to lose." Ted Daffan, himself a product of rural poverty, used the phrase to begin what is the arch-principle song of this category, adding the revealing line, "And now I'm losing you."

A tragic love affair, then, is the final insult—and perhaps the focus for economic and social frustrations it would be unmanly to admit. This defensiveness in being merely poor folks is expressed a different way in several poor boy-rich girl songs like "A Mansion On The Hill" and "Pick Me Up On Your Way Down." In both cases, wealth cannot buy happiness or real love.

The song of unrequited love is central to the development of hillbilly music, and is one form whose popularity has never waned—and probably never will. Chances are, the country composer will never run out of new and inventive ways of saying the same thing, nor will he run short of homely metaphors, whether it be "the pillow that you dream on," "the blackboard of my heart," or "gold statuettes for tears and regrets."

ADDRESS UNKNOWN

"Everybody gets a letter sometime marked 'address unknown' or 'return to sender.' Mine was an accident. I don't recall where I got the idea from. There was a pop song by the same title around the same time, but I hadn't heard it. It was by the Ink Spots, and a very dear friend of mine, Johnny Marks, wrote it. I kid him about his and he kids me about mine. Of course we came up together. He was struggling to get a break early in the forties and we had our first big songs at the same time."

—Vaughn Horton

ADDRESS UNKNOWN

by Vaughn Horton, Gene Autry, and Denver Darling

I waited each day for your letter
Although I knew what it would cost

But, dear, when it came, I knew that your game
Had been won and I knew that I had lost.

But I just couldn't open your letter
I know you're no longer my own
The moment it came, I wrote 'neath my name
These heart-breakin' words, "Address Unknown."

I wanted to open your letter
To see if you missed me sometimes
But you have a way of makin' me pay
'Cause I know what you write between the lines.

I know I'd be so glad to see you
In spite of the hurt you're the one
But deep down inside, I can't lose my pride
And forgive you for what you have done.

BLACKBOARD OF MY HEART

"This was about 1951 and I had just started writing songs. I got the idea from a waitress who worked where I ate breakfast every morning. She came over to the table one day and said, 'Hey, I've got a great idea for a song for you. How about "my tears have washed 'I love you' from the blackboard of my heart"?' And I said, 'How about it?' She said, 'Well, doesn't it give you a picture?' And I said, 'Come to think of it, I guess it does.' I got the first verse and the chorus written right away. Then it took me almost two years to get a second verse for it."

—Lyle Gaston

BLACKBOARD OF MY HEART

by Lyle Gaston and Hank Thompson

When I was young and went to school, they taught me how to write
To take the chalk and make a mark, and hope it turns out right
Well, that's the way it is with love and what you did to me
I wrote it so you'd know that I was yours eternally.

But my tears have washed "I love you" from the blackboard of my heart

It's too late to clean the slate and make another start
I'm satisfied the way things are, although we're far apart
My tears have washed "I love you" from the blackboard of my
heart.

If you'd been true the way you should, and not have gone astray
Those tears would not have fallen down and washed the words away
No need to talk, for if the chalk should write these words again
It will be for someone else, not things that might have been.

BLUE MOON OF KENTUCKY

"Back in those days, it seems every trip we made was from Kentucky to Florida driving back and forth. I always thought about Kentucky, and I wanted to write a song about the moon we could always see over it. The best way to do this was to bring a girl into the song. I wanted words to this, because most of my songs were instrumentals. 'Kentucky Waltz' had come earlier and I knew I could write both words and music, so I wrote it in the car on the way home from one of those Florida trips."

—Bill Monroe

BLUE MOON OF KENTUCKY

by Bill Monroe

Blue moon of Kentucky, keep on shining
Shine on the one that's gone and left me blue
Blue moon of Kentucky, keep on shining
Shine on the one that's gone and left me blue
It was on one moonlight night
Stars shinin' bright
Whisper on high
Love said good-bye
Blue moon of Kentucky, keep on shining
Shine on the one that's gone and left me blue.

"About four o'clock one morning in Cincinnati's Gibson Hotel, Alton and Rabon Delmore and I were getting ready for a recording session the next day. Alton knew a guitar riff he had learned from Henry Glover, a black songwriter on the King Records staff at the time. We decided to put words to it and a song was born. We recorded it the next day."

—Wayne Raney

BLUES, STAY AWAY FROM ME

by Wayne Raney, Alton and Rabon Delmore, and Henry Glover

Blues, stay away from me
Blues, why don't you let me be?
Don't know why you keep on haunting me.

Love was never meant for me
True love was never meant for me
Seems somehow we never did agree.

Tears, so many I can't see
Years don't mean a thing to me
Time goes by and still I can't be free.

BORN TO LOSE

"The source of inspiration for 'Born To Lose' will have to remain my secret. It is true that I sometimes played penny ante poker, but I almost always won."

—Ted Daffan

BORN TO LOSE

by Ted Daffan

Born to lose, I've lived my life in vain
Every dream has only brought me pain
All my life, I've always been so blue
Born to lose, and now I'm losing you.

Born to lose, it seems so hard to bear
How I long to always have you near

You've grown tired, and now you say we're through
Born to lose, and now I'm losing you.

Born to lose, my every hope is gone
It's so hard to face that empty dawn
You were all the happiness I knew
Born to lose, and now I'm losing you.

There's no use to dream of happiness
All I see is only loneliness
All my life, I've always been so blue
Born to lose, and now I'm losing you.

BOUQUET OF ROSES

"I had what I believed to be a very beautiful melody running around in my head. One day I met Bob Hilliard at a recording studio, and I sang it to him. He agreed that it was a 'sweet' tune, and as the word 'sweet' implied something romantic and flowery, we pursued that direction and finally came up with the title 'Bouquet Of Roses,' and then started to collaborate on the lyrics. The song was finished the following day."

—Steve Nelson

BOUQUET OF ROSES

by Steve Nelson and Bob Hilliard

I'm sending you a big bouquet of roses
One for every time you broke my heart
And as the door of love between us closes
Tears will fall like petals when we part.

I begged you to be different
But you'll always be untrue
Now I'm tired of forgiving
And there's nothing left to do
So I'm sending you a big bouquet of roses
One for every time you broke my heart.

You made our lover's lane a road of sorrow
Till at last we had to say goodbye

You're leaving me to face each new tomorrow
With a broken heart you taught to cry.

I know that I should hate you
After all you put me through
But how can I be bitter
When I'm still in love with you?
So I'm sending you a big bouquet of roses
One for every time you broke my heart.

BURY ME BENEATH THE WILLOW

"This was a song we've known all our lives. We used to sing it when we had get-togethers and parties. It was the first song we recorded in 1927 in Bristol, Tennessee, for RCA Victor." —Mother Maybelle Carter, of the original Carter Family

BURY ME BENEATH THE WILLOW

by Bradley Kincaid

Bury me beneath the willow
'Neath the weeping willow tree
When he hears his love is sleeping
Maybe then he'll think of me.

My heart is sad and I am lonely
Thinking of the one I love
Will I see him never, never
Till we meet in heaven above.

He told me that he dearly loved me
How could I believe him untrue
Then one day some neighbors told me
"He has proven untrue to you."

Place on my grave a snow-white lily
To prove that I was true to him
And tell him that I died to save him
When his love I could not win.

Then bury me beneath the willow
'Neath the weeping willow tree
And tell some brown-eyed boy I'm sleeping
Then perhaps he'll weep for me.

CANDY KISSES

"This song was written over a busted-up romance I had many years ago and was addressed to the girl I was going with. I was driving to work one day to a radio program that I was doing in Wooster, Ohio. I was thinking about her and the thought crossed my mind that I didn't mean as much to her as the candy kisses that my mother used to bring home on Saturday when she went grocery shopping—not the Hershey candy kisses—those candy kisses wrapped in paper with peanut butter in them. I wrote it in my head in ten minutes and sang it when I got to the station that morning. It is my theme song and also my most requested song."

—George Morgan

CANDY KISSES
by George Morgan

Candy kisses, wrapped in paper
Mean more to you than any of mine
Candy kisses, wrapped in paper
You'd rather have them any old time.

You don't mean it when you whisper
Those sweet love words in my ear
Candy kisses, wrapped in paper
Mean more to you than mine do, dear.

I built a castle out of dreams, dear
I thought that you were building, too
Now my castles all have fallen
And I am left alone and blue.

Once my heart was filled with gladness
Now there's sadness, only tears

Candy kisses, wrapped in paper
Mean more to you than mine do, dear.

COLD, COLD HEART

"I was in the hospital for some minor ailment. We had had an argument. He and the children had come to visit me and brought me the first fur coat I ever owned. During the entire visit I spoke to the children, but I didn't speak to Hank. On his way home he told our housekeeper, Audrey Ragland, 'She's got the coldest heart I've ever seen.' That same night he wrote this song. Among the 100 songs Hank Williams wrote, this song was his favorite."

—Audrey Williams

COLD, COLD HEART

by Hank Williams

I tried so hard, my dear, to show
That you're my every dream
Yet you're afraid each thing I do
Is just some evil scheme
A memory from your lonesome past
Keeps us so far apart
Why can't I free your doubtful mind
And melt your cold, cold heart?

Another love before my time
Made your heart sad and blue
And so my heart is paying now
For things I didn't do
In anger, unkind words are said
That make the teardrops start
Why can't I free your doubtful mind
And melt your cold, cold heart?

You'll never know how much it hurts
To see you sit and cry
You know you need and want my love
Yet you're afraid to try
Why do you run and hide from life

To try, it just ain't smart
Why can't I free your doubtful mind
And melt your cold, cold heart?

There was a time when I believed
That you belonged to me
But now I know your heart is shackled
To a memory
The more I learn to care for you
The more we drift apart
Why can't I free your doubtful mind
And melt your cold, cold heart?

CRAZY ARMS

"When I was about twenty-two years old, I was a heavy drinker. My wife and I and our baby girl lived in Las Vegas, Nevada, in 1949. Each night at the club where I played steel guitar, I would get so drunk that I almost had to crawl home. I never drank in the daytime. One day my wife and I were uptown shopping and I ran into a musician friend who invited me to have a drink and I did. That was all my wife could take of my drinking, so she left me and went home to her mama in Los Angeles. After she left on the bus, I sat down with my guitar and wrote 'Blue ain't the word for the way that I feel, and a storm is brewing in this heart of mine.' I wrote the whole song in a few minutes. I went back to Los Angeles to get my wife back a few days later. (My wife and I have been married twenty-six years now, our daughter is twenty-three, our son is fourteen, and we have a grandson who is two years old.)" —Ralph Mooney

CRAZY ARMS

by Ralph Mooney and Charles Seals

Now blue ain't the word for the way that I feel
And a storm is brewing in this heart of mine
This ain't no crazy dream, I know that it's real
You're someone else's love now, you're not mine.

Crazy arms that reach to hold somebody new
For my yearning heart keeps sayin' you're not mine

My troubled mind knows soon to another you'll be wed
And that's why I'm lonely all the time.

So please take the treasured dreams I had for you and me
And take all the love I thought was mine
Someday my crazy arms may hold somebody new
But now I'm so lonely all the time.

FADED LOVE

"I came from a family of fiddlers, and this song was originally an old fiddle tune that had been in the family for years. My father John Wills taught me the tune, and it was just a matter of putting words to it. My younger brother Billy Jack helped me with the words."

—Bob Wills

FADED LOVE

by Bob and John Wills

As I look at the letters that you wrote to me
It's you that I'm thinking of
As I read the lines that to me were so sweet
I remember our faded love.

I miss you, darling, more and more ev'ry day
As heaven would miss the stars above
With every heartbeat I still think of you
And remember our faded love.

I think of the past and all the pleasures we had
As I watch the mating of the dove
It was in the springtime that you said goodbye
I remember our faded love.

"I lived just a ten-minute drive from Pamper Music's office in a trailer house, and I wrote this song one afternoon while driving to the office. Somewhere during the trip the line that I had heard someone say probably a thousand times in my life, 'It's funny how time slips away,' came to me. I thought, 'It's funny there's never been a song by that title,' and it started coming to me. It has been my most successful song financially to date. It has been recorded maybe 80 or 90 times so far—on the average, someone records it once a month."
—Willie Nelson

FUNNY HOW TIME SLIPS AWAY
by Willie Nelson

Well, hello there
My, it's been a long, long time
How'm I doin'?
Oh, I guess that I'm doin' fine
It's been so long now, but it seems how that it was yesterday
Oh, ain't it funny how time slips away?

Say, how's your new love?
I hope he's doin' fine
I heard you told him
That you'd love him till the end of time
Now that's the same thing that you told me, it seems like yesterday
Oh, ain't it funny how time slips away?

I gotta go now
I hope I see you around
But I don't know when, though
Never know when I'll be back in town
But remember what I tell you, in time you're gonna pay
Oh, ain't it funny how time slips away?

HALF AS MUCH

"My husband Curley just got up from the supper table one night and went down to the radio station where he was working in Anniston, Alabama. He stayed down there about thirty minutes, and when he came back, he said, 'Baby, I wrote us a good song tonight.' He played and sang it for me, and of course I thought it was good, but next day he played it for the boys in his band, the Georgia Peach Pickers, and they all laughed at him. Then he recorded it and sent it to Acuff-Rose, and instead of writing back like they usually did, Fred Rose called him and said, 'I just want you to know you've got a damned hit!' Curley had the first record on it at Columbia, but just as it started to go big up in Gaston, Anniston and up in there, the Columbia pressing plant went on strike for seven weeks, and when they came off, Christmas songs were in and that killed his version of it. Then Rosemary Clooney came out with it and made it popular in the pop field, and then Hank Williams picked it up."

—Louise (Mrs. Curley) Williams

HALF AS MUCH
by Curley Williams

If you loved me half as much as I love you
You wouldn't worry me half as much as you do
You're nice to me when there's no one else around
You only build me up to let me down.

If you missed me half as much as I miss you
You wouldn't stay away half as much as you do
I know that I would never be this blue
If you only loved me half as much as I love you.

HAVE YOU EVER BEEN LONELY?

"Just before writing 'Last Round-Up,' my father had disliked greatly the term 'Hill Billy' music; so he wrote under the name of 'George Brown.' After 'Round-Up' became a hit, he became more accepting of the term and went back to his real name, 'Billy Hill.' "

—Lee Hill Taylor

HAVE YOU EVER BEEN LONELY (HAVE YOU EVER BEEN BLUE)?
by George Brown (Billy Hill) and Peter De Rose

Two of a kind everywhere I see
Lovers in the moonlight, robins in a tree

Now that we have parted what am I to do
But make this plea to you?

Have you ever been lonely, have you ever been blue?
Have you ever loved someone just as I love you?
Can't you see I'm sorry for each mistake I've made?
Can't you see I've changed, dear, can't you see I've paid?
Be a little forgiving, take me back in your heart
How can I go on living, now that we're apart?
If you knew what I've been through, you would know why I ask you
Have you ever been lonely, have you ever been blue?

My happiness two alone can share
Now that I have lost you, life is hard to bear
You and I have quarreled, I'm a fool, it's true
Why can't we start anew?

HEARTACHES BY THE NUMBER

"I was in the Army as a paratrooper for three years. Everything was done by the numbers. We even ran by the numbers and had to count cadence. Back when I wrote this song, I was writing 8 or 10 songs at a time. I had used several terms and expressions that are used almost exclusively in the service. I was really just fooling around with words and seeing if I could take this Army expression and put it into a love song. That's the game songwriters play. Sometimes it works and sometimes it don't. In this case it did."

—Harlan Howard

HEARTACHES BY THE NUMBER

by Harlan Howard

Heartache number one was when you left me
I never knew that I could hurt this way
And heartache number two was when you came back again
You came back and never meant to stay.

Now I've got heartaches by the number, troubles by the score
Everyday you love me less, each day I love you more

Yes I've got heartaches by the number, a love that I can't win
But the day that I stop counting, that's the day my world will end.

Heartache number three was when you called me
And said that you were coming back to stay
With hopeful heart I waited for your knock on the door
I waited but you must have lost your way.

HE'LL HAVE TO GO

"My wife has a very soft voice, and when I used to call home I couldn't hear her. I'd have to say, 'If you don't talk louder, put your mouth closer to the phone.' I came home one day and she had the first line of this song written. She didn't even have a title for it. I sat down and we finished it and gave it that title. It's a lost love song, but it's a positive approach to the problem."

—Joe Allison

HE'LL HAVE TO GO

by Joe and Audrey Allison

Put your sweet lips a little closer to the phone
Let's pretend that we're together all alone
I'll tell the man to turn the jukebox way down low
And you can tell your friend there with you
He'll have to go.
Whisper, hang up or will you tell him he'll have to go?

You can't say the words I want to hear
While you're with another man
If you want me, answer "yes" or "no"
Darling, I will understand.

Put your sweet lips a little closer to the phone
Let's pretend that we're together all alone
I'll tell the man to turn the jukebox way down low
And you can tell your friend there with you
He'll have to go.

Whisper to me, tell me do you love me true
Or is he holding you the way I do?
Though love is blind, make up your mind, I've got to know
And you can tell your friend there with you
He'll have to go.
Whisper, hang up or will you tell him he'll have to go?

I CAN'T STOP LOVING YOU

"This song was written in Knoxville in a house trailer on the Clinton highway. I sat down to write a lost love ballad. After writing several lines to the song, I looked back and saw the line 'I can't stop loving you.' I said, 'That would be a good title,' so I went ahead and rewrote it in its present form. I also wrote 'Oh, Lonesome Me' that same afternoon."

—Don Gibson

I CAN'T STOP LOVING YOU

by Don Gibson

I can't stop loving you
So I've made up my mind
To live in memory
Of old lonesome times
I can't stop wanting you
It's useless to say
So I'll just live my life
In dreams of yesterday.

Those happy hours
That we once knew
So long ago
Still make me blue
They say that time
Heals a broken heart
But time has stood still
Since we've been apart.

I can't stop loving you
There's no use to try
Pretend there's someone new

I can't live a lie
I can't stop wanting you
The way that I do
There's only been one love for me
That one love is you.

I FORGOT MORE THAN YOU'LL EVER KNOW

"I wrote 'I Forgot More Than You'll Ever Know' in 1947, but it wasn't recorded until 1953. It was turned down by nearly everybody in the business. The song stems from an old saying. So many times I've heard people say 'I forgot more than you'll ever know about this job or this thing or whatever.' I thought it would be a good idea for a song because everybody was already familiar with the title. This song was not written from true life. If every songwriter wrote true things about himself, most wives would have left long ago." —Cecil Null

I FORGOT MORE THAN YOU'LL EVER KNOW

by Cecil Null

You think you know the smile on his lips
The thrill at the touch of his fingertips
But I forgot more than you'll ever know about him.

You think you'll find a heaven of bliss
In each caress, each tender kiss
But I forgot more than you'll ever know about him.

You stole his love from me one day
You didn't care how you hurt me
But you can never steal away
Memories of what used to be.

You think he's yours to have and to hold
Someday you'll learn when his love grows cold
That I forgot more than you'll ever know about him.

"In 1940, the Jimmy Wakely Trio was in California awaiting word on our employment on the Gene Autry Radio Show, 'Melody Ranch,' and we had nothing to do but write songs for promised recording sessions. Before that all my songs had been cowboy, but I was convinced we'd have quicker success with a hillbilly love song. In the verse of a song we had sung on the radio in Oklahoma I found the line 'I wonder where you are tonight,' and the idea was born. Over the years, many people have come to the conclusion that it is an old Public Domain song, and several newer songs have come to life using the identical melody. The most touching moment of infringement came when a blind man sang me what he called 'my church song,' written around an old P. D. song. It was a painful duty to remind the poor man that I was the composer. He was quite embarrassed when I did so reluctantly. 'Don't worry, my friend,' I told him. 'I won't sue you!' "

—Johnny Bond

I WONDER WHERE YOU ARE TONIGHT

by Johnny Bond

Tonight I'm sad, my heart is weary
Wondering if I'm wrong or right
To dream about you though you left me
I wonder where you are tonight.

The rain is cold and slowly falling
Upon my window pane tonight
And though your love grows even colder
I wonder where you are tonight.

Your heart was cold, you never loved me
Though you often said you cared
And now you've gone to find another
Someone who'll know the love I've shared.

'Twas spring, the birds were gaily singing
And trees were blossoming so sweet
No lovers ever looked so happy
No other love was so complete.

Then came the dawn the day you left me
I tried to smile with all my might
But you could see the pain within me
That lingers in my heart tonight.

I've died a million times my darling
Ever since you went away

Just watching, waiting, hoping, praying
That you'll be coming back someday.

The loneliness within my cabin
Has left its mark upon my heart
'Cause I have never been the same, dear
Since that sad day we had to part.

If I could only make amends, dear
For all the things that were not right
I wouldn't have to walk and worry
And wonder where you are tonight.

I'LL TWINE 'MID THE RINGLETS

Written in 1860 by Maud Irving and J. P. Webster, a popular songwriting team, this is the original song the Carter Family remembered as "Wildwood Flower."
—D. H.

I'LL TWINE 'MID THE RINGLETS
by Maud Irving and P. J. Webster

I'll twine 'mid the ringlets of my raven black hair
The lilies so pale and the roses so fair
The myrtle so bright with an emerald hue
And the pale aronatus with eyes of bright blue.

I'll sing and I'll dance, my laugh shall be gay
I'll cease this wild weeping, drive sorrow away
Tho' my heart is now breaking, he never shall know
That his name made me tremble and my pale cheeks to glow.

I'll think of him never, I'll be wildly gay
I'll charm ev'ry heart, and the crowd I will sway
I'll live yet to see him regret the dark hour
When he won, then neglected, the frail wildwood flower.

He told me he loved me and promis'd to love
Through ill and misfortune, all others above
Another has won him; ah, misery to tell
He left me in silence, no word of farewell.

He taught me to love him, he call'd me his flower
That blossom'd for him all the brighter each hour
But I woke from my dreaming, my idol was clay
My visions of love have all faded away.

I'M A FOOL TO CARE

"This song was inspired by the lovely records made by the Ink Spots. I created the melody and lyrics for the high tenor voice of the lead singer, and the bridge was meant to be spoken by the bass singer. Decca, who owned the Ink Spots, turned it down. I recorded it in 1940, and it was a hit then and several times since." —Ted Daffan

I'M A FOOL TO CARE
by Ted Daffan

I'm a fool to care,
When you treat me this way
I love you so, but, darling, I know
I'm a fool to care.

I'm a fool to cry
Since you told me goodbye
You can't be true, so what can I do
I'm a fool to care.

I know I should laugh
And call it a day
But I know I would cry, dear
If you went away.

I'm a fool to care
When you don't care for me
Why should I pretend, I'd lose in the end
I'm a fool to care.

"I met Hank when he came to Nashville about three years before he died. We wrote a book together called 'How To Write Folk And Western Music To Sell.' One day I was over at Acuff-Rose, our mutual publisher, and Hank handed me a piece of paper and said, 'Do you think people will understand what I'm trying to say when I say this?' The line was 'Did you ever see a robin weep when leaves begin to die? It's because he's lost the will to live; I'm so lonesome I could cry.' Hank had this lonesome streak, and I think it was largely caused by his marital problems. I think he wrote it out of a feeling of loneliness that stayed very much with him. He would be the natural person to write 'I'm so lonesome I could cry!' "

—Jimmy Rule

I'M SO LONESOME I COULD CRY
by Hank Williams

Hear that lonesome whippoorwill?
He sounds too blue to fly
The midnight train is whining low
I'm so lonesome I could cry.

I've never seen a night so 'lone
When time goes crawling by
The moon just went behind a cloud
To hide its face and cry.

Did you ever see a robin weep
When leaves begin to die?
That means he's lost the will to live
I'm so lonesome I could cry.

The silence of a falling star
Lights up a purple sky
And as I wonder where you are
I'm so lonesome I could cry.

I'M THINKING TONIGHT OF MY BLUE EYES

One of the most popular lost and unrequited love songs of all time, this song entered country music tradition in 1929 when it was recorded and made famous by the original Carter Family. The tune is practically the same as a number of later songs, including "Great Speckled Bird," "Wild Side Of Life," and "It Wasn't God Who Made Honky Tonk Angels."

—D. H.

"This was an old song I've known all my life. I used to sing it when I was a little girl. I guess it's a real old tune the people used."

—Sara Carter, of the original Carter Family

I'M THINKING TONIGHT OF MY BLUE EYES

by A. P. Carter

'T would be better for us both had we never
In this wide and wicked world ever met
For the pleasures that we've both seen together
I am sure, love, I'll never forget.

Oh, I'm thinking tonight of my blue eyes
Who is sailing far over the sea
Oh, I'm thinking tonight of my blue eyes
And I wonder if he ever thinks of me.

Oh, you told me once, dear, that you loved me
And you said that we never would part
But a link in the chain has been broken
Leaves me with a sad and aching heart.

When the cold, cold grave shall enclose me
Will you come, dear, and shed just one tear?
And say to the strangers around you
A poor heart you have broken lies here?

IT MAKES NO DIFFERENCE NOW

"1938, it was. I was sitting in my car in a drive-in having a cold one waiting for a phone call. It never came. 'Oh, well,' I said, 'it makes no difference now.' The first verse flowed out in my mind as if I were hearing it on the radio. I borrowed a pencil from the car hop and wrote it on the back of an envelope containing a bill. At the time, I was working with a band in

Houston, The Blue Ridge Playboys, and we tried it on our radio program and the results were sensational. The requests were pouring in, and even the newsboys were selling the lyrics in the streets (as was the custom in those days with popular songs). The recording man for Vocalion listened to it and agreed it was all right for radio, but he explained that jukeboxes were where the sales were, and all of the operators had requested fast or swinging music. It was turned down. Later, Cliff Bruner recorded it, and it was a smash. One jukebox operator told me he had doubled his plays since 'It Makes No Difference Now.' I sold the song for a few hundred dollars, but I got it back in 1966 when the copyright was renewed. Besides many of the country bands, it was one of the first country songs ever recorded by Bing Crosby. It's still selling."
—Floyd Tillman

IT MAKES NO DIFFERENCE NOW
by Floyd Tillman and Jimmie Davis.

Makes no difference now what kind of life fate hands me
I'll get along without you now, that's plain to see
I don't care what happens next, for I'll get by somehow
I don't worry, 'cause it makes no difference now.

It was just a year ago when I first met you
I learned to love you and I thought you'd love me too
But that's all in the past and I'll forget somehow
I don't worry, 'cause it makes no difference now.

Now that we have really parted I can't believe we're through
I don't blame myself, I'm sure I can't blame you
There was something had to happen, and it happened somehow
I don't worry, 'cause it makes no difference now.

After all is said and done I'll soon forget you
Altho' I know that it will be so hard to do
Let things happen as they will, and I'll get by somehow
I don't worry, 'cause it makes no difference now.

KENTUCKY WALTZ

"'Kentucky Waltz' was my first try at writing words to a song. I had written 74 instrumentals before I wrote it."
—Bill Monroe

KENTUCKY WALTZ

by Bill Monroe

We were waltzing that night in Kentucky
Beneath the beautiful harvest moon
And I was the boy that was lucky
But it all ended too soon
As I sit alone in the moonlight
I see your smiling face
And I long once more for your embrace
In that beautiful Kentucky Waltz.

THE LAST LETTER

"Rex told me that at the time he wrote 'The Last Letter' he lived in New Orleans at the Tutweiler Hotel. It was the largest hotel they had at that time. He was married to a girl named Margaret. They didn't get along too well, as they were both young. He said at the time he wrote the song was the only time they had gotten along. They were getting along just fine. One day he came in and sat down to the baby grand piano he had in the apartment and wrote 'The Last Letter.' It wasn't in any way a song about him or his life in general, just a song." —Dorothy Griffin Smith

THE LAST LETTER

by Rex Griffin

Why do you treat me as if I were only a friend?
What have I done that makes you so different and cold?
Sometimes I wonder if you'll be contented again
Will you be happy when you are withered and old?

I cannot offer you diamonds and mansions so fine
I cannot offer you clothes that your young body craves
But if you say that you long to forever be mine
Think of the heartaches, the tears and the sorrow you'll save.

When you are lonely and tired of another man's gold
When you are weary, remember this letter, my own
Don't try to answer though I suffer anguish untold
If you don't love me I wish you would leave me alone.

While I am writing this letter I think of the past
And of the promises that you are breaking so free
But to this world I will soon say my farewell at last
I will be gone when you read this last letter from me.

(I'D BE) A LEGEND IN MY TIME

"This song was written on the road to Knoxville, Tennessee, in a car with Mel Foree. I was reading an article in a magazine I had picked up about an entertainer. He was talking about show business and his career and how he would like to be a legend in his time. I told Mel that that would be a good title for a song, so I started humming."

—Don Gibson

(I'D BE) A LEGEND IN MY TIME
by Don Gibson

If heartaches brought fame in love's crazy game
I'd be a legend in my time
If they gave gold statuettes for tears and regrets
I'd be a legend in my time.

But they don't give awards, and there's no praise or fame
For a heart that's been broken over love that's in vain.

If loneliness meant world acclaim then everyone would know my name
I'd be a legend in my time.

"I am 82 and was a flier-pilot in the First World War at Wright Field, Dayton, Ohio. I was impressed by the lovesick boys who left their young wives and sweethearts for the service, blue. I had been writing songs since I was 12. So I wrote 'Lovesick Blues.' After the war I went to New York City. Cliff Edwards (Ukelele Ike) recorded the song on Perfect Records —a good job, but the song, ahead of its time, was a flop. I took the song back from Jack Mills. Twenty years went by, and Fate stepped in in the guise of a stranger in Alabama who met Hank Williams and sold him 'Lovesick Blues' as *his* song for $100. Fred Rose published it, but I had the copyright. When Williams' record hit the market, I flew to Nashville and took all the money, since I was also the publisher. Meanwhile, Frank Ifield in England had sold 4 million, and altogether, the song has sold 10 million."

—Cliff Friend

LOVESICK BLUES

by Cliff Friend and Irving Mills

I'm in love, I'm in love with a beautiful gal
That's what's the matter with me
I'm in love, I'm in love with a beautiful gal
But she don't care about me
Lord, I tried and I tried to keep her satisfied
But she just wouldn't stay
So now that she is leaving me
This is all I can say:

I got a feeling called the blues, oh Lord
Since my baby said goodbye
Lord, I don't know what I'll do
All I do is sit and sigh, oh Lord
That last long day she said goodbye
Well, Lord, I thought I would cry
She'll do me, she'll do you, she's got that kind of lovin'
How I love to hear her when she calls me sweet da-ad-ad-dy
Such a beautiful dream
I hate to think it's all over
I've lost my heart, it seems
I've grown so used to you, somehow
I'm nobody's sugar daddy now
And I'm lonesome, I've got the lovesick blues.

"Hank went to see Fred Rose, the publisher, at his office at WSM, and the very first day he took four of Hank's songs—'Never Again Will I Knock On Your Door,' 'I Saw The Light,' and several others. We were so happy and delighted. But then Fred said, 'Boy, I don't know whether you wrote these songs, whether you bought them off somebody or where you got them. I'll tell you what I want you to do: I'm going to give you a title, and I want you to go back and write a song to it.' And this song was 'Mansion On The Hill.' "

—Audrey Williams

A MANSION ON THE HILL

by Hank Williams and Fred Rose

Tonight, down here in the valley
I'm lonesome, and oh how I feel
As I sit here alone in my cabin
I can see your mansion on the hill.

Do you recall when we parted?
The story to me you revealed
You said you could live without love, dear
In your loveless mansion on the hill.

I've waited all through the years, love
To give you a heart true and real
'Cause I know you're living in sorrow
In your loveless mansion on the hill.

The light shines bright from your window
The trees stand so silent and still
I know you're alone with your pride, dear
In your loveless mansion on the hill.

NO ONE WILL EVER KNOW

"Fred Rose, on a business trip to New York, invited me to come up and visit with him a couple of days. I got a three-day pass from Naval duty and accepted the invitation. While walking down Broadway, Fred remarked he had a great title for a song and asked me if I would like to take a crack

at it. 'Just cry your heart out in the lyrics,' he said. I took the title back to the Naval Base and was immediately summoned to guard duty. Walking back and forth on a guard post, the lyrics to 'No One Will Ever Know' were born. I sent a lead sheet to Fred. He made some revisions and got it recorded by Roy Acuff in 1945."
—Mel Foree

NO ONE WILL EVER KNOW
by Mel Foree and Fred Rose

No one will ever know my heart is breaking
Although a million teardrops start to flow
I'll cry myself to sleep and wake up smiling
I'll miss you, but no one will ever know.

I'll tell them we grew tired of each other
And realized our dreams could never be
I'll even make believe I never loved you
Then no one will ever know the truth but me.

No one will ever know how much I'm pining
Each time the past comes back to haunt me so
No one will ever know the tears I'm hiding
You've hurt me, but no one will ever know.

I'll tell them I found true love with another
That I was glad the day you set me free
I'll even make believe I never loved you
Then no one will ever know the truth but me.

OH, LONESOME ME

"It must have been the mood or the way I was feeling. The period of time I was going through had a reflection on me, the way I felt. So I sat down and started writing a melody and singing the words. Originally it was 'Ole Lonesome Me.' When I gave it to the publisher they interpreted it to be 'Oh, Lonesome Me,' but I just let it stand. It was printed that way on the sheet music and record and it was too late to change it back."
—Don Gibson

OH, LONESOME ME
by Don Gibson

Everybody's goin' out and havin' fun
I'm just a fool for stayin' home and havin' none
I can't get over how she set me free
Oh, lonesome me.

I'll bet she's not like me, she's out and fancy free
Flirting with the boys with all her charms
But I still love her so, and brother don't you know
I'd welcome her right back here in my arms.

Well, there must be some way I can lose these lonesome blues
Forget about the past and find somebody new
I've thought of every thing from A to Z
Oh, lonesome me.

A bad mistake I'm makin' by just hangin' 'round
I know that I should have some fun and paint the town
A love-sick fool that's blind and just can't see
Oh, lonesome me.

PICK ME UP ON YOUR WAY DOWN

"I was a factory worker out in California in about 1957. I was sitting in a night club called George's Roundup. Wynn Stewart had a band there, and I was waiting for him to finish so we could go get some coffee. I heard a couple arguing at the table next to me, and the girl got mad and got up and the guy said to her, 'Well, you can just pick me up on your way down!' I had no idea what the conversation involved, but that struck me as a title. I carried it around mentally for about a year, then all of a sudden, I sat down and just wrote the song from beginning to end, and I've never changed a word. It just kind of fell in place, which lets me know that I wrote it subconsciously. That's how songwriters say they 'wrote that song in two minutes.' Well, I wrote that song in one year and two minutes."

—Harlan Howard

PICK ME UP ON YOUR WAY DOWN

by Harlan Howard

You were mine for just a while, now you're puttin' on the style
And you've never once looked back at your home across the track
You're the gossip of the town, but my heart can still be found
Where you tossed it on the ground; pick me up on your way down.

Pick me up on your way down, when you're blue and all alone
When their glamor starts to bore you, come on back where you belong
You may be their pride and joy, but they'll find another toy
Then they'll take away your crown; pick me up on your way down.

They have changed your attitude, made you haughty and so rude
Your new friends can take the blame, underneath you're still the same
When you learn these things are true, I'll be waiting here for you
As you tumble to the ground, pick me up on your way down.

RELEASE ME

"Years ago I was playing a one-nighter near San Francisco. I happened to overhear a couple arguing at the corner table right next to the bandstand. I heard the woman say, 'If you'd release me, we wouldn't have any problems and everything would be all right.' It didn't hit me then, but it did later, just thinking about them arguing. I had never heard it said like that before. I had always felt that divorce was a dirty word in a song, and I felt that 'Release Me' was a softer way of saying it. The song has sold over 18 million records and has been recorded over 300 times."

—Eddie Miller

RELEASE ME

by Eddie Miller, Dub Williams, Robert Yount, and W. S. Stevenson

Please release me, let me go
For I don't love you anymore
To live together is a sin
Release me, and let me love again.

I have found a new love, dear
And I will always want her near
Her lips are warm while yours are cold
Release me, my darling, let me go.

I once loved your lovely face
But now someone will take your place
Can't you see that you can't win
Release me, and let me love again.

REMEMBER ME WHEN THE CANDLE LIGHTS ARE GLEAMING

"This song was written in 1939 when Lulu Belle and I spent a year at radio station WLW, Cincinnati. In our guest room at home when I was a child there was a fancy old cup and saucer which sat on the dresser. The phrase, 'Remember Me,' was on the cup in fancy gold lettering. We children were not allowed to touch this momento of the sentimental Gay Nineties, somehow connected with the courtship of Mother and Dad. Feeling a bit homesick and sentimental during the bustle of radio shows and road trips, I 'made up' the song while riding in the car to personal appearance jobs. The lyric was not intended to apply to any particular person."
—Scott Wiseman

REMEMBER ME WHEN THE CANDLE LIGHTS ARE GLEAMING
by Scott Wiseman

Remember me when the candle lights are gleaming
Remember me at the close of a long, long day
It would be so sweet when all alone I'm dreaming
Just to know you still remember me.

The sweetest songs belong to lovers in the gloaming
The sweetest days are days that used to be
The saddest words I ever heard were words of parting
When you said "Sweetheart remember me."

You told me once that you were mine alone forever
And I was yours till the end of eternity

But all those vows are broken now, and we will never
Be the same except in memory.

A brighter face may take my place when we're apart, dear
A sweeter smile, a love more bold and free
But in the end, fair weather friends may break your heart, dear
If they do, sweetheart remember me.

SAN ANTONIO ROSE

"When I was a very young man, I was living in Roy, New Mexico, working as a barber and playing for dances on Saturday night. Since most of the population of Roy was Mexican, I wrote a tune for them to dance to and called it 'Spanish Two-Step.' When I did my first recording session with Columbia in 1935, 'Spanish Two-Step' was one of the tunes I recorded. On November 28, 1938, I went to Dallas to record again for Columbia. After we had cut several tunes, Uncle Art Satherly, who was the A & R man on this session, asked me if I had another tune like 'Spanish Two-Step.' I said, 'No, I don't, but if you give me a few minutes, maybe I can come up with something.' In a few minutes I had written and recorded the tune. Uncle Art asked me what I wanted to name the tune. I told him I didn't know. So he said, 'Let's name it "San Antonio Rose."' This was an instrumental and it sold very well. The recording company asked me to record it again with lyrics. I worked for two years before finally finishing the words and recorded 'New San Antonio Rose' in April, 1940."

—Bob Wills

SAN ANTONIO ROSE
by Bob Wills

Deep within my heart lies a melody
A song of old San Antone
Where in dreams I live with a memory
Beneath the stars all alone.

It was there I found beside the Alamo
Enchantment strange as the blue up above

A moonlit pass that only she would know
Still hears my broken song of love.

Moon in all your splendor knows only my heart
Call back my Rose, Rose of San Antone
Lips so sweet and tender like petals falling apart
Speak once again of my love, my own.

Broken song, empty words I know
Still live in my heart all alone
For that moonlit pass by the Alamo
And Rose, my Rose of San Antone.

SHE THINKS I STILL CARE

"This was a true, inspirational song. It was basically about a girl I used to be in love with who later shafted me. If she hadn't done that, I probably never would have written the song. The way things turned out, I'm glad the romance ended the way it did."
—Dickey Lee

SHE THINKS I STILL CARE

by Dickey Lee

Just because I asked a friend about her
Just because I spoke her name somewhere
Just because I rang her number by mistake today
She thinks I still care.

Just because I haunt the same old places
Where the mem'ry of her lingers everywhere
Just because I'm not the happy guy I used to be
She thinks I still care.

But if she's happy thinking I still need her
Then let that silly notion bring her cheer
But how could she ever be so foolish?
Where would she get such an idea?

Just because I asked a friend about her
Just because I spoke her name somewhere
Just because I saw her, then went all to pieces
She thinks I still care.

T FOR TEXAS

"In Asheville, before that first broadcast (over WWNC), I told myself: 'He'll either make it good in a big way, or he'll do what he calls a complete flop.' . . . I was even doubtful about his 'T For Texas,' although it might be termed lively. Still, what in the world would people think if he sang over the radio 'I'm goin' to shoot poor Thelma, just to see her jump and fall'? . . . About the third week in June, there in Asheville, in 1927, my Jimmie came home one day without his usual teasingly gay greeting. . . . 'You see, Mother—I've been—let out—up at WWNC. They gave my spot to another entertainer.' 'But, darling—you made good, didn't you?' Jimmie said, a little bitterly: 'Oh, I reckon I made good, okay.' From his hip pocket, he drew a bundle of letters, fan letters, and threw them on the bed. . . . Raves about his sobbing yodeling, about the sweetness of his crooning lullabies, and waves of raves about—of all things—'T For Texas.' "

—Mrs. Carrie Rodgers
(from *My Husband, Jimmie Rodgers*)

T FOR TEXAS (BLUE YODEL)
by Jimmie Rodgers

T for Texas, T for Tennessee
T for Texas, T for Tennessee
T for Thelma, that gal that made a wreck out of me.

If you don't want me, Mama, you sure don't have to stall
If you don't want me, Mama, you sure don't have to stall
'Cause I can get more women than a passenger train can haul.

I'm gonna buy me a pistol just as long as I'm tall
I'm gonna buy me a pistol just as long as I'm tall
I'm gonna shoot poor Thelma just to see her jump and fall.

I'm going where the water drinks like cherry wine
I'm going where the water drinks like cherry wine
'Cause the Georgia water tastes like turpentine.

I'm gonna buy me a shotgun with a great long shiny barrel
I'm gonna buy me a shotgun with a great long shiny barrel
I'm gonna shoot that rounder that stole away my gal.

Rather drink muddy water and sleep in a hollow log
Rather drink muddy water and sleep in a hollow log
Than to be in Atlanta, treated like a dirty dog.

TAKE THESE CHAINS FROM MY HEART

" 'Take These Chains From My Heart' was written in Nashville some time during 1952 and was one of the last songs recorded by the late, great genius, Hank Williams. It was released shortly before his death on January 1, 1953, and almost every radio station in the United States kept playing it repeatedly as a tribute to him. It was one of the songs that broke the barrier between country and pop music, and also brought country music into the rhythm and blues field. Dean Martin and Ray Charles are two among many artists credited with this. It is also credited with being one of the songs instrumental in bringing a stream of pop writers and artists into Nashville and the field of country music."

—Rose (Mrs. Hy) Heath

TAKE THESE CHAINS FROM MY HEART
by Hy Heath and Fred Rose

Take these chains from my heart and set me free
You've grown cold and no longer care for me
All my faith in you is gone, but the heartaches linger on
Take these chains from my heart and set me free.

Take these tears from my eyes and let me see
Just a spark of the love that used to be

If you love somebody new, let me find a new love, too
Take these chains from my heart and set me free.

Give my heart just a word of sympathy
Be as fair to a heart as you can be
Then if you no longer care for the love that's beating there
Take these chains from my heart and set me free.

TENNESSEE WALTZ

"While driving back to Nashville from some dates in Texas, Redd Stewart and I were listening to the radio and heard Bill Monroe's 'Kentucky Waltz' and Redd remarked, 'It's odd no one ever did a "Tennessee Waltz," since we make our living on the Grand Ole Opry.' On the back of an old-fashioned match box, the lyrics were composed. A song was born. Governor Frank Clement signed the bill officially on February 17, 1965, making it the Tennessee state song." —Pee Wee King

TENNESSEE WALTZ

by Pee Wee King and Redd Stewart

I was waltzing with my darlin' to the Tennessee Waltz
When an old friend I happened to see
Introduced him to my loved one and while they were waltzing
My friend stole my sweetheart from me.

I remember the night and the Tennessee Waltz
Now I know just how much I have lost
Yes I lost my little darlin' the night they were playin'
The beautiful Tennessee Waltz.

"This song was inspired by a broken marriage between two friends of mine. It is my best-selling song to date."
—Dallas Frazier

THERE GOES MY EVERYTHING
by Dallas Frazier

I hear footsteps slowly walking
As they gently walk across a lonely floor
And a voice is softly saying, "Darling
This will be goodbye for ever more."

There goes my reason for living
There goes the one of my dreams
There goes my only possession
There goes my everything.

As my memory turns back the pages
I can see the happy years we had before
Now the love that kept this old heart beating
Has been shattered by the closing of the door.

THEY'LL NEVER TAKE HER LOVE FROM ME

"Leon said he wrote this song for me."
—Myrtie (Mrs. Leon) Payne

THEY'LL NEVER TAKE HER LOVE FROM ME
by Leon Payne

If today the sun should set on all my hopes and cares
There is one whose smiling face the gods would see
'Cause she'll walk along beside me up the golden stairs
Oh, they'll never, never take her love from me.

What a fool I was to go and break the trust she gave
And to see her love turn into sympathy
It's the one regret I'll carry with me to my grave
Oh, they'll never, never take her love from me.

I'm so thankful for each golden hour of happiness
That we shared together in the used-to-be
Someone else's arms may hold her now in fond caress
But they'll never, never take her love from me.

I thought I'd make her happy if I stepped aside
But I knew her love would never set me free
And even on the day she became another's bride
I said they'll never, never take her love from me.

TOO LATE

"I had a brother-in-law that was always knocking his wife around and drank a lot. I got to thinking that maybe one day she'd just have enough and leave, so I wrote a song called 'Too Late.' I recorded it as my first number on Decca and it was a smash. I went back to Oklahoma City and I ran into my brother-in-law. (Meanwhile, I had written some other songs.) And he said, 'Man, you never wrote anything as pretty as "Too Late" in your life.' I said, 'You should like it, you son of a bitch, it's the story of your life.' "

—Jimmy Wakely

TOO LATE

by Jimmy Wakely

Too late, too late to ask forgiveness
Too late, too late for me to cry
She's gone, she's gone, she left this morning
And this is how she said goodbye:

Upon my pillow was a letter
It said "I still don't want to go
But if you don't change your way of living
May God have mercy on your soul.

"You know I love you as no other
But you have played around too long

Goodbye, good luck, and don't forget me
For I will be a long time gone."

Too late, too late, my heart keeps crying
You should have known she'd go away
Too late, for now you'll have to suffer
It always seems to end this way.

WALKING THE FLOOR OVER YOU

"I was living in Fort Worth, Texas, and had a sponsored radio program on KGKO. I had worked my way up from ten dollars a week I was making in a drug store to seventy-five dollars a week on the radio. This was in 1941. I had just written 'Walking The Floor Over You,' and Dave Kapp happened to be in town with his recording equipment, so we set up a date. I had four songs altogether, and Dave liked 'I Wonder Why You Said Goodbye' and wanted to release it next. But I said, 'Mr. Kapp, do me a favor and release "Walking The Floor Over You" next and I'll never ask you another favor.' Well, he agreed, and that record was such a hit that I guess I'm the only Decca artist who has picked all my releases since 1941."

—Ernest Tubb

WALKING THE FLOOR OVER YOU
by Ernest Tubb

You left me and you went away
You said that you'd be back in just a day
You've broken your promise, and you left me here alone
I don't know why you did, dear, but I do know that you're gone.

I'm walking the floor over you
I can't sleep a wink, that is true
I'm hoping and I'm praying
As my heart breaks right in two
Walking the floor over you.

Now, darling, you know I love you well
Love you more than I can ever tell

I thought that you wanted me and always would be mine
But you went and left me here with troubles on my mind.

Now someday you may be lonesome too
Walking the floor is good for you
Just keep right on walking, and it won't hurt you to cry
Remember that I love you and I will the day I die.

WHEN MY BLUE MOON TURNS TO GOLD AGAIN

"In 1940, my partner Wiley Walker and I recorded a session for Columbia, and it was a mistake. We didn't have any idea about original songs; we were just going to do songs we thought we liked. Art Satherly, Columbia A & R man, kicked most of them out, and we had to learn and record six songs in one day. It didn't come off. After the session, he sat us down and said, 'You're going to have to write your own songs if you're interested in the recording business.' Because of this, I started trying to write songs. Shortly after, we were moving from Lubbock, Texas, to Oklahoma City to take a new job. I had everything I owned in the car including my wife and two kids. I drove all night across the west Texas prairie, looking right into a full moon. It was so bright on that flat ground I could turn my headlights out and still see the road. That's where the idea struck me for this song. Everybody was asleep, and as I drove along, I started putting the song together." —Gene Sullivan

WHEN MY BLUE MOON TURNS TO GOLD AGAIN

by Gene Sullivan and Wiley Walker

Memories that linger in my heart
Memories that make my heart grow cold
But someday they'll live again, sweetheart
And my blue moon again will turn to gold.

When my blue moon turns to gold again
When the rainbow turns the clouds away
When my blue moon turns to gold again
You'll be back in my arms to stay.

The lips that used to thrill me so
Your kisses were meant for only me
In my dreams they live again, sweetheart
But my golden moon is just a memory.

The castles we built of dreams together
Were the sweetest stories ever told
Maybe we will live them all again
And my blue moon again will turn to gold.

WILDWOOD FLOWER

"The first time I heard this song, I was just a kid. My mother sang it and her mother sang it. It has been handed down for years and years. It's the most popular song we ever recorded, and there's hardly a country group who doesn't use this song."

—Mother Maybelle Carter,
of the original Carter Family

WILDWOOD FLOWER[1]

by A. P. Carter

Oh, I'll twine with my mingles and waving black hair
With the roses so red and the lilies so fair
And the myrtles so bright with emerald dew
The pale and the leader and eyes look like blue.

Oh, I'll dance, I will sing, and my laugh shall be gay
I will charm ev'ry heart, in his crown I will sway
When I woke from my dreaming, idols were clay
All portions of love then had all flown away.

Oh, he taught me to love him and promised to love
And to cherish me over all others above
How my heart now is wond'ring misery can tell
He's left me no warning, no words of farewell.

Oh, he taught me to love him and called me his flow'r
That was blooming to cheer him thru life's dreary hour

[1]See p. 157, "I'll Twine 'Mid The Ringlets."

Oh, I'm longing to see him thru life's dark hour
He's gone and neglected this pale wildwood flower.

WORRIED MIND

"This song was an attempt to catch the mood of the people who haunted the little taverns where jukeboxes were the only source of entertainment. The title was suggested by a cheating girl friend." —Ted Daffan

WORRIED MIND

by Ted Daffan and Jimmie Davis

You promised me love that would never die
That promise you made was only a lie
Now after you've gone, all alone I'll pine
For all that I've got is a worried mind.

I gave you a ring, I gave you a home
You promised me true that you'd never roam
I bought you fine clothes and I bought you wine
But all that you gave is a worried mind.

And when I was down, you just left me there
I needed you so, but you didn't care
You found a new love and a home so fine
But all that I've got is a worried mind.

You promised me love that would never die
That promise you made was only a lie
Now after you've gone, all alone I'll pine
For all that I've got is a worried mind.

"This has been my most popular song by far, and it has been recorded more than 300 times. It was used in both my campaigns for the governorship of Louisiana, in 1944 and 1959. It was used in a number of movies, including one called *Louisiana* in which I had the leading role. It also has been the theme song on radio stations, and the tune has been used to advertise various products on TV and radio with other words."

—Jimmie Davis

YOU ARE MY SUNSHINE

by Jimmie Davis and Charles Mitchell

The other night, dear, as I lay sleeping
I dreamed I held you in my arms
When I awoke, dear, I was mistaken
And I hung my head and cried.

You are my sunshine, my only sunshine
You make me happy when skies are gray
You'll never know, dear, how much I love you
Please don't take my sunshine away.

I'll always love you and make you happy
If you will only say the same
But if you leave me to love another
You'll regret it all some day.

You told me once, dear, you really loved me
And no one else could come between
But now you've left me and love another
You have shattered all my dreams.

7 | Cheatin' Songs

Slipping Around

For the first twenty-five years of recorded hillbilly music, songwriters almost exclusively avoided the issues of infidelity and illicit love. In a structured, church-centered society, cheating not only was a sin, it was taboo in polite society.

But in the forties, with the advent of World War II, rural society began to change, and this change was reflected in country music. The love song took on a hopeless, pitiful note. A surge in unrequited love songs reflected this self-pity and went as far as a suicide threat in "The Last Letter." And a whole new type of song—the honky-tonk song—appeared to celebrate that new institution and to lament the new life-style it symbolized. Clearly, many were "Headin' Down The Wrong Highway."

Inevitably, in the upheaval of a wartime society, with women working, husbands and wives separated, easy social and geographical mobility, and honky tonks no longer populated exclusively by women of easy virtue, country writers began first to flirt with, then to address directly, the subject of cheating.

Infidelity was nothing new, of course, but before the war it was chancy, furtive, and shameful—and seldom mentioned. Little changed in this regard during the forties and fifties except that cheating became common enough to qualify as a subject for popular song.

As Webb Pierce said, "I think the reason 'Back Street Affair' hit is that there were a lot of people having back street affairs, and it was something they were keeping hidden. Then, when the record came out in 1952, it became an emotional outlet for them. They hear somebody singing about back street affairs, they kind of smile and say, 'That's us, honey, let's play that one. Let's buy that one.' There were enough people saying 'That's us, honey' that it sold a lot of records and got a lot of plays."

Even before Pierce's hit recording of Billy Wallace's "Back Street Affair," though, country composers were gradually getting around to discussing the subject. In 1943, Ernest Tubb's "Try Me One More Time" and Jenny Lou Carson's "You Two-Timed Me One Time Too Often" in 1945, hinted at the matter of cheating, but both were vague and general enough so that they could be taken either way—as a one-sided courtship or a violation of the marriage vows. The word "untrue" is common to both, though the relationships (perhaps deliberately) are never clearly spelled out.

Then, in 1948, Hal Blair frankly stated the case: "One Has My Name, The Other Has My Heart," a song that offered little but wishful thinking as a solution to the dilemma of "brown eyes" versus "blue eyes." Marriage, after all, was inviolate, even if it didn't include love.

Floyd Tillman wrote in 1949 what is probably the classic cheating song, "Slipping Around," and established a pattern that persists to this day. Although cheating is wrong in the eyes of society and sinful in the sight of God, the temptation is just too great. Even though such a relationship evokes guilt and fear, there is always the vague hope that things can be "made right" some way short of divorce.

That same year, Tillman himself wrote an answer song called "I'll Never Slip Around Again," and raised the provocative question of whether one who has cheated on one mate can be expected to be true to another. The Louvin Brothers gave this idea a more subtle twist in a sophisticated 1956 song called "I Take The Chance." The lines "But, dear, you know to one I've been untrue/I wonder if you think I'd do the same to you/I take the chance of causing you to doubt my love" manage without contrivance to highlight the dishonesty and dangers of a cheating relationship.

Inevitably, a number of country songs have taken the opposite viewpoint—that of the person cheated on—usually introducing a note of retribution. One of the best of these was Hank Williams's "Your Cheatin' Heart," which tells the offender that he or she will pay for the sin of cheating: "Your cheatin' heart will make you weep." Revenge usually is not a factor in the cheating song; usually the singer is content with a mournful "I told you so."

The sixties produced a stream of cheating songs in the established manner, but as with all country songs, this category also took on a new maturity and realism. Cheating was justified in two songs about "The Other Woman" by Betty Sue Perry and Don Rollins. In Betty Sue Perry's hit published in 1965, the cheater's wife "gave him the right to seek that other woman" by being the first to cheat, and Rollins's 1965 "answer" echoes this sentiment, blaming the wife for leaving him "prey to another woman's charms." Both are addressed to the wife and rationalize the cheating game.

In "Margie's At The Lincoln Park Inn," which even the writer, Tom T. Hall, admitted was "ahead of its time," cheating (or at least the intention to cheat) receives neither apology nor rationalization, though one can read into it a subtle social message concerning the quality of middle-class life.

Sexual needs, long a taboo in country music, are given as the reason for cheating in the tragic "Ruby, Don't Take Your Love To Town." Its threat of violence is alien to the traditionally lovesick cheating song, but no more alien than its frank admission of damaged manhood. It is an angry, defiant song and more akin to "You Ain't Woman Enough" than to the classic cheating songs. This Loretta Lynn hit is a challenge to the other woman and also contains more than a hint of violence.

So the cheating song has achieved a new sophistication and willingness to deal with real issues. And from their popularity, it's apparent that there are, indeed, plenty of people saying "That's us, honey."

BACK STREET AFFAIR

"There had been songs about slipping around and stepping out, but none with young girls involved. As I looked around, I saw that lots of married men were going out with young girls. Then I, of all people, fell in this snare. This girl had soft, dark eyes, a winning smile, and made a married man feel at ease. I hope she's happy. I was happy in the light of her understanding smile. That's life. That's a back street affair. I know it. I've lived it."

—Billy Wallace

BACK STREET AFFAIR
by Billy Wallace

You didn't know I wasn't free
When you fell in love with me
And with all your young heart you learned to care
It brought you shame and disgrace
The world has tumbled in your face
'Cause they call our love a back street affair.

They say you wrecked my home
I'm a husband that's gone wrong
They don't know the sorrow that we had to bear

For the one I'm tied to
Was the first to be untrue
Now they call our love a back street affair.

We have each other now
That's all that matters anyhow
For the judgement of gossip's never fair
We'll just be brave and strong
Someday they'll see they're wrong
Let them call our love a back street affair.

When the mist rolls away
We'll be free to love someday
And more happiness God meant for us to share
I'll climb a mountain, dear
Just so the world can hear
That our love's not a back street affair.

DON'T LET ME CROSS OVER

"I was on tour on the road between Knoxville and Cincinnati, just riding along watching the 'No Passing' signs that tell you not to cross over the yellow line, and that's where I got the idea. I made it 'love's cheating line,' but I got the idea from those road signs. It's sold well over a million copies. I wrote an answer, 'Just Over The Line,' and that was a hit, too."

—Penny Jay

DON'T LET ME CROSS OVER

by Penny Jay

I'm tempted, my darling, to steal you away
Don't let me cross over, stay out of my way
You know that I love you, and I'm not the stealing kind
But I'm faced with heartaches at love's cheating line.

Don't let me cross over love's cheating line
You belong to another and can never be mine
I know one step closer would be heaven divine
Don't let me cross over love's cheating line.

I tried to forget you, but what else can I do
When your eyes keep saying that you love me too?
I know if I lose you, not a dream will I have left
I don't want to cheat, dear, but I can't help myself.

I TAKE THE CHANCE

"My brother basically wrote this song. The title is exactly like it says. At the time, I guess he liked somebody else better than he liked his wife, and the song is almost self-explanatory. When the title came up, Ira and I worked on the song, and whichever came up with the best line, we used it."

—Charlie Louvin

I TAKE THE CHANCE

by Charlie and Ira Louvin

I've tried to live my life the best I can
I prayed I'd never cheat to heed my heart's command
But, dear, you know to one I've been untrue
I wonder if you think I'd do the same to you.

I take the chance
Of causing you to doubt my love
I take the chance to be with you.

I know it's wrong for us to steal a kiss
And when you hold me in your arms I can't resist
I have a home and someone kind and true
I know I'd lose it all if I was seen with you.

I take the chance
To lose my soul, my life, my pride
I take the chance to be with you.

"It was the natural thing to do to write an answer song. A popular network show called 'The Lucky Strike Hit Parade' had chosen 'Slipping Around' to do on the network. I received a frantic letter from the publisher that two lines were censored as immoral: 'Though you're tied up with someone else/And I'm all tied up too.' I changed them to 'I guess I had it comin,' there's nothing I can do.' It was then I decided to write an answer to 'Slipping Around,' the reverse, 'I'll Never Slip Around Again.' That was my only answer song.' —Floyd Tillman

I'LL NEVER SLIP AROUND AGAIN
by Floyd Tillman

I'll never slip around again
I've learned a lot, somehow
The gal I slipped around with then
Is married to me now
I know just how it feels
To live in lonely misery
'Cause the gal I slipped around with then
She's slippin' 'round on me.

I guess I had it comin'
There's nothin' I can do
I left the truest sweetheart
To fall in love with you
I had to learn the hard way
That slippin' 'round don't pay
And I'll never slip around again
Until my dyin' day.

MARGIE'S AT THE LINCOLN PARK INN

"This is a very adult song. It was never a great success, but it's one of my mainstays. I think it's a little bitter, a little too broad and ahead of its time. The song pushed people around too much. They didn't want to hear about that just yet, because it wasn't as clever as 'Harper Valley,' and the fellow that was getting ready to go to the Lincoln Park Inn was speaking in the first person. I think that, socially, we've always apologized for our desires. Like 'Please Help Me, I'm Falling,' that's an apology for a desire and a plea for forgiveness. But in this song, people just weren't ready to face the reality of the need without the apology."

—Tom T. Hall

MARGIE'S AT THE LINCOLN PARK INN
by Tom T. Hall

My name's in the paper where I took the Boy Scouts to hike
My hands are all dirty from working on my little boy's bike
The preacher came by, and I talked for a minute with him
My wife's in the kitchen, and Margie's at the Lincoln Park Inn.

And I know why she's there, 'cause I've been there before
But I made a promise that I wouldn't cheat anymore
I tried to ignore it, but I know she's in there, my friend
My mind's on a number, and Margie's at the Lincoln Park Inn.

Next Sunday, it's my turn to speak to the young people's class
They expect answers to all of the questions they ask
What would they say if I spoke on a modern-day sin
And all of the Margies at all of the Lincoln Park Inns?

The bike is all fixed, and my little boy is in bed asleep
His little old puppy is curled in a ball at my feet
My wife's baking cookies to feed to the bridge club again
I'm almost out of cigarettes, and Margie's at the Lincoln Park Inn.

And I know why she's there.

ONE HAS MY NAME, THE OTHER HAS MY HEART

"I wrote the lyrics, Eddie Dean was the composer and his wife Dearest Dean mothered the title. The song, as far as I have been able to determine was the first of the 'cheating' songs, and daring enough at the time to be banned by certain church leagues and others. Time has changed all that. It is now considered mild. This song is a true story and concerned only me, not Eddie and Dearest. I was engaged to a girl when I came home from overseas, and due to a misunderstanding, we were not married. I very brilliantly, on the rebound, married someone else. The story line of the song is very simple and self-explanatory. However, as a little addendum to the tale, the ultimate ending is not entirely negative. The 'blue-eyed girl' of the lyric has remained a fast friend through these many years, and I know and love her family."

—Hal Blair

ONE HAS MY NAME, THE OTHER HAS MY HEART

by Hal Blair, Eddie Dean, and Dearest Dean

One has my name, the other has my heart
With one I'll remain, that's how my heartaches start
One has brown eyes, the other's eyes are blue
To one I am tied, to the other I am true
One has my love, the other only me
But what good is love to a heart that can't be free?
So I'll go on living my life just the same
While one has my heart, the other has my name.

One has my name, the other has my heart
With one I'll remain, that's how my heartaches start
One has brown eyes, the other's eyes are blue
To one I am tied, to the other I am true
One has my love, the other only me
But what good is love to a heart that can't be free?
If I could live over, my life I would change
The one who has my heart would also have my name.

THE OTHER WOMAN

"In my younger years, I had similar experiences and probably drew from my subconscious when I wrote this song. I also have empathy for people who get involved in this sort of thing. I'd like to believe that some women who get criticized for being 'the other woman' are not always scalawags. His wife may be doing him wrong. One of the most dramatic incidents relating to the song occurred one night when Loretta Lynn was singing it on stage. A woman came out of the audience, flashed a gun at Loretta and said, 'You're the so-and-so who's been running around with my husband. I'm gonna kill you right now!' Loretta said, 'Oh, no, I'm not running around with your husband. Someone else wrote the song, and she's not the other woman either.' That's how much people identify with the song."

—Betty Sue Perry

THE OTHER WOMAN

by Betty Sue Perry

I'd like to introduce myself, I'm the other woman
The other woman in your husband's life
The whole town's buzzin' 'bout us and our stolen moments
They're calling you the true and faithful wife.

But you gave him the right to seek that other woman
And you know who was first to cheat on who
I just accepted love from him you never wanted
The other woman didn't steal from you.

Now everybody's blaming me, I'm the other woman
But who are they to judge who's wrong or right
Their whispers might be different if they knew what I know
The husband still beats you home every night.

THE OTHER WOMAN (IN MY LIFE)

"At the time that Ray Price's hit recording of this song was released, there was speculation in Nashville that it was a true song. However, I am certain that it was not based on a real incident. In fact, my brother wrote the song several years before it was actually published. Listening to some old tapes, he came across 'The Other Woman.' When some friends heard it, they assured him it was a hit, which prompted him to try to get it published."

—Rosemary Rollins Smartt

THE OTHER WOMAN (IN MY LIFE)

by Don Rollins

Don't accuse me of being without feeling
I didn't mean to bring you any harm
Maybe you are the one who was careless
And left me prey to another woman's charms.

The other woman isn't prettier than you
But the other woman soothed my wounded pride
And more important I feel wanted again
I can't give up the other woman in my life.

I'm afloat down the middle of a river
And I can't climb out of either side
And if I go over the deep end
It won't be because I haven't tried.

PLEASE HELP ME, I'M FALLING

"Don Robertson started the song and backed away from completing it when he realized he was writing his own story. When Don showed me the partially completed work, I was immediately interested in working on the song, for I, too, was personally living the song. Don and I debated for some time about showing this song, and finally exposed it and ourselves to the publisher. 'Please Help Me, I'm Falling' is sincerely written and is true and factual."

—Hal Blair

PLEASE HELP ME, I'M FALLING (IN LOVE WITH YOU)
by Hal Blair and Don Robertson

Please help me, I'm falling in love with you
Close the door to temptation, don't let me walk through
Turn away from me, darling, I'm begging you to
Please help me, I'm falling in love with you.

I belong to another whose arms have grown cold
But I promised forever to have and to hold
I can never be free, dear, but when I'm with you
I know that I'm losing the will to be true.

Please help me, I'm falling, and that could be sin
Close the door to temptation, don't let me walk in
For I mustn't want you, but darling I do
Please help me, I'm falling in love with you.

" 'Ruby' is based on a true story of a man from my home town in Florida. This particular man was injured during World War II in Germany and was sent to England to recuperate. While he was in England, he met a nurse that helped nurse him back to health. He married her and brought her back home. They lived behind our house in a little apartment. His wounds kept recurring, and he'd have to go to the veterans hospital to get treated. Then one day, he went to the hospital and became temporarily paralyzed. This lasted four or five months. During this time, his problems started increasing. 'Ruby' stood by him till she could stand it no longer. Then she started fixing her hair, putting flowers in it, painting her lips, and walking back and forth in front of the pool room. She was lonesome, needed attention. She was a good girl, actually, but the way I wrote it, I put the blame on her. At the time, I didn't know what was going on, because I was only 12 or 13 years old. Twenty-three years later, I realized what was happening. I just changed the wars and brought it up to date and wrote the story in about an hour. Eventually, it was a couple of years ago, he killed her and himself too. That's a true story."

—Mel Tillis

RUBY, DON'T TAKE YOUR LOVE TO TOWN
by Mel Tillis

You have painted up your lips and rolled and curled your tinted hair
Ruby, are you contemplating going out somewhere?
The shadows on the wall tell me the sun is going down
Oh, Ruby, don't take your love to town.

For it wasn't me that started that old crazy Asian war
But I was proud to go and do my patriotic chores
Oh, I know, Ruby, that I'm not the man I used to be
But, Ruby, I still need your company.

It's hard to love a man whose legs are bent and paralyzed
And the wants and needs of a woman your age, Ruby, I realize
But it won't be long, I've heard them say, until I'm not around
Oh, Ruby, don't take your love to town.

She's leaving now, 'cause I just heard the slamming of a door
The way I know I've heard it slam one hundred times before
And if I could move, I'd get my gun and put her in the ground
Oh, Ruby, don't take your love to town.

"About three o'clock in the morning, after playing a job a few hundred miles out of Houston, we stopped at an all-night cafe on the way home. There was a telephone nearby, and a lady was talking on it. I couldn't help but overhear the conversation. She said, 'Now, Honey, you call me, and if a man answers, hang up.' I thought, 'Poor girl, she's just like me . . . slipping around.' "

—Floyd Tillman

SLIPPING AROUND

by Floyd Tillman

Seems I always have to slip around
To be with you, my dear
Slipping around
Afraid we might be found
I know I can't forget you
And I've got to have you near
But we just have to slip around
And live in constant fear.

Though you're tied up with someone else
And I'm all tied up too
I know I've made mistakes, dear
But I'm so in love with you
I hope some day I'll find a way
To bring you back with me
Then I won't have to slip around
To have your company.

YOU AIN'T WOMAN ENOUGH

"I think that all women get upset when they think that some other woman is messin' with their husband or their man. I try to write everyday living, everyday life."

—Loretta Lynn

YOU AIN'T WOMAN ENOUGH

by Loretta Lynn

You've come to tell me something you say I ought to know
That he don't love me anymore, and I'll have to let him go

You say you're gonna take him, but I don't think that you can
'Cause you ain't woman enough to take my man.

Women like you, they're a dime a dozen, you can buy 'em anywhere
For you to get to him, I'd have to move over and I'm gonna stand right here
It'll be over my dead body, so get out while you can
Oh, you ain't woman enough to take my man.

Sometimes a man's caught lookin' at things that he don't need
He took a second look at you, but he's in love with me
I don't know where that leaves you, but I know where I stand
And you ain't woman enough to take my man.

YOUR CHEATIN' HEART

"Whereas I am privileged to tell any truth that existed during my life with my husband, my wish is not to hurt anyone. All living things have problems, maybe even the dead; most certainly Hank was no different. He laughed and he cried. I saw both. Like all of us he had a past, some good and some bad. What man don't? Out of his past and present came ideas for songs as did 'Cheatin' Heart.' Hank and I became engaged in Nashville, Tennessee. We decided to drive down to my home in the bayou country in Louisiana to tell my mom and dad that we were to be married. This was early summer, 1952. I didn't know much about Hank's past and didn't really care, but I was young and had not experienced misery. Hank started telling me about his problems with his ex-wife, Audrey. He said that one day her 'Cheatin' Heart' would pay. Then he said, 'Hey, that'd make a good song! Get out my tablet, Baby; me and you are gonna write us a song!' Just about as fast as I could write, Hank quoted the words to me in a matter of minutes. Then he looked over at me, my hair flying in his convertible car, eating an ice cream cone, and said, 'One thing, Baby, Ole Hank could never be ashamed of you.' Once again his eyes brightened as he said, 'Write this down for Ole Hank.' And so it was—another thought from the heart of a gentle man with the soul of a giant and the needs of a child—tender love." —Billie Jean Williams Horton

YOUR CHEATIN' HEART

by Hank Williams

Your cheatin' heart will make you weep
You'll cry and cry and try to sleep
But sleep won't come the whole night through
Your cheatin' heart will tell on you.

When tears come down like fallin' rain
You'll toss around and call my name
You'll walk the floor the way I do
Your cheatin' heart will tell on you.

Your cheatin' heart will pine some day
And crave the love you threw away
The time will come when you'll be blue
Your cheatin' heart will tell on you.

8 | Honky-Tonk Songs

Wild Side of Life

Since the mid-forties, the action of many songs written about cheating and broken love affairs has been played out on a new stage, the honky tonk. This period has also marked the appearance of an entirely new kind of song, the honky-tonk song.

Centering on the places themselves and the churning activity that characterizes them, honky-tonk songs have made up an increasing share of new compositions since World War II. The honky tonk as a fact of hillbilly life has become a major factor in hillbilly song.

Although the origin of the term honky tonk is obscure, it was probably borrowed from ragtime and has been in use in the rural South at least since the 1920s. Ragtime, an enormously popular musical style, was born in Sedalia, Missouri, in 1890, and quickly spread throughout the Midwest and South. One of its musical characteristics was the "honky tonk" piano, and, by extension, the saloons and bawdy houses where it was played became urban "honky tonks." One of the earliest uses of the term was in a song entitled "Honka-Tonk Rag," written in 1910 by Earl Jones and L. Albert. Country boys visiting these saloons probably brought the name home with them. When the Model T found its way to the back country, the new mobility it provided gave rise to the roadside tavern, located safely away from the judgments of a fundamentalist society and on the outskirts of the law, and these became country honky tonks.

Prohibition gave these places new importance, while their secrecy and air of wickedness made them more attractive—particularly when women were welcomed for the first time into the traditionally all-male saloon. Where liquor flows, entertainment flourishes, and here the country musician found an alternative to the barn dance, the fiddlers' grove, and the medicine wagon in which to play.

Jack Cardwell, an Alabama musician and songwriter who played in some of the same honky tonks as Hank Williams during the forties, recalled his early experiences: "The first one I recall going to was Thigpen's Log Cabin, halfway between Georgiana and Chapman, Alabama. It was just a big barn—a big open building with the rafters showing—and they had a band stand maybe 8 feet by 10 feet. There was no whiskey sold legally, but there was plenty of it there; they'd hide bottles all over the woods."

As they spread, honky tonks became a training ground for country performers who, in the beginning, worked at music as an avocation, often for no pay. Beginning with pioneers like Al Dexter, Jimmy Skinner, and Floyd Tillman during the forties, a distinct honky-tonk style developed further with fifties stars like Lefty Frizzell, Hank Williams, and Webb Pierce, and matured during the next decade with singers like Buck Owens and George Jones.

As these artists grew in stature and success and became paid, professional honky-tonk singers, their music underwent a number of changes. Steel guitar, drums, and eventually amplified instruments were added so the band could be heard over the din of a barroom jammed with dancing couples. Singing styles and song content changed, too, though more subtly and over time.

Songs of church and home, obviously, didn't fit with the smells of beer and cheap perfume, and performers dug deep in their song bags for more lively numbers or composed their own. Some were raucous and off color and thus appropriate to the crowds of laborers and farmhands who comprised the honky tonks' early audiences.

"A man didn't carry his wife or girlfriend there," Cardwell said. "The women were there hunting a good time just like the men. There were lots of fights. People who are less 'cultured' have a tendency to drink a little more, and men at that time farmed or worked in the logging woods or did hard labor. Transportation was at a nil, and when they did get a chance to blow off, why, they would."

By the mid-thirties, the coin-operated phonograph had become a fixture in many honky tonks, providing entertainment during the band's off hours and bringing the new sounds to smaller places that couldn't afford live entertainment. Borrowed from the so-called juke joints that sprang up in England around 1910, the machines were called "jukeboxes," and they, too, influenced the development of a honky-tonk style.

As early as 1935, records were issued on the Mel-odee label (and presumably others) which bore the inscription "manufactured for juke boxes"; Gene Autry's "Nighttime In Nevada" was one of these. The jukebox not only assured record manufacturers a new, steady source of distribution, but also created a fairly homogeneous audience throughout the South and Southwest (and, by the late forties, parts of the North as well). Thus, it paved the way for a true national honky-tonk singing style where earlier hillbilly records had more closely followed individual regional styles.

As the honky tonk became a firmly established bit of Americana, it afforded the scenario for a rash of songs about the honky-tonk life-style. The songs that make up this chapter are those specifically about the honky tonk and the honky-tonk experience—drinking, dancing, hell raising, loose morality, and, almost always, loneliness. Often their subject matter touches on that of other chapters, but the songs in this selection stand apart as a distinct phenomenon.

One of the first honky-tonk songs to attain widespread popularity was Ted Daffan's "Headin' Down The Wrong Highway," copyrighted in 1945. Like "Bubbles In My Beer" and many of those that followed it, it expresses guilt and regret at a misspent life—not unmixed with self-pity. By the fifties, songs like "There Stands The Glass" and "Warm Red Wine" began to celebrate the act of drinking itself, but always as an escape from "tears," "fears," or "the dreams that are gone."

But not all honky-tonk songs are quite so piteous; "If You've Got The Money, I've Got The Time" and "Honky Tonk Man" get caught up in the sheer exuberance of a Saturday night on the town—though usually at the expense of the female. This note of male chauvinism is common to a great many country songs, but nowhere does it show itself more clearly than in the honky-tonk song. "But if you run short of money, I'll run short of time, 'cause you with no more money, honey, I've got no more time," writes Lefty Frizzell, while the male protagonist in "Honky Tonk Man" says, "And when my money's all gone, I'm on the telephone, callin' 'Hey, hey, mama, can your daddy come home?' "

The double standard apparent in these songs is made clear in the concept of the "honky-tonk angel." Basically a good woman lured by the gay night life, she will "never make a wife." It is, after all, *God* who makes honky-tonk angels, according to the song "The Wild Side Of Life." Even the answer song, "I Didn't Know God Made Honky Tonk Angels," which was written by a man but claims to represent the female point of view, casts her as a victim and thus perpetuates her subordinate role.

Loretta Lynn's "Don't Come Home A-Drinkin' " represents the budding independence and increasing consciousness of women that characterized the 1960s. Though far from being a statement of women's liberation, it is clear that she will no longer suffer the abuses of the past.

The term "honky tonk" has in recent years acquired a wider connotation; it has come to mean any place where dancing and drinking go on that enters the consciousness of the country boy. Thus, Bill Anderson, in his songs "City Lights" and "Bright Lights," injects what borders upon a note of alienation—not only from his lost love but from the entire urban experience. Anderson, though born a southerner, did not have roots in rural poverty. Nonetheless, he managed to capture the spirit of a great many country music fans with these two honky-tonk songs.

Perhaps Bill Anderson's songs signal the beginning of the end of the honky tonk of the past as it merges with and becomes indistinguishable from the city-and-suburban lounge.

BRIGHT LIGHTS AND COUNTRY MUSIC

"I was performing for a week in a nightclub in Toronto, Canada, and on Saturday we were scheduled to play two shows. About Thursday of that week, I got a letter from a lady by the name of Monna Tanner who lived about 200 miles from town, saying she was coming to see our show on Saturday. 'I'll be there for the night show instead of the afternoon show,' she said, 'because I like soft lights with my country music.' And the phrase 'soft lights and country music' really struck me, but I realized the best way to say it was 'bright lights and country music.' After our show that Saturday night, I told Jimmy Gateley about the letter, and we wrote the song outside the dressing room at this club. We stood in the hall while about 40 or 50 people waited for our autographs, and we wrote it right there in front of an audience."

—Bill Anderson

BRIGHT LIGHTS AND COUNTRY MUSIC
by Bill Anderson and Jimmy Gateley

I won't stay home and cry tonight like all the nights before
I just learned that I don't really need you anymore
I found a little place downtown where guys like me can go
And they've got bright lights and country music.

Bright lights and country music, a bottle and a glass
Soon I'll be forgetting that there ever was a past
And when everybody asks me what helped me forget so fast
I'll say "bright lights and country music."

A table by the bandstand, a bottle filled with wine
Honky tonks were made for men with women on their minds
Nothing else can take away this loneliness of mine
Quite like bright lights and country music.

"The great Tommy Duncan called me one day and said, 'Cindy, I've got a great song title for you.' I hadn't written a square song all day and was hungry for a good title. Tommy took a deep breath and said, 'Watching the Bubbles in My Beer.' I couldn't have been more surprised if he had hit me in the face with a wet squirrel. I said, 'You're kidding,' but I could tell by the silence on the other end of the line that he wasn't kidding. So I said, 'Tell me what you had in mind.' He said, 'Well, you see a lonely man sitting in a barroom not talking to anyone, just thinking of someone or something that happened in the past—just remembering and watching the bubbles in his beer.' You can bet I didn't wait for the water to get hot before I started to put that one on paper." —Cindy Walker

BUBBLES IN MY BEER
by Cindy Walker, Tommy Duncan, and Bob Wills

Tonight in a bar alone I'm sitting
Apart from the laughter and cheer
While scenes from the past rise before me
Just watching the bubbles in my beer.

I'm seeing the road that I've traveled
A road paved with heartaches and tears
And I'm seeing the past that I've wasted
While watching the bubbles in my beer.

A vision of someone who loved me
Brings a lone silent tear to my eye
As I think of the heart that I've broken
And of the golden chances that have passed me by.

Oh, I know that my life's been a failure
I've lost everything that made life dear
And the dreams I once made now are empty
As empty as the bubbles in my beer.

CITY LIGHTS

" 'City Lights' was the first song I ever wrote that was a commercial success. I was living in a little three-story hotel in the town of Commerce,

Georgia, at the time. I was only 19 years old, and I was going to school at the University of Georgia, working part-time as a disc jockey in Commerce. I went out on top of the hotel one night, and I was looking down at the lights of the town. It was a very clear night, and as I looked up at the stars, I started with the second verse, 'The world was dark and God made stars to brighten up the night; did the God who put those stars above make those city lights?' I wrote it as a question. Ray Price changed it later, but I was asking could that same God who made the stars that were so beautiful and clean make the lights of the town which sometimes tended to be kind of dirty?"

—Bill Anderson

CITY LIGHTS
by Bill Anderson

The bright array of city lights as far as I can see
The Great White Way shines through the night for lonely guys like me
The cabarets and honky tonks, their flashing signs invite
A broken heart to lose itself in the glow of city lights.

Lights that say "Forget her in a glass of sherry wine"
Lights that offer other girls for empty hearts like mine
They paint a pretty picture of a world that's gay and bright
But it's just a mask for loneliness behind those city lights.

The world was dark, and God made stars to brighten up the night
Did the God who put those stars above make those city lights?
Did He make a place for men to cry when things don't turn out right?
Are we just supposed to run and hide behind those city lights?

Lights that say "Forget her love in a different atmosphere"
Lights that lure are nothing but a masquerade for tears
They paint a pretty picture, but my arms can't hold them tight
And I just can't say "I love you" to a street of city lights.

DIM LIGHTS, THICK SMOKE

"I was a country entertainer, and I had been at all the barn dance shows —the National Barn Dance in Chicago, the Old Dominion Barn Dance in

Richmond, Virginia, and the Boone Country Jamboree in Cincinnati—in the days before television. We used acoustical instruments and played for a seated audience in theaters and auditoriums and places like that. Then I moved to California and got into Western Swing. So the first date that I played was at Bakersfield, a place called The Blackboard, and it was the loudest band I had ever heard in my life. I had never worked with drums or electrical instruments. The smoke was thick, and I wasn't used to that. And there were women and men out there dancing, and that was new to me. On the way home—I had about 100 miles to drive between Bakersfield and the San Fernando Valley—I came up with this idea, 'dim lights, thick smoke, and loud music.' The original title of the song was 'Honky Tonk Heart,' but Max Fidler thought the first line would make a better title. Consequently, I got used to drums, and now I wouldn't be without them. The band that was playing there at that time was Bill Woods, and Buck Owens was singing in the band; he was one of the musicians that backed me."

—Joe Maphis

DIM LIGHTS, THICK SMOKE (AND LOUD, LOUD MUSIC)
by Joe Maphis, Rose Lee Maphis, and Max Fidler

A home and little children mean nothing to you
A house filled with love and a husband so true
You'd rather have a drink with the first guy you meet
And the only home you know is the club down the street.

Dim lights, thick smoke and loud, loud music
Is the only kind of life you'll ever understand
Dim lights, thick smoke and loud, loud music
You'll never make a wife to a home-lovin' man.

A-drinkin' and a-dancin' to a honky tonk band
Is the only kind of life you'll ever understand
Go on and have your fun, you think you've played it smart
I feel sorry for you and your honky tonk heart.

202

DON'T COME HOME A-DRINKIN'

"My little sister had started a song called 'I Come Home Last Night As Drunk As I Could Be,' so I thought, 'Well, I'm gonna try to help her get in the business.' So I changed it around to 'Don't Come Home A-Drinkin' With Lovin' On Your Mind,' 'cause that's about the way it happens, don't it?"

—Loretta Lynn

DON'T COME HOME A-DRINKIN'

by Loretta Lynn

Well, you thought I'd be waitin' up when you came home last night
You'd been out with all the boys, and you ended up half tight
But liquor and love they just don't mix; leave the bottle or me behind
And don't come home a-drinkin' with lovin' on your mind.

No, don't come home a-drinkin' with lovin' on your mind
Just stay out there on the town and see what you can find
'Cause if you want that kind of love,
Well, you don't need none of mine
So don't come home a-drinkin' with lovin' on your mind.

You never take me anywhere, because you're always gone
And many a night I've laid awake and cried there all alone
Then you come in a-kissin' on me, it happens every time
So don't come home a-drinkin' with lovin' on your mind.

FOUR WALLS

"My co-writer was a very busy pianist, writing by day and playing by night, and the song was inspired by a day-to-day observation of the marvelous manner in which his wife took the rough edges of life with no complaint. It was a number of years after it was written that Jim Reeves recorded it and made it a smash hit. Chet Atkins told me later how he happened to connect with the song. It seems Chet had a stack of material on his desk while Jim was in the room, and, through some movement or other, the stack toppled into his wastebasket. Jim joined the rescue effort, putting the sheet music and demonstration records back on the desk. And while doing so, he saw the title, asked about it, listened to it, liked it, and recorded it."

—Marvin Moore

FOUR WALLS

by Marvin Moore and George Campbell

Out where the bright lights are glowing
You're drawn like a moth to a flame
You laugh while the wine's overflowing
While I sit and whisper your name.

Four walls to hear me
Four walls to see
Four walls too near me
Closing in on me.

Sometimes I ask why I'm waiting
But my walls have nothing to say
I'm made for love, not for hating
So here, where you left me, I'll stay.

One night with you is like heaven
And so, while I'm walking the floor
I listen for steps in the hallway
And wait for your knock on my door.

HEADIN' DOWN THE WRONG HIGHWAY

"This song was inspired by a personal experience. Heavy drinking is an occupational hazard with musicians and band leaders. I woke up one Monday morning with a horrible hangover. I lived in a small penthouse on top of a hotel on the beach in Los Angeles. There was nothing left to drink in the place, so I went downstairs and around the corner to a bar. I ordered my drink (a double, of course) and looked around. It was early in the morning, and there were only two other customers. Both looked very seedy and seemed to have the shakes. I said to myself, 'Boy we're on the wrong road.' Instantly 'Headin' Down The Wrong Highway' hit me, and the lyrics started flowing. I left the drink and dashed back to the little penthouse and got the lyrics down on paper. It took about ten minutes including the melody. I stopped drinking 25 years ago."

—Ted Daffan

HEADIN' DOWN THE WRONG HIGHWAY

by Ted Daffan

Too many sweethearts, and none of them true
Done too many things that I shouldn't do
Made lots of money, all spent the wrong way
Headin' down the wrong highway.

Made lots of friends, and now they're all gone
Too many memories still linger on
Had too many drinks, both night and day
Headin' down the wrong highway.

Too many heartaches and too many tears
Crowded too much in just a few years
I want to go right, but I've lost my way
Headin' down the wrong highway.

Lost everything, lost all my friends
God only knows how this all will end
Drinking and drinking, each night and day
Headin' down the wrong highway.

HONKY TONK MAN

"They say a writer has to live what he writes, but I wouldn't say it's necessarily so. Of course, I know what goes on in honky tonks, but that doesn't mean I'm a honky tonker. I owned a club for four years in Huntsville, Alabama, a couple of years before I wrote this song. It was the first song I ever tried to write. I always could write lyrics, but I didn't know anything about writing a tune. So I bought myself an old Stella guitar and learned to play three chords—the same three chords that are in 'Honky Tonk Man.' It was the song Johnny Horton used to get on Columbia Records; he didn't even have a record contract when he got it."

—Howard Hausey

HONKY TONK MAN

by Howard Hausey, Johnny Horton, and Tillman Franks

I'm livin' fast and dangerously
But I've got plenty of company
When the moon comes up and the sun goes down
That's when I want to see the lights of town.

'Cause I'm a honky tonk man, and I can't seem to stop
I love to give the girls a whirl to the music of an old jukebox
And when my money's all gone I'm on the telephone
Callin' "Hey, Hey, mama, can your daddy come home?"

It takes a purty little gal and a jug of wine
That's what it takes to make a honky tonk mind
With the jukebox whinin' honky tonk style
That's when I want to lay my money down.

IF YOU'VE GOT THE MONEY, I'VE GOT THE TIME

"I was working in West Texas at a night club and I had a friend from Oklahoma to come visiting. He wanted to go somewhere and he said, 'Lefty, you want to go?' and I said, 'Well if you got the money, I got the time!' and it dawned on me this would be a beautiful idea for a song."

—Lefty Frizzell

IF YOU'VE GOT THE MONEY, I'VE GOT THE TIME

by Lefty Frizzell and Jim Beck

If you've got the money, I've got the time,
We'll go honky tonkin' and we'll have a time
We'll make all the night spots
Dance, drink beer and wine
If you've got the money, honey
I've got the time.

There ain't no use to tarry
So let's start out tonight

We'll spread joy, oh boy, oh boy
And we'll spread it right
We'll have more fun, baby
All the way down the line
If you've got the money, honey
I've got the time.

If you've got the money, I've got the time
We'll go honky tonkin' and we'll have a time
Bring along your Cadillac
Leave my old wreck behind
If you've got the money, honey
I've got the time.

Yes, we'll go honky tonkin'
Make every club in town
We'll go to the park where it's dark
We won't fool around
But if you run short of money
I'll run short of time
'Cause you with no more money, honey
I've got no more time.

IT WASN'T GOD WHO MADE HONKY TONK ANGELS

"I was returning from a trip to the neighboring town of Rayne, Louisiana. I had my car radio on and was listening to a country program. The song playing was 'Wild Side of Life' by Hank Thompson. This was a real big country record at the time, and I had thought of writing a sequel on several occasions; however, the lyric ideas I had had were not, in my opinion, strong enough. On this trip, the set of lyrics came to my mind I felt I had been searching for. I pulled my car on the side of Highway 90, took a tablet I kept in my glove compartment for such occasions and began to write the lyrics down as they came to my mind. Kitty Wells' recording of the song became an immediate hit, and in a very short period it was the number one country song and record in the nation."

—Jay Miller

IT WASN'T GOD WHO MADE HONKY TONK ANGELS

by J. D. Miller

As I sit here tonight, the jukebox playing
The tune about the wild side of life
As I listen to the words you are saying
It brings mem'ries when I was a trusting wife.

It wasn't God who made honky tonk angels
As you said in the words of your song
Too many times married men think they're still single
That has caused many a good girl to go wrong.

It's a shame that all the blame is on us women
It's not true that only you men feel the same
From the start, 'most every heart that's ever broken
Was because there always was a man to blame.

THERE STANDS THE GLASS

"This song was originally started by Mary Jean Schurz. I liked it very much and my wife liked the idea of the song, so I took and finished it up and recorded it. I put it in the name of Audrey Grisham which is my wife's former name. Both Jim Denny of the Grand Ole Opry and Fred Rose said recording it would ruin my career because it tolerated drinking. I went ahead and put it out anyway, and it's still one of my most requested songs. 'There Stands The Glass' is like the national anthem of barroom songs. It took care of all the drinking songs when it happened."

—Webb Pierce

THERE STANDS THE GLASS

by Audrey Grisham, Mary Jean Schurz, and Russ Hall

There stands the glass
That will ease all my pain
That will settle my brain
It's my first one today.

There stands the glass
That will hide all my tears

That will drown all my fears
Brother, I'm on my way.

I'm wond'ring where you are tonight
Wond'ring if you are all right
Wond'ring if you think of me
In my misery.

There stands the glass
Fill it up to the brim
Let my troubles grow dim
It's my first one today.

WARM RED WINE

" 'Warm Red Wine' was written into a song after I read Proverbs 23: 29–35* in the Bible."
—Cindy Walker

WARM RED WINE
by Cindy Walker

Put a nickel in the jukebox and let it play
For my heart is cold with its pain
Take the cork from the bottle of the warm red wine
And fill my glass up again
Till it flows o'er the rim, fill my glass to the brim
Like the tears flow in this heart of mine
While I say so long to the dreams that are gone
On account of the warm red wine.

Oh, the prison of stone with its cold iron bars is no more a prison than mine

*"Who hath woe? Who hath sorrow? Who hath contentions? Who hath babbling? Who hath wounds without cause? Who hath redness of eyes? They that tarry long at the wine; they that go to seek mixed wine. Look not thou upon the wine when it is red, when it giveth its color in the cup, when it moveth itself aright. At the last it biteth like a serpent and stingeth like an adder. Thine eyes shall behold strange women, and thine heart shall utter perverse things. Yea, thou shalt be as he that lieth down in the midst of the sea, or as he that lieth upon the top of a mast. They have stricken me, shalt thou say, and I was not sick; they have beaten me, and I felt it not: when shall I awake? I will seek it yet again."

I'm a prisoner of drink who'll never escape from the chains of the
warm red wine
Oh, the wine is red, so warm and red
Like a ruby it sparkles and gleams
But I paid for the wine, the warm red wine
With all my hopes and dreams.

THE WILD SIDE OF LIFE

"I had been married for about seven or eight months, and my wife asked me for a divorce. I asked her why, and she said I reminded her of her ex-husband more than she thought I would. I told her I didn't believe her, but I went out and got her a divorce anyway. Later on, I went to a dance with a buddy of mine, and she came in with his wife. They sat over at a table with two guys that had on suits of clothes and big ties and were drinking big fifths of whiskey. Well, we weren't able to afford that kind of drinking. We were just a couple of country boys drinking beer. They were drinking and having such a good time that I said, 'She didn't quit me because she didn't think nothing of me, she just quit me to go back to the wild side of life.' And I got to looking at her and the way she was dressed, and I thought, 'She is, she's just a perfect angel,' and that gave me the idea for the song.

"I got home that night, and I was sitting on the side of my bed, feeling just as low as a person could feel. After seeing her down there, I was hurting, you know. She had told me when we separated, 'Don't write me. If you do, I'll just tear the letters up. And if you call me on the phone, I'll just hang up.' But I wanted to talk to her, so I wrote it in the words of a song. I went down there the next week and went up on the bandstand. Jimmy Heath and the Melody Masters were playing there then, and he announced that a friend of theirs wanted to sing a song that he'd written. They asked me the tune, and I said I had kind of copied 'Thinking Tonight Of My Blue Eyes,' which is a real old tune. So they gave me an introduction, and I sang 'The Wild Side Of Life.' She knew it was about her right off the bat, and a friend of mine overheard her say, 'I ought to go up there and pull that grey-headed son of a gun's hair all out.' I've never talked to her since. I did see her a time or two at a distance."

—William Warren

THE WILD SIDE OF LIFE

by William Warren and Arlie A. Carter

You wouldn't read my letter if I wrote you
You asked me not to call you on the phone
But there's something I'm wanting to tell you
So I wrote it in the words of this song:

I didn't know God made honky tonk angels
I might have known you'd never make a wife
You gave up the only one that ever loved you
And went back to the wild side of life.

The glamour of the gay night life has lured you
To the places where the wine and liquor flow
Where you wait to be anybody's baby
And forget the truest love you'll ever know.
It hurt me to know that you don't love me
Though I know our love's forever gone
And it killed my soul and pride, dear, inside me
When I saw you in that stranger's arms so long.

I'll just live my life alone with mem'ries of you
And dream of kisses you traded for my tears
And no one will ever know how much I loved you
And I pray that you'll be happy through the years.

9 | Social Commentary

That's How It Is When You're Po' Folks

A review of the body of hillbilly recordings from 1923 to 1973 reveals few songs of genuine "protest"—expressions of communal outrage at economic or social injustices, or appeals for action against them. In its place has developed a vigorous tradition of social commentary, dating back at least to the thirties. Individual, personal, and ironic but seldom bitter, these songs provide revealing insights to the rural South and its approach to life.

One would imagine that the South, which perhaps has suffered more social injustice than any other region in the past hundred years, would provide fertile soil for the growth of radical movements. Reconstruction, industrialization, the Depression, the Dust Bowl—all could be expected to radicalize a good many white southern Americans, but this has rarely been the case, or at least such protest has seldom found expression in hillbilly song.

There have been isolated individuals who were both militant and musical, such as "Aunt" Molly Jackson, the wife of a Kentucky coal miner and union member, and Oklahoma's Woodrow Guthrie (cousin of country singer Jack Guthrie). However, both of them spent much of their time with and gained most of their support from radical groups in the North; there is little evidence of a southern musical tradition of protest.

Archie Green, writing in *Only a Miner,* cites several early hillbilly records with radical themes or dealing with revolutionary figures, including Gene Autry's "The Death Of Mother Jones" and the Martin Brothers' "The North Carolina Textile Strike" and "The Marion Massacre." But the very rarity of these examples and the scarcity of the records themselves marks them as exceptions to the rule.

Nor is country music reactionary, as it has recently been labeled, the "music of the Silent Majority." For example, much has been made of Merle Haggard's "Okie From Muskogee," a 1969 antihippie song, and "The Fightin' Side Of Me," a patriotic song written and recorded in 1970 in support of the soldiers in Vietnam. A close reading of the lyrics, however, reveals them as "reactive," but hardly reactionary. They reflect the revulsion many Americans, from North and South, felt toward the hippie life-style and its close identification with the antiwar movement. They are not the product of political reaction per se, but of the defense of a treasured life-style perceived to be under attack. Both were commercially crafted songs designed to appeal to a wide audience, and any wide deviation from popular opinion could not have produced their enormous successes. (Perhaps the fact that Haggard recently wrote and recorded "Irma Jackson," a love song lamenting black–white marriage taboos, is an indication of changing times.)

One obvious reason for the lack of a strong bias, right or left, in country music is that it is by definition a popular, *commercial* form that must closely follow the middle of the road. Executives of recording companies have seldom been known for advanced social thinking; their success, however, has depended on their ability to predict public tastes more than to formulate them, and it is a reasonable assumption that a strong demand for real protest music would have been filled. Not that hillbilly music has not had its occasional political extreme. Individual records and artists have voiced opinions both left and right over more than half a century; but these have seldom achieved any large measure of popularity or commercial success.

Even stronger reasons for the scarcity of popular protest material in country music were the enduring social values we encounter throughout this book. From the early frontier days, the rugged southern citizen has been a strong individualist, suspicious of governments and "movements," jealous of his privacy and freedoms. Not that he hasn't had troubles with governments, suffered from invasions of his privacy or breaches of his freedom, but he has seldom sacrificed his individualism or self-imposed isolation long enough to join with like thinkers to form a movement or mount a protest. In this his attitudes have been supported not only by his society and religion but in some ways by the realities of the commercial music form he calls his own.

These individualistic convictions were not swayed—in some ways they were supported—by the paternalism of the planters of the Old South which survived the Civil War and lasted well into the twentieth century. The meanest sharecropper or tenant farmer saw the planter not as a member of a distinct and antagonistic class so much as another individual—more fortunate, perhaps, but also perhaps more "deserving."

Calvinistic doctrines of personal sin and retribution contributed, too, to the lack of social protest in hillbilly music. Faced with hardships or social ills, the southern rural white blamed not the system but himself and his own individual sins. He remained largely content, or at least was fatalistic about his low station in life. In the extreme this fatalism expressed itself in songs like "Born To Lose."

Despite episodes like the formation of the Farmers' Alliance and the Populist movement of the eighties and nineties, much southern outrage was directed outward at the North and East, since those areas threatened the South's equilibrium; but this feeling was shared by all southern classes and served to unify the South even more. When, toward the end of the century, it became apparent that the region was progressing under a semblance of the prewar order, the individualistic outlook was reconfirmed, as W. J. Cash pointed out in *The Mind of the South:* "In the late nineties the common white was not only drawing away from every thought of revolt; he was drawing away with cheerfulness. The ranks of the South were closing, not merely because of the Negro; the impulse toward class awareness and class action was dying down, not only because it had been signally demonstrated that the way to its development was hopelessly blocked, but also because the tensions and irritations that had given rise to it in the first place were being removed. . . ."

Intense pride in the South itself and a consistent feeling of unity in the face of outside "hostility" persists to this day and continues to minimize internal dissension. Consider, for example, several songs that have been selected by radical northern folklorists (largely from old hillbilly records) for anthologies which purport to portray the radicalized South of the thirties (See "The Working Man"):

From Bob Miller's " 'Leven Cent Cotton and Forty Cent Meat":

> No use talking, any man is beat
> With 'leven cent cotton and forty cent meat.

The Delmore Brothers' "Fifteen Miles From Birmingham":*

> When a feller's broke he can't find a friend
> Nobody's got a dime to lend
> But when he's rich they sit and itch
> On him their money spend
> On him their money spend.

And Dorsey Dixon's "Weaveroom Blues":

> Our hearts are aching, let us take a little booze
> For we're going crazy with them weaveroom blues.

One would have to stretch his imagination to call these songs "revolutionary," yet they are among the more radical expressions of discontent recorded during the depth of the Depression. They focus on fatalism, personal solutions, criticism of hypocrisy, expressions which characterize much of the social comment of country music.

By and large, the songs that follow are highly personal expressions of discontent. The skepticism of some southerners about a federal dole, for example, is apparent in two songs, "Old Age Pension Check" (which satirizes the unsuccessful Townsend Plan of the thirties) and "Welfare Cadilac" (which presents a fairly common view of the program among noncity dwellers in both North and South). Perhaps the bitterest of these songs, and the only one to go as far as to mention "a world of greed and hate," is "No Vacancy," by Merle Travis and Cliffie Stone; expressive of the physical and social dislocation that to this day plagues the returning veteran, it still vaguely hopes that "the hand of fate" (rather than direct action) will solve the problem.

A number of songs lament changes in social values. "Rockin' Alone In An Old Rockin' Chair," for example, deplores popular attitudes toward old people; written in the thirties, it expresses an idea that is gaining new currency today. Two more recent songs that mourn the passing of traditional American values are "Married By The Bible, Divorced By The Law" and "Where Have All Our Heroes Gone?"

Hypocrisy is the major target of the country composer today, and this, too, is an expression of his individualism. In songs like "Harper Valley PTA," "Skip A Rope," and "Sunday Morning Christian," he lashes out at those who pay lip service to the old values but live their own less-than-virtuous lives. Though by no means a new development in country music, the modern, sophisticated treatment the theme receives in these songs is an indication of how country music has changed.

Songs about the virtues of poverty comprise the final category of social commentary and echo a theme often expressed in other kinds of country songs—unrequited love songs, for example. Money won't buy "A Satisfied Mind," and the "new" will quickly wear off "Crystal Chandeliers," but "Po' Folks" have something money can't buy—they "set the table with love."

Even in these later songs there is very little really radical spirit, little genuine protest. Perhaps the best expression of fatalism, of the inevitability of some measure of injustice, is one of the closing lines of the Bill Anderson song: "That's how it is when you're po' folks."

"This song was inspired by a rich girl–poor boy situation in my own life, where two people had come into unbelievable wealth and whose marriage subsequently had ended in separation. Long after, I was called upon to entertain at a social gathering where one of the partners was present, alone as far as the marriage was concerned, but surrounded by people. They were up to their p's and q's on all of the social graces, but essentially artificial. In the center of the room was a crystal chandelier. I thought, 'Boy, that's it! It's the greatest symbol of the tinsel world in existence. It's so beautiful, and at the same time so cold and lifeless. It offers you nothing outside of the beauty you behold.' " —Ted Harris

CRYSTAL CHANDELIERS
by Ted Harris

Oh, the crystal chandeliers light up the paintings on your wall
The marble statuettes are standing stately in the hall
But will the timely crowd that has you laughing loud help you dry your tears
When the new wears off of your crystal chandeliers?

I never did fit in too well with folks you knew
And it's plain to see that the likes of me don't fit with you
So you traded me for the gaiety of the well-to-do
And you turned away from the love I offered you.

I see your picture in the news most every day
You're the chosen girl of the social world, so the stories say
But a paper smile only lasts a while, then it fades away
When the love we knew will come home to you some day.

DARK AS A DUNGEON

"The saddest songs are written when a person is happy. I was driving home after a date with a beautiful girl in Redondo Beach, California. I had a recording session to do the next morning and needed some material. I parked my car under a street light and wrote the verses to 'Dark As A Dungeon.' I got the idea from growing up around the coal mines in Kentucky. My father and brothers were coal miners."

—Merle Travis

DARK AS A DUNGEON

by Merle Travis

Come listen, you fellers, so young and so fine
And seek not your fortune in the dark dreary mine
It'll form as a habit and seep in your soul
Till the stream of your blood is as black as the coal.

It's dark as a dungeon and damp as the dew
Where danger is double and pleasures are few
Where the rain never falls and the sun never shines
It's dark as a dungeon 'way down in the mine.

It's many a man I have known in my day
Who lived just to labor his young life away
Like a fiend with his dope and a drunkard his wine
A man will have lust for the lure of the mine.

I hope when I'm gone and the ages shall roll
My body will blacken and turn into coal
Then I'll look from the door of my heavenly home
And pity the miner a-diggin' my bones.

HARPER VALLEY PTA

"I wanted to write a song about my home town or something I remembered. When I couldn't get a song out of my father's grocery store in Carter City, Kentucky, in my mind I moved down the road about four miles, and I ran across this lady whose child had been spanked in school, and who took on the entire PTA. The song pretty much is true with the exception of the miniskirt, because they didn't wear them in those days. But she was a pretty flashy dresser, a young widow woman, very attractive, and she liked to have music around the house. People would sit around on the porch and drink beer, and of course this was a tremendous sin in those days. When I wrote the song, it dawned on me how much we are unaware of what we are, and I discovered there are millions of Harper Valleys all over the world. The song proved it by selling as it did.

—Tom T. Hall

HARPER VALLEY PTA

by Tom T. Hall

I want to tell you all a story 'bout a Harper Valley widowed wife
Who had a teenage daughter who attended Harper Valley Junior High
Well, her daughter came home one afternoon and didn't even stop to play
She said, "Mom, I got a note here from the Harper Valley PTA."

The note said, "Mrs. Johnson, you are wearing your dresses 'way too high
It's reported you've been drinking and running 'round with men and going wild
And we don't believe you ought to be a-bringing up your little girl this way"
It was signed by the secretary, Harper Valley PTA.

Well, it happened that the PTA was gonna meet that very afternoon
They were sure surprised when Mrs. Johnson wore her miniskirt into the room
As she walked up to the blackboard, I still recall the words she had to say
She said, "I'd like to address this meeting of the Harper Valley PTA.

Well, there's Bobby Taylor sittin' there, and seven times he's asked me for a date
And Mrs. Taylor sure seems to use a lot of ice when he's away
And, Mr. Baker, can you tell us why your secretary had to leave this town?
And shouldn't widow Jones be told to keep her window shades all pulled completely down?

Well, Mr. Harper couldn't be here 'cause he stayed too long at Kelly's Bar again
And if you smell Shirley Thompson's breath, you'll find she's had a little nip of gin
Then you have the nerve to tell me you think that as a mother I'm not fit
Well, this is just a little Peyton Place, and you're all Harper Valley hypocrites."

No, I wouldn't put you on, because it really did, it happened just this way
The day my Mama socked it to the Harper Valley PTA.

"The idea for the song came to me over a period of time due to the fact that marriages were begun by the Bible and ended by the law. Numerous ministers have commented as to how much truth there is in the song."

—Johnny Rector

MARRIED BY THE BIBLE, DIVORCED BY THE LAW

by Johnny Rector, Pee Wee Truebitt, Neva Starns, K. Loury, and Cookie Longhorn

What a strange world we live in; what a shame! What a shame!
Someone's always quarrelin', their marriage don't remain
Divorces by the thousands; is the human race insane?
I always thought that marriage should be a sacred thing.

Married by the Bible, divorced by the law
Every day there's more and more, the worst I ever saw
Things have changed, they're not the same as the days of Ma and Pa
They were married by the Bible, no divorces by the law.

Steps are often taken without thinking twice
And ofttimes there's a child or two who's left to pay the price
Those little hearts so innocent, they don't know who's to blame
No mom and dad to love them; what a shame! Oh, what a shame!

NO VACANCY

"Right after World War II, the most popular sign all over the country was the 'No Vacancy' sign. Returning veterans and other people as well had a hard time finding a place to live. One night after playing a date, Cliffie Stone and I drove a couple of hundred miles from California looking for a motel to spend the night. Every motel we passed had a 'No vacancy' sign, and this gave us the idea to write the song." —Merle Travis

NO VACANCY

by Merle Travis and Cliffie Stone

All along the road of life I roam
Lookin' for a place to call my home

Not a fancy mansion or a bungalow for me
Ev'rywhere I go I seem to find
Hangin' on the door that same old sign
And my heart beats slower when I read on the door, "No Vacancy."

No Vacancy, No Vacancy
All along the line it's the same old sign waitin' for me
No Vacancy, No Vacancy
And my heart beats slower when I read on the door, "No Vacancy."

Not so long ago when the bullets screamed
Many was the happy dream I dreamed
Of a little nest where I could rest when the world was free
Now the mighty war over there is won
Troubles and trials have just begun
As I face that terrible enemy sign, "No Vacancy."

Brother, if you live a life of ease
Better take a moment on your knees
Thank the Lord above for all his love, then think of me
Livin' in a world of greed and hate
Hoping ev'ry day the hand of fate
Will remove that sign that's a-hangin' on the door, "No Vacancy."

THE OLD AGE PENSION CHECK

"I bought this number from a boy that lived in Knoxville, and as far as I know, he wrote it. I can't remember his name at the present time. Some people resented the song, but it still sold well. Songs like this are not received one hundred per cent. There are some words in it that are a little touchy for some people: 'Send your dime to Washington—get on relief.' It was more of a comedy song for me, but it was taken a little bit politically by some."

—Roy Acuff

THE OLD AGE PENSION CHECK

by Roy Acuff

When our old age pension check comes to our door
We won't have to dread the poor house anymore
Though we're old and thin and gray
Good times will be back to stay
When our old age pension check comes to our door.

When her old age pension check comes to her door
Dear old grandma won't be lonesome any more
She'll be waiting at the gate
Every night she'll have a date
When her old age pension check comes to her door.

Grow a flowing long white beard and use a cane
'Cause you're in your second childhood, don't complain
Life will just begin at sixty
We'll all feel very frisky
When our old age pension check comes to our door.

Powder and paint will be abolished on that day
And hoop skirts will then be brought back into play
Painted cheeks will be the rage
And old maids will tell their age
When their old age pension check comes to their door.

All the drug stores will go bankrupt on that day
For cosmetics, they will all be put away
I'll put a flapper on the shelf
Get a grandma for myself
When her old age pension check comes to her door.

There's a man that turned this country upside-down
With his old age pension rumor going 'round
If you want in on the fun
Send your dime to Washington
And that old age pension man will be around.

"I didn't grow up in poverty or near anything like what I wrote this song about, but I always wished I had come from a rural background, I always wished I had grown up on a farm, I always wished I had come from a large family. I wrote the song kind of tongue-in-cheek, because so many of the people I know and have associated with came from rural backgrounds and from large families. I know they had a lot of rough times, but these were some of the happiest people I ever knew. It was almost like nobody ever told them they were poor. I was trying to show that, even though things could be bad, you could laugh at them, you could smile, and that the most important thing, after all, was love." —Bill Anderson

PO' FOLKS

by Bill Anderson

There's a whole lotta people lookin' down their noses at me
'Cause I didn't come from a wealthy family
There was ten of us living in a two-room shack
On the banks of the river by the railroad track
And we kept chickens in a pen in the back
And ev'rybody said we was po' folks.

My daddy was a farmer, but all he ever raised was us
Dug a forty-foot well, struck thirty-six gallons of dust
The Salvation Army gave us clothes to wear
A man from the County came to cut our hair
We lived next door to a millionaire
But we wasn't nothin' but po' folks.

We was po' folks livin' in a rich folks' world
We sure was a hungry bunch
If the wolf had ever come to our front door
He'd a had to brought a picnic lunch.

My granddaddy's pension was a dollar and thirty-three cents
That was ten dollars less than the landlord wanted for rent
The landlord's letters got nasty, indeed
He wrote, "Git out!" but paw couldn't read
And he was too broke to even pay heed
But that's how it is when you're po' folks.

But we had something in our house money can't buy
Kept us warm in the winter, cool when the sun was high
For whenever we didn't have food enough

And the howling winds would get pretty rough
We patched the cracks and set the table with love
'Cause that's what you do when you're po' folks
And we wasn't nothin' but po' folks.

ROCKIN' ALONE IN AN OLD ROCKIN' CHAIR

Written in 1932, this song has enjoyed periodic revivals ever since. Bob Miller was known for his creation during the twenties and thirties of what he called "Main Street Music," which included a good deal of social commentary and a number of "mother songs" like "My Mother's Tears" and "Story Of A Dear Old Lady."
—D. H.

ROCKIN' ALONE IN AN OLD ROCKIN' CHAIR
by Bob Miller

Sitting alone in an old rockin' chair
I saw an old mother with silvery hair
She seemed so neglected by those who should care
Rockin' alone in an old rockin' chair.

Her hands were all calloused and wrinkled and old
A life of hard work was the story they told
And I thought of angels as I saw her there
Rockin' alone in an old rockin' chair.

Bless her old heart, do you think she'd complain?
Though life has been bitter, she'd live it again
And carry the cross that is more than her share
Rockin' alone in an old rockin' chair.

It wouldn't take much just to gladden her heart
Just some small remembrance on somebody's part
A letter would brighten her empty life there
Rockin' alone in an old rockin' chair.

I look at her and I think, "What a shame,
The ones who forgot her she loves just the same"
And I think of angels as I see her there
Rockin' alone in an old rockin' chair.

A SATISFIED MIND

"The song came from my mother. Everything in the song are things I heard her say over the years. I put a lot of thought into the song before I came up with the title. One day my father-in-law asked me who I thought the richest man in the world was, and I mentioned some names. He said, 'You're wrong, it is the man with a satisfied mind.' It has been done a lot in churches. I came out of the Opry one night and a church service was going on nearby. The first thing I heard was the congregation singing 'Satisfied Mind.' I got down on my knees."

—Red Hayes (as quoted in *Country Music People,* July 1973)

A SATISFIED MIND

by J. H. Hayes and Jack Rhodes

How many times have you heard someone say
"If I had his money, I would do things my way"
But little they know that it's so hard to find
One rich man in ten with a satisfied mind.

Once I was winning in fortune and fame
Everything that I dreamed for to get a start in life's game
But suddenly it happened I lost every dime
But I'm richer by far with a satisfied mind.

Money can't buy back your youth when you're old
Or a friend when you're lonely or a love that's grown cold
The wealthiest person is a pauper at times
Compared to the man with a satisfied mind.

When life has ended, my time has run out
My friends and my loved ones I'll leave, there's no doubt

But one thing for certain, when it comes my time
I'll leave this old world with a satisfied mind.

SKIP A ROPE

"My co-writer, Jack Moran, was the originator of the idea for 'Skip A Rope,' one of the first songs to tell it like it really is. The majority of parents did not like the song. They did not like being cast as the *heavy.* They did not want to admit that they were even partially responsible for the behavior patterns and general attitudes toward society of their children. Had it not been for the children, the song never would have become a success. It started a new trend in country music songwriting. I believe it opened the door to freedom of expression, and things that used to be taboo for us country writers were all of a sudden all right. I'm glad we wrote it and I'm glad it was a hit and I'm grateful to the children of America."

—Glenn D. Tubb

SKIP A ROPE
by Jack Moran and Glenn D. Tubb

Skip a rope, skip a rope
Oh, listen to the children while they play
Now, ain't it kinda funny what the children say?
Skip a rope
Daddy hates Mommy, Mommy hates Dad
Last night you should have heard the fight they had
Gave little sister another bad dream
She woke us all up with a terrible scream
Skip a rope, skip a rope.

Oh, listen to the children while they play
Now, ain't it kinda funny what the children say?
Skip a rope
Cheat on your taxes, don't be a fool
What was that they said about the Golden Rule?
Never mind the rules, just play to win
And hate your neighbor for the shade of his skin
Skip a rope.

Oh, listen to the children while they play
Now, ain't it kinda funny what the children say?
Skip a rope
Stab 'em in the back, that's the name of the game
And Mommy and Daddy are who's to blame
Skip a rope, skip a rope
Just listen to the children while they play
It's really not very funny what the children say
Skip a rope.

STUCK UP BLUES

"Back in the fifties and even before, many people looked down on country music and country people. I always felt that these same people who were putting on airs and putting down our music had the very same background I and other country performers did. This simple little song seemed to tell that story so well I always liked it." —Roy Acuff

STUCK UP BLUES

Arr. by Roy Acuff

I look yonder at that high-headed feller, his nose turned to the sun
He'll tell you that he built this world, without him it wouldn't run
His ev'ry action shows just how important he feels
When just like me, he was raised on wild onions and borrowed meal.

Hey, hey, hey don't pull that stuff on me
I am just a country boy, plain as I can be
I'm not so very smart, dumb as any old mule
Show me a hundred stuck up folks, I'll show you a hundred fools.

You need not turn your head when you pass me on the street
I know you feel so important now to everybody but me
You may fool the rest of this world, but you're sure not fooling me
For I knew you when you wore a straw hat to the Christmas tree.

The other day I met a man of high society
He tried to pull that stuff on me, his social dignity

I says, "Now look here, John, I know where you come from
And your old man always used the words, 'by crackie and by gum.' "

SUNDAY MORNING CHRISTIAN

"The story is just my own personal beliefs about religion and how I feel about religious phonies. I've always felt that a person, by merely going to church, could not be a very good Christian person and have high hopes of going to Heaven or wherever we're going afterward. I've also observed religious fanatics that carry their religion like it was a banner. In fact, they're even egotistical about their religion. People like that turn me off, and I was trying to say that in this song. I've just got a thing in my head that religion is a 24-hour-a-day business. If you're not a Christian on Monday, then the two hours you spend going to church on Sunday, wearing your finest clothes and donating ten dollars and making sure everybody can see it, isn't going to get you through."

—Harlan Howard

SUNDAY MORNING CHRISTIAN

by Harlan Howard and Lawrence Reynolds

Mister Jones, this car you sold me isn't all that I desired
You swore it was young and healthy, now I find it's old and tired
But a deal's a deal, you tell me, and there's nothing to be done
Mister Jones, I'd like you better if you robbed me with a gun.

You're a Sunday morning Christian, Sir
Singing louder than the rest
Beg forgiveness at the altar
With your chin down on your chest
But tomorrow will be Monday
You'll revert back to your ways
Gougin', kickin', cheatin', shovin'
With no thoughts of God or lovin'
Don't let me stand in your way
Surely God will forgive you next Sunday.

Mrs. Smith, your fine attendance shows the Christian life you live
But I know your little secret, you expect God to forgive

You'll kiss your husband Monday morning, see him safely on his way
Then get ready for your lover; it's a long time till Sunday.

WELFARE CADILAC

"In 1969, I came from Greenville, Kentucky, to Nashville with a tune called 'Welfare Cadilac.' I believed the song was a hit and took it to all the major labels in Music City. The record executives laughed me off, and they kept laughing until 'Welfare Cadilac' became the number one hit in the nation. Me and my wife gathered up an armload of records and took off to various radio stations in the South. We were gone three weeks and when we got back to Nashville 'Welfare Cadilac' was high on the charts and stayed there for 34 weeks. It made me feel good to know that an ole country boy had made a fool out of those big Nashville Cats."

—Guy Drake

WELFARE CADILAC

by Guy Drake

I've never worked much, in fact, I've been poor all my life
I guess all I really own is ten kids and a wife
This house I live in is mine, but it's really a shack
But I've always managed somehow to drive me a brand new
  Cadilac.

The back door steps, they done fell plumb down
The front screen door's off and laying somewhere out there on the
  ground
The wind just now whooped up another piece of that tar roofing off
  the back
I sure hope it don't skin up that new Cadilac.

The front porch posts fell loose at the bottom
It don't make no sense to fix 'em, 'cause that floor's just too darn
  rotten
In winter time we sometimes have some snow that blows in through
  the cracks
If it gets too bad we all just pile up and sleep out there in that new
  Cadilac.

I know the place ain't much, but I sure don't pay no rent
I get a check the first of every month from this here Federal Government
Every Wednesday I get commodities, sometimes four or five sacks
Pick 'em up down at the welfare office, driving that new Cadilac.

Some folks say I'm crazy, and I've even been called a fool
But my kids get free books, and all them there free lunches at school
We get peanut butter and cheese, and, man! They give us flour by the sack
'Course them welfare checks, they meet the payments on this new Cadilac.

Now the way that I see it, these other folks are the fools
They're working and paying taxes, just to send my young 'uns through school
The Salvation Army cuts their hair, and gives them clothes to wear on their backs
So we can dress up and ride around, and show off this new Cadilac.

But things are still gonna get better yet, at least that's what I understand
They tell me this new President has put in a whole new poverty plan
He's gonna send us poor folks money, they say we're gonna get it out there in stacks
In fact, my wife's already shopping around, for her new Cadilac.

WHERE HAVE ALL OUR HEROES GONE?

"I got the idea to write this song along with a boy by the name of Bob Talbert, who is a newspaper writer in Detroit. Bob and I both grew up in Columbia, South Carolina, and, though we didn't know each other then, we went to all the same picture shows, saw the same Roy Rogers and Gene Autry pictures and idolized the same ballplayers. We grew up in the World War II era when General MacArthur and General Eisenhower were so in the news. One time we got to talking about how things are for kids today compared with what they were when we grew up. Bob turned to me and made a very simple statement, 'Where have all the heroes gone?' I said, 'That's a fabulous idea for a song,' and I wrote it down just that way. When I got back to Nashville, he wrote me a three-page, single-spaced typewritten letter with all his thoughts on the subject. Since Bob can't write music, my job was to condense those three pages down to what I thought was a commercial song. It's a very misunderstood song. People try to read things into it that I didn't intend to be there. They say it's an 'Establishment song,' that I'm anti-this or pro-that or that I don't like long hair. That's ridiculous; the song doesn't say anything about that. All the song says is that kids today don't have any heroes. They don't have anybody to look up to and say, 'Gee, that's who I want to be like.' That's why I wrote the song—I felt there was a real need for it."

—Bill Anderson

WHERE HAVE ALL OUR HEROES GONE?

by Bill Anderson and Bob Talbert

Where have all our heroes gone?
What's come over our great land
America is still my home, sweet home
But where have all our heroes gone?

Recitation:

I saw a group of boys the other day, standing in a corner of a playground, looking and laughing at a magazine; and I overheard one of the boys say, "Man, is he ever cool." And he pointed to the man whose picture was on the magazine cover. And everybody kinda said under their breath, "Yeah, he's cool, all right." And I got sick to my stomach, because I'd seen the cover, and the "man" that they were talkin' about had instigated a riot in one of our major cities last summer. And the magazine was writing about how the police were unkind to him, the judges were unfair with him, and how he talked back and slung his long hair about, and cussed and did his thing. And they made him into a regular hero. And inside this magazine was the story of the baseball player who got involved with the gamblers. Of the football player who said that football was not the end, just a means to an end, meaning the girls and the good times. And a story of the folk singer who proudly claims to be both a member of a party alien to our government and a non-tax-paying citizen. These young boys read with open eyes and open minds. And I thought to myself, "My God, are these the people that these young boys look up to? Are these their idols? Are these the heroes of the Now Generation?" I had heroes when I was a kid. We all did. And our heroes did their thing, too. Like General Douglas MacArthur, who returned like he said he would. Like Gene Autry and Roy Rogers, who chased the bad guys right off the screen. Like Lindberg, who flew the ocean, and Jesse Owens, who showed Hitler, and John Wayne and Gary Cooper. After all, didn't they really win the war? And General Ike, bless your soul, 'cause you made us feel sad. We've killed some of our recent heroes—the Kennedys, the Kings. And, even as great as their space feats are, how many of the astronauts can you name? Huh? How many? My heroes were people like Joe DiMaggio, who proved that nice guys can finish first, and Stan Musial, who never had an unkind word for anybody. And Winston Churchill, whose two fingers raised together meant victory, not just a let-your-enemy-have-it-all kind of artificial peace. This country needs a lot of things today, friends. But it doesn't need any one thing any more than it needs some real heroes. Men who know what it means to be looked up to by a grimy-faced kid. Men who want to sign autograph books and not deals under the table. Men who are willing to play the game with the people who made them heroes. Men who don't mind putting on a white hat and saying "thank you" and "please." I wish I knew just one man that I'd be proud for my son to look up to and say, "Daddy, when I grow up, I want to be just like him."

10 | Songs of War and Patriotism

There's a Star-Spangled Banner Waving Somewhere

When country music got its commercial beginning, the memory of World War I was still fresh. Of the years since, fully one-third can be described as war years, times that deeply affected the rural southern consciousness and way of life.

Since 1916, when the Selective Service Act instituted a truly national draft, southerners have fought alongside northerners in four American wars which have touched the lives of three generations. Southerners brought to these wars their music and their traditional values and took away with them broader horizons and notions of patriotism.

Over the fifty years of commercial country music history, the southern states have given more than their proportionate share of soldiers both to the nation's standing army and to troops mobilized for war. Federal military service, offering job security and early retirement, provides an attractive alternative to the struggle for existence on a small farm or in a rural mill, despite its disregard for personal liberties. And in recent years, when draft laws favored the affluent and educated, a disproportionately large share of our fighting men (both black and white) have been contributed by the rural South.

Typically, the attitude of the hillbilly and his music toward war is a personal one, more concerned with its effects than its causes. During World War I, for example, while northern city audiences sang such cheerful and optimistic ditties as "Over There" and "Goodbye, Broadway, Hello, France," their country counterparts favored songs like "Goodbye, Ma, Goodbye, Pa, Goodbye, Mule" and Jimmie Rodgers's first recorded song, "The Soldier's Sweetheart."

A country audience likes nothing better than a tragic song, and what better setting for it than a war? It has all the elements of drama—separation, loneliness, betrayal, danger, disfigurement, and death—and hillbilly songs about the experience of war have managed to cover them all. As a result, many of the songs that follow have lived on as more than mere nostalgia. In fact, the barracks itself has proven a means of oral transmission where songs from one war have been passed on from soldier to soldier, reshaped and made to fit another.

Few country songs (in contrast to popular songs) are exclusively patriotic in theme, though some, like "Smoke On The Water," provide an apocalyptic vision of war's outcome. The most popular hillbilly war song of all, "There's A Star-Spangled Banner Waving Somewhere," while it evinces soul-stirring patriotic emotion, also manages to be a classic country song: it tells a good story and also manages to interweave elements of history, pathos, religion, and bravery.

In the line "God gave me the right to be a free American/And for that precious right, I'd gladly die," composer Bob Miller summed up the patriotic feelings of most Americans during World War II—feelings that overrode the individualism and resistance to regimentation that typifies the southerner. Responding to the high feelings and expert propaganda of that period, southerners perceived it as a truly national effort and gave their all.

These probably were not the same emotions at play during the sixties, however, when country music produced such superpatriotic songs as "Tell Them What We're Fighting For" and "The Minute Men Are Turning In Their Graves." Southerners, steeped in reverence for God, home, and country and slower to change their ways, stood not so much in favor of the war in Southeast Asia as opposed to the war protesters, whom they considered unpatriotic.

Jimmie Rodgers struck what is still the most popular note in war songs—the death of a loved one—in "The Soldier's Sweetheart" (written during World War I). The dramatic device of a final communication from the battlefield was echoed in "Soldier's Last Letter," one of the most popular and enduring songs of World War II, and in Loretta Lynn's "Dear Uncle Sam," written during the conflict in Vietnam.

The theme of separation, too, has prompted a number of war songs, including "Each Night At Nine," written as a letter from a barracks overseas, and "Silver Dew On The Blue Grass Tonight," which might almost be its answer song.

Two of the songs in this selection express longing for girls left behind overseas. "Filipino Baby" was originally written about the Spanish-American War, but was successfully revived during World War II, when Manila Bay again became important to American servicemen. And the sentiment of "Fraulein" (lingering love for a foreign girl) will prevail as long as soldiers are sent overseas. One of the most recent examples of this kind of song is Buck Owens's "Made In Japan."

Others express the anxiety and often the tragedy of the returning veteran. Tin Pan Alley writer Frank Loesser caught the uncertainty of the returning soldier long away as well as the essence of a country lyric in "Have I Stayed Away Too Long?" Much more tragic is the hero of "Molly," who has kept his affliction from his wife until their pathetic reunion.

The songs that follow originated in the nation's wars of the past century, yet the emotions they express apply to all wars everywhere. As long as country boys are called to serve away from home, they'll take their battered guitars and many of these songs with them.

THE BALLAD OF THE GREEN BERETS

"Barry Sadler and I were both members of the Special Forces—the 'Green Berets'—stationed at Fort Bragg. He was always singing and playing his guitar. Barry got the idea for the song in 1963, and we wrote it together. It was published in 1965 and released January 1, 1966, long before the Vietnam War had run its course. Of course, the Green Berets were the first American fighting forces in Vietnam. Within six months of its release, 7 million records had been sold, and 48 single recordings of the song were made." —Robin Moore, Jr.

THE BALLAD OF THE GREEN BERETS

by S/Sgt. Barry Sadler and Robin Moore, Jr.

Fighting soldiers from the sky
Fearless men who jump and die
Men who mean just what they say
The brave men of the Green Berets.

Silver wings upon their chests
These are men, America's best
One hundred men will test today
But only three win the Green Beret.

Trained to live off nature's land
Trained in combat, hand-to-hand
Men who fight by night and day
Courage deep from the Green Berets.

Back at home, a young wife waits
Her Green Beret has met his fate
He has died for those oppressed
Leaving her his last request.

"Put silver wings on my son's chest
Make him one of America's Best
He'll be a man they'll test one day
Have him win the Green Beret."

THE BATTLE OF NEW ORLEANS

"I originally wrote this song to help my students in Snowball, Arkansas, learn something about the War of 1812."

—Jimmie Driftwood

Written to an old square-dance tune, "The Eighth Of January," this song tells the story of how Andrew Jackson defeated the army of British commander Pakenham in the last battle of the war. The battle actually took place on January 8, 1815, after the war was over, since neither side had received word of the Treaty of Ghent, signed December 24, 1814.

—D. H.

THE BATTLE OF NEW ORLEANS
by Jimmie Driftwood

In eighteen and fourteen we took a little trip
Along with Colonel Jackson down the mighty Mississip'
We took a little bacon and we took a little beans
And we met the bloody British near the town of New Orleans.

We fired our guns and the British kept a-comin'
But there wasn't nigh as many as they was a while ago
We fired once more and they began to runnin'
On down the Mississippi to the Gulf of Mexico.

Well, I seen Marse Jackson a-walkin' down the street
And a-talkin' to a pirate by the name of Jean Lafitte
He gave Jean a drink that he brought from Tennessee
And the pirate said he'd help us drive the British in the sea.

The French told Andrew you'd better run
For Pakenham's a-comin' with a bullet in his gun
Old Hickory said he didn't give a damn
He was gonna whip the britches off of Colonel Pakenham.

Well, we looked down the river and we seen the British come
There must have been a hundred of 'em beatin' on the drum
They stepped so high and they made their bugles ring
While we stood beside our cotton bales and didn't say a thing.

Old Hick'ry said we'd take 'em by surprise
If we didn't fire a musket till we looked 'em in the eyes
We held our fire till we seen their faces well
Then we opened up our squirrel guns and really gave 'em hell.

They ran through the briars and they ran through the brambles
And they ran through the bushes where a rabbit couldn't go
They ran so fast that the hounds couldn't catch 'em
On down the Mississippi to the Gulf of Mexico.

We fired our cannon till the barrel melted down
So we grabbed an alligator and we fought another round
We filled his head with minnie balls and powdered his behind
Then when we touched the powder off, the 'gator lost his mind.

They lost their pants and their pretty shoddy coats
And their tails were always showin' like a bunch of billy goats
They run down the river with their tongues a-hangin' out
And they said they got a lickin' which there wasn't any doubt.

We marched back to town in our dirty ragged pants
And we danced all night with them pretty girls from France
We couldn't understand them but they had the sweetest charms
And we understood them better when we got them in our arms.

The guide who brung the British from the sea
Came a-limpin' in the camp just as sick as he could be
He said the dying words of the Colonel Pakenham
Was "You'd better quit your foolin' with your cousin Uncle Sam."

We'll march back home, but we'll never be content
Till we make Old Hickory the people's president
And every time we think about the bacon and the beans
We'll think about the fun we had way down in New Orleans.

"As far as I know, Billy Barton wrote this song. I first heard him sing it when we were working at the Clover Club in Bakersfield, California. I figured the song was a hit, and I traded a 1947 Kaiser for it. I turned around and gave him back a third of the song, and then sold Fuzzy Owen the other third. I've heard about 'Dear John' letters all my life, and the fact that people use the term a lot probably made it a hit."

—Lewis Talley

A DEAR JOHN LETTER

by Lewis Talley, Fuzzy Owen, and Billy Barton

Dear John, Oh, how I hate to write
Dear John, I must let you know tonight
That my love for you has died away like grass upon the lawn
And tonight I wed another, Dear John.

Recitation:

I was overseas in battle when the postman came to me
And he handed me a letter, I was happy as could be
For the fighting was all over and the battle had been won
Then I opened up the letter and it started, "Dear John."

Will you please send back my picture, my husband wants it now
When I tell you who I'm wedding, you won't care, dear anyhow
Now the ceremony has started and I wed your brother Don
Will you wish us happiness forever, Dear John?

DEAR UNCLE SAM

" 'Dear Uncle Sam' I wrote when Vietnam was in real bad shape. I kind of put myself in the place of some woman or girl who lost her husband or boyfriend. Many have that I've known."

—Loretta Lynn

DEAR UNCLE SAM
by Loretta Lynn

Dear Uncle Sam, I know you're a busy man
And tonight I write to you through tears with a tremblin' hand
My darling answered when he got that call from you
You said you really need him, but you don't need him like I do.

Don't misunderstand, I know he's fighting for our land
I really love my country, but I also love my man
He proudly wears the colors of the old red, white and blue
While I wear a heartache since he left me for you.

Dear Uncle Sam, I just got your telegram
And I can't believe that this is me shakin' like I am
For it said, "I'm sorry to inform you . . ."

EACH NIGHT AT NINE

"This was a song born in the barracks. It was a natural at the time, as easy to write as a letter. I was still in the Air Force at Ellington Field, restricted to camp. Rumors of overseas shipments . . . any day now I would be gone. I was wrong at least about the overseas shipment. I went to New York and Dave Kapp recorded it. It got a lot of play on network radio, but was hard to buy because of the shellac shortage." —Floyd Tillman

EACH NIGHT AT NINE
by Floyd Tillman

A thousand miles, dear, a thousand more
Across the water, across the shore
I'll say a prayer, dear, for you and mine
Please think of me, dear, each night at nine.

I hold your picture close to my heart
It takes your place, dear, while we're apart
Helps to remind me that you're still mine
Please think of me, dear, each night at nine.

The bugle's playing, out goes the lights
Gee, but it's lonely these army nights
Go tell the kiddies I'm doing fine
Give them my love, dear, each night at nine.

A thousand miles, dear, a thousand more
Across the water, across the shore
I'll say a prayer, dear, for you and mine
Please think of me, dear, each night at nine.

FILIPINO BABY

"I rewrote this song; that's how my name is on it. Billy Cox, who recorded it, sent me the lyrics. It was originally about a 'colored sailor with a face as black as jet' and was written by Charles K. Harris at the time of the Spanish-American War. I rewrote it and that's what made it a hit."

—Clarke Van Ness

FILIPINO BABY

by Billy Cox and Clarke Van Ness

There's a warship from Manila sailing proudly o'er the foam
Many sailors' hearts were filled with sad regret
Looking backward to this island where they spent such happy hours
Making love to every pretty girl they met.

When up stepped a little sailor with his bright eyes all aglow
Saying "take a look at my gal's photograph"
Then the sailors gathered 'round him just to look upon her face
And he said, "I love my Filipino baby."

"She's my Filipino baby, she's my treasure and my pet
Her teeth are bright and pearly and her hair is black as jet
Oh, her lips are sweet as honey and her heart is pure I know
And I love my little Filipino baby."

In a little rustic cottage in the far off Philippines
Dwells a pretty little maiden all alone
And she's thinking of her true love, though he's far across the sea
And her heart beats true for him and him alone.

Then one day he whispered, "Darlin' I've come back from Caroline,
I've come back to claim the only girl I love"
And that night there was a wedding while the ship's crew gathered
'round
And he wed his little Filipino baby.

FRAULEIN

"During World War II, I met a little blonde-headed German girl who I got serious with. In fact we were engaged for five years. That, plus the fact that my mother was German and that I've been around Germans all my life inspired me to write this song. I grew up with the idea that instead of saying 'Miss' you could say 'Fraulein.' Actually my Fraulein wasn't from Germany—she was from a German settlement in South Texas named Raccoon Bend, just outside of Hempstead, Texas, which is known as 'Shotgun Junction.' I cut my teeth in radio on station KTRH, Houston, and she was in the traffic department. She was a Texas Fraulein."

—Lawton Williams

FRAULEIN

by Lawton Williams

Far across deep blue waters lives an old German's daughter
By the banks of the old river Rhine
Where I loved her and left her, I can't forget her
I miss my pretty Fraulein.

Fraulein, Fraulein, look up towards the heavens
Each night when the stars start to shine
By the same stars above you, I swear that I love you
You are my pretty Fraulein.

When my memories wander away over yonder
To the sweetheart that I left behind
In a moment of glory, a face comes before me
The face of my pretty Fraulein.

"When he first started Frank Music, his publishing company, Frank had an office next to Nat Tannen, who distributed his songs. Nat was also a major country music publisher, and all of the country people used to come there. Frank used to meet them and he loved them. He truly enjoyed country music and admired that kind of writing very much. When he wrote 'Have I Stayed Away Too Long?' he was trying to write a song in the country idiom both musically and lyrically. He never wrote 'down.' He had respect for whatever form of song he wrote, which is probably the reason he had success with so many different types of songs. A lot of the songs he wrote in 1943 were based on our being at war—as 'They're Either Too Young Or Too Old,' 'In My Arms' and 'What Do You Do In The Infantry?' "

—Lynn (Mrs. Frank) Loesser

HAVE I STAYED AWAY TOO LONG?

by Frank Loesser

Have I stayed away too long?
Have I stayed away too long?
If I came home tonight
Would you still be my darling
Or have I stayed away too long?

I'm just outside of town
I'll soon be at your door
Or maybe I'd be wrong to hurry there
I'd best keep out of town
And worry you no more
For maybe someone else has made you care.

Have all of my dreams gone wrong?
My beautiful dreams gone wrong?
If I'd come home tonight
Would you still be my darling
Or have I stayed away too long?

The love light that's shone so strong
Sweet love light that's shone so strong
If I'd come home tonight
Would that same light be burning
Or have I stayed away too long?

Written in 1901 by popular writers Gus Edwards and Will D. Cobb, this song was originally credited to the mythical Pen name combination of Will Whitmore and Harry Hilliard. Edwards and Cobb had a number of popular hits in the early 1900s, including "In My Merry Oldsmobile," "School Days," and "Sunbonnet Sue." "I'll Be With You When The Roses Bloom Again" has survived as a country classic and was especially popular during the two world wars. —D. H.

I'LL BE WITH YOU WHEN THE ROSES BLOOM AGAIN

by Will Cobb and Gus Edwards

They were strolling through the gloaming
As the roses were in bloom
A soldier and his sweetheart fond and true
And their hearts were filled with sorrow
As their thoughts were of tomorrow
As she pinned a rose upon his coat of blue.

Do not ask me, love, to linger
For you know not what to say
For duty calls your sweetheart's name again
And your heart need not be sighing
If I be among the dying
I'll be with you when the roses bloom again.

When the roses bloom again beside the river
And the robin redbreast sings his sweet refrain
I'll be with you, sweetheart mine
I'll be with you when the roses bloom again.

Midst the rattle of the battle
Came a whisper soft and low
A soldier who had fallen in the fray
"I am dying, Captain, dying
And I know I have to go
But I want you to promise e'er I pass away.

"There's a far and distant river
Where the roses are in bloom
A maiden who is waiting there for me
And it's there I pray you take me
I've been faithful, don't forsake me
I'll be with you when the roses bloom again."

" 'Molly' was written when I was eighteen years old. I've never known a girl named Molly, nor have I known anyone with a similar experience. This song was God-sent. It was my first record and also Bobby Goldsboro's first record and hit."
—Steve Karliski

MOLLY
by Steve Karliski

The war began and Henry left his farm
Left his darlin' Molly with a baby in her arms
Now the war was over and their life could begin
Molly saw her darlin' standing at the door again.

It's so nice to hear your voice again, Molly
So nice to hear your voice again, Molly
Oh, how happy I'd be if I only could see you
Sweet, sweet Molly, please don't cry.

Recitation:

Maybe I should have written to let you know ahead of time
But I was afraid you'd worry if you knew that I'd gone blind
Do I hear you cryin', Molly? Please don't cry, you silly thing
See what you've done? You even brought a tear to my eye
Oh, how happy I'd be if I only could see you
Sweet, sweet Molly, please don't cry.

Where's my son? What does he look like, Molly?
Everyone says he took after me; Lord, I wish I could see!
Come here, little man; don't be afraid, I'm your daddy
Guess he'll get used to me in time, won't he, Molly?

SILVER DEW ON THE BLUE GRASS TONIGHT

"I wrote this during the Second World War. I thought my husband was going into the service; I was feeling very blue, and I thought, 'This is really the end of my life.' As it turned out, he didn't have to go after all. When I took the song to my publisher, he advised me to use a pseudonym because ordinarily women don't get very far. So they decided to use the beginning of my first name and the ending of my last name—'Ed Burt.' Bob Wills was the first to record it, and after the war, they updated the lyrics to make it a more general song, but I think the original lyrics were prettier and more heartrending." —Edith Berbert

SILVER DEW ON THE BLUE GRASS TONIGHT

by Ed Burt

The moon was softly shining on an old Kentucky home
The fragrance of magnolia filled the air
A lonely girl was writing to her sweetheart 'cross the foam
"May God protect you, darling, over there!"

Silver dew on the blue grass tonight
How it shines in the moon's silver light!
Soldier boy so far from me, how I wish that you could see
Silver dew on the blue grass tonight.

Stars of gold on the old flag tonight
While you fight for a cause that is right
You will keep that flag on high for those boys who had to die
Stars of gold on the old flag tonight!

Silver dew on the blue grass tonight
While I pray you'll come safe through the fight
Close your eyes and think of me, then, my darling, you will see
Silver dew on the blue grass tonight.

SMOKE ON THE WATER

"This was a vision that I had—well, it was actually a dream—from a passage in the Bible. It said that when God put a rainbow in the sky, the world would not be destroyed by water again, it would be destroyed by fire. I felt possibly the war would consume the world with fire as the Bible stated it would be. Earl Nunn and I worked the song out together. In 1944 or 1945, the Los Angeles paper carried a story about a bunch of sailors that came back to San Diego. They were on the first ship—I believe it was the *Wasp*—that was hit by a *kamikaze.* In an interview with a newspaper reporter, he asked the sailor what he was thinking right after the ship was hit, and he said, 'Well, I was thinking about a song I had heard called "Smoke On The Water." ' Years later, a man was in my office in Nashville, and when he found out that I wrote 'Smoke On The Water,' he almost flew apart. He said his outfit in the Marines had a key word when they'd go into any kind of a dive. If they wanted to find their bunch, they'd holler out 'Smoke On The Water!' One night he was half drunk and he got into a fight with another guy. The guy knocked him down and was a-stompin' him and he knew he was being killed. In the midst of being beat to death, he just hollered 'Smoke On The Water!' as loud as he could, and three or four of his buddies came and pulled the guy off of him. He said, 'That song saved my life as sure as I'm standing here.' "

—Zeke Clements

SMOKE ON THE WATER

by Zeke Clements and Earl Nunn

There will be a sad day comin' for the souls of all mankind
They must answer to the people, and it's troublin' their minds
Everybody who must fear them will rejoice on that great day
When the powers of dictators shall be taken all away.

There'll be smoke on the water, on the land and the sea
When our army and navy overtakes the enemy
There'll be smoke on the mountains when the heathen gods stay
And the sun that is risin' will go down on that day.

For there is a great destroyer made of fire and flesh and steel
Rollin' towards the foes of freedom; they'll go down beneath its wheels
There'll be nothin' left but vultures to inhabit all that land
When our modern ships and bombers make a graveyard of Japan.

Hirohito, 'long with Hitler, will be ridin' on a rail
Mussolini'll beg for mercy; as a leader he has failed
But there'll be no time for pity when the screamin' eagle flies
That will be the end of Axis, they must answer with their lives.

" 'Soldier's Last Letter' was written back in the early years of World War II. I suppose the inspiration was that of seeing so many GIs not coming home from the war. The song was not of any personal experience of myself, relatives or friends, but it was relative to many men of that war. Ernest Tubb was most instrumental in making it so popular. His Decca record was a big hit both at home and overseas."

—Redd (Sgt. Henry) Stewart

"I know this song was a true story to a lot of mothers, for I met quite a number of them and autographed their 'last letters' for them, 1944–45."

—Ernest Tubb

SOLDIER'S LAST LETTER

by Sgt. Henry Stewart and Ernest Tubb

When the postman delivered a letter
It filled her dear heart full of joy
But she didn't know till she read the inside
It was the last one from her darling boy.

"Dear Mom," was the way that it started
"I miss you so much," it went on
"Mom, I didn't know that I loved you so
But I'll prove it when this war is won.

I'm writing this down in a trench, Mom
Don't scold if it isn't so neat
You know, as you did when I was a kid
And I'd come home with mud on my feet.

The captain just gave us our orders
And Mom, we will carry them through
I'll finish this letter the first chance I get
But for now, Mom, I'll say I love you."

Then the mother's old hands began to tremble
As she fought against tears in her eyes
But they came unashamed, for there was no name
And she knew that her darling had died.

That night as she knelt by her bedside
She prayed, "Lord above, hear my plea

And protect all the sons that are fighting tonight
And, dear God, keep America free."

THE SOLDIER'S SWEETHEART

"A pal of Jimmie's, Sammy Williams, told his sweetheart good-bye and went to France—to be killed in action. So before the war was over, Jimmie found time to pick out words and air to his first composition, a sentimental song. . . . From the first his railroad buddies liked the song, and the young fellows in Meridian who were his boon companions liked it. With banjo, guitar, uke, they hung around the all-night places or strolled the streets playing and singing Jimmie's song along with 'Sweet Adeline' and other sentimental ballads. But it was not until some ten years later that the world heard—and approved of it."

—Mrs. Carrie Rodgers (from *My Husband, Jimmie Rodgers*)

THE SOLDIER'S SWEETHEART
by Jimmie Rodgers

Once I had a sweetheart
A sweetheart brave and true
His hair was dark and curly
His loving eyes were blue.

He told me that he loved me
And he often proved it so
And he often came to see me
When the ev'ning sun was low.

But fate took him away
To this awful German war
And when he came to say goodbye
My heart did overflow.

He says, "Goodbye, little darling
To France I must go."

He takes the golden finger ring
And he placed it on my hand
Said, "Remember me, little darling
When I'm in no man's land."

He promised he would write to me
That promise he's kept true
And when I read this letter, friend
I pray the war is through.

The second letter I got from him
The war was just ahead
The third one, wrote by his captain
My darling dear was dead.

I'll keep all of his letters
I'll keep his gold ring, too
And I'll always live a single life
For the soldier who was so true.

THAT CRAZY WAR

"This is an old song which I revised and adapted. I heard a blind singer do it at Toe River Fair, Spruce Pine, North Carolina, when I was about ten years old. He called it 'That Bloody War.' That was about the time of World War I, but I have a feeling it might have originated during the Spanish-American War. I enjoyed making up verses about raw recruits who came from the nearby mountains and had never been away from home before. But I knew WLS radio [Chicago], would never let me sing 'Bloody War,' so I changed it to 'Crazy War.' We recorded it for Columbia, and it did pretty well. I got the ideas from neighborhood boys and two older brothers of mine who went to fight with Pershing."

—Scott Wiseman

THAT CRAZY WAR
by Scott Wiseman

Now, over there, across the sea, they've got another war
But, oh, I wonder if they know just what they're fighting for
In that war, that crazy war?

In 1917, you know, we helped them win their fight
But all we got was a lesson in what Sherman said was right
In that war, that crazy war.

I was a simple country lad, I lived down on the farm
I'd never even killed a gnat, nor done a body harm
Until that war, that crazy war.

One day the Sheriff caught me, said, "Come along, my son
Your Uncle Sammy's needin' you to help him tote a gun
In that war, that crazy war."

They took me down to the courthouse, my head was in a whirl
And when the doctors passed on me, I wished I'd been a girl
In that war, that crazy war.

They took me out to the rifle range to hear the bullets sing
I shot and shot that whole day long and never hit a thing
In that war, that crazy war.

The captain said to fire at will, and I said, "Who is he?"
The old coot got so ravin' mad he fired his gun at me
In that war, that crazy war.

When first we got to sunny France, I looked around with glee
But rain and kilometers was all that I could see
In that war, that crazy war.

A cannonball flew overhead, I started home right then
The corporal, he was after me, but the general beat us in
In that war, that crazy war.

And now we're back at home again from over there in France
The enemy lost the battle, and we lost all our pants
In that war, that crazy war.

THERE'S A STAR-SPANGLED BANNER WAVING SOMEWHERE

"With Bob Miller, it's either hillbilly or it isn't, and no compromises. He tries to confine his offerings to authentic outlets, and this has caused him some embarrassment. When 'There's A Star-Spangled Banner Waving Somewhere' hit its third million in record and sheet music sales, Miller inserted an ad in *Variety* asking big-name band leaders 'not' to play it, please. And when the song made the Hit Parade he threatened to sue if it was played. He explains that his reputation as a writer and publisher was at stake. This music, he insists, must have the common touch. It is violated unless done by a true son of the soil, one to the manner born. . . . To streamline such a number is, says Miller, to break faith with his clientele."

—Doron K. Antrim, *Colliers* magazine

THERE'S A STAR-SPANGLED BANNER WAVING SOMEWHERE

by Shelby Darnell (Bob Miller) and Paul Roberts

There's a Star-Spangled Banner waving somewhere
In a distant land so many miles away
Only Uncle Sam's great heroes get to go there
Where I wish that I could also live some day
I'd see Lincoln, Custer, Washington and Perry
And Nathan Hale and Collin Kelly too
There's a Star-Spangled Banner waving somewhere
Waving o'er the land of heroes brave and true.

In this war with its mad schemes of destruction
Of our country fair and our sweet liberty
By the mad dictators, leaders of corruption
Can't the U.S. use a mountain boy like me?
God gave me the right to be a free American
And for that precious right I'd gladly die
There's a Star-Spangled Banner waving somewhere
That is where I want to live when I die.

Though I realize I'm crippled, that is true, sir
Please don't judge my courage by my twisted leg
Let me show my Uncle Sam what I can do, sir
Let me help to bring the Axis down a peg
If I do some great deed I will be a hero
And a hero brave is what I want to be
There's a Star-Spangled Banner waving somewhere
In that heaven there should be a place for me.

11 | Prison Songs

Doin' My Time

The continuing popularity of the prison song in the country repertory is easy to understand—some of the most dramatic and poignant lyrics written over the years fall into this category—but its origins remain a puzzle. Some scholars explain it as an outgrowth of the common prison theme in many native American folk ballads, others see it as a commentary on the disproportionate number of poor people (South and North, black and white) who did time behind bars, whereas a few treat it merely as a commercial formula that began with the first great hillbilly hit, "The Prisoner's Song," itself a reworking of older folk fragments.

All three sides have good arguments. Consider, for example, these songs picked at random from the Combs collection *(Folk-Songs of the Southern United States).* From "Floyd Frazier,"

> Floyd Frazier is now in prison
> And ought to hang-ed be
> For the killing of an innocent woman
> This world may plainly see.

From "The Tolliver Song,"

> He was put in jail at Roand [Rowan]
> There to remain a while
> In the hands of law and justice
> To bravely stand his trial.

And from "Ellen Smith,"

O now I am a prisoner
And I'm confined in jail
My friends all gathered round
But none was worth my bail.

Whatever the folk influence on the composed, commercial songs of the country tradition, it is certain that a term in jail, especially for vagrancy, was not uncommon (and little to be ashamed of) for countless men during the Golden Age of country music. According to Robert Goldston *(The Great Depression),* "If the bulls caught you they'd beat you with their sticks, perhaps kill you, or turn you over to a local sheriff. If this happened down South, in Georgia or Florida, for example, you were sent to the chain gang."

And the influence of "The Prisoner's Song" cannot be minimized. Recorded by Vernon Dalhart in 1924, it became Victor's best-selling pre-electric recording, boosted the sales of records in a declining market, and firmly established Dalhart's reputation as a hillbilly singer. It still is being recorded and, to some extent, imitated today.

We can say with some assurance, however, that violence (and, inevitably, imprisonment) was common in the lives of white southerners during the formative years of country music. W. J. Cash treated the subject at length in *The Mind of the South.* He argued that the existence of large masses of "inferior" blacks (both before and after slavery) gave even the poorest white security and independence without the slightest need to work for it. This attitude, he said, worked to preserve not only Jeffersonian democracy, but also frontier attitudes.

"This character is of the utmost significance," Cash wrote, "for its corollary was the perpetuation and acceleration of the tendency to violence which had grown up in the Southern backwoods as it naturally grows up on all frontiers. . . . However careful they might be to walk softly, such men as these of the South were bound to come often into conflict. And being what they were—simple, direct, and immensely personal—and their world being what it was—conflict with them could only mean immediate physical clashing, could only mean fisticuffs, the gouging ring, and knife and gun play."

Inevitably, such behavior led to the death and tragedy we have seen throughout this book, and often to prison.

So Dalhart's success in 1924 was not accidental; prisons and prisoners were not alien to the southern whites who made up the original audience for hillbilly music, and their attitudes were strongly sympathetic. For these songs almost never dwell on the prisoner's crime; often he has been wrongly imprisoned and always, at least in the early songs, dramatic impact is achieved by the separation of the prisoner from his wife, sweetheart, or mother.

Thus, in "The Convict And The Rose," the rose symbolizes both love and innocence; the prisoner who has finished his sentence in "I'm Free" was "falsely suspected" and is going home to sweetheart and mother, and even in "Twenty-One Years," where the narrator is doing time for his girl friend, he still holds out hope that she will arrange for his pardon or parole.

During the thirties and forties, when crimes were mentioned, many were of the rowdy sort typical of Jimmie Rodgers's "Campbell" of "In The Jailhouse Now" or of the prisoner in "Doin' My Time." During this period many artists recorded one or two prison songs, as they did railroad songs; Roy Acuff found the tragic-prisoner image especially compatible in songs like "Branded Wherever I Go" and "Behind Those Walls Of Gray."

Beginning with the fifties, prison songs took on a much more serious note as the repressed violence and anger of "Folsom Prison Blues" made its impact. Johnny Cash's protagonist "shot a man in Reno just to watch him die" and expresses not remorse but self-pity. Cash's use of the train as a symbol of freedom is a connection often made both in prison and in railroad songs and is reminiscent of Bob Miller's "Twenty-One Years."

Stonewall Jackson is another artist strongly identified with the prison song, and his success with "Life To Go" and "I Washed My Hands In Muddy Water" prompted him to go back and record such classics as "Shackles And Chains," "I'm Here To Get My Baby Out Of Jail," and the old British-American ballad "Knoxville Girl."

A few country artists have themselves spent time in jail and have thus brought a note of real sincerity to their efforts. Jimmie Tarleton, most famous for his recomposition of the folk-derived "Birmingham Jail" and "Columbus Stockade Blues," was caught riding the rods home from a recording session in 1932 and spent time in the Atlanta jail. More recently, Merle Haggard, who spent three years in San Quentin during the early sixties, has brought renewed interest to this category with his sensitive interpretations. Haggard's first two number-one hits, "Branded Man" and "I'm A Lonesome Fugitive," were prison songs.

To this day, "Doin' My Time" is largely a poor man's worry, and it has found its most eloquent expression in poor man's music—black blues and country music.

THE CONVICT AND THE ROSE

"This song was written 'tongue-in-cheek'; my husband never expected it to be the hit it was. He was a sentimental man and wrote many sentimental songs like 'The Trail Of The Lonesome Pine' and 'Rose Of Washington Square,' but he was a little ashamed of this song because it was so 'syrupy.' He came home one day and said, 'I put your name on a song,' then he told me the title of it, and I remember dying laughing because I thought it was just a corny song, but that was before I read the lyrics for the first time." —Elizabeth Chapin (Mrs. Ballard) MacDonald

THE CONVICT AND THE ROSE

by Ballard MacDonald, Betty Chapin, and R. A. King

Within my prison cell so dreary
Alone I sit with weary heart
I'm thinking of my lonely darling
From her forever I must part.

A rose she sent me as a token
She sent it just to light my gloom
To tell me that her heart is broken
To cheer me 'fore I meet my doom.

She wrote "I took it from the garden
Where once we wandered side by side
But now you hold no hope of pardon
And I can never be your bride."

The judge would not believe my story
The jury said I had to pay
But to the rose in all its glory
"Not guilty" is all that I can say.

Goodbye, sweetheart, for in the morning
I meet my Maker and repose
And when I go at daylight's dawning
Against my heart they'll find this rose.

DOIN' MY TIME

"It was the early thirties and times were hard. I was drifting from place to place and my pockets were usually empty. I could strum a few chords on a guitar and sing some Jimmie Rodgers songs. I was also trying to write, but I knew I had a long way to go. A Model A Ford carried me into Grand Rapids, Michigan, on a cold December day. My gas tank was empty and 35 cents was all my pockets showed. A cousin gave me a welcome and a warm meal. I couldn't find a job, but I did have a little $35 Gibson guitar I could strum, and the blues came easy to a boy who was broke and who would have liked them anyway, even if he had been a millionaire. One day, my cousin handed me a *True Detective* magazine. In it was a story called 'I'm a Fugitive From a Georgia Chain Gang.' Robert Burns was the author. He was a native of New Jersey who had escaped and was writing while in hiding. His story created a world of publicity regarding the chain gang system and how it worked, and a top movie was made starring Paul Muni with the same title. From this story also came the idea for 'Doin' My Time.' "

—Jimmie Skinner

DOIN' MY TIME
by Jimmie Skinner

On this old rock pile with a ball and chain
They call me by a number, not a name, Lord, Lord
Gotta do my time, gotta do my time
With an aching heart and a worried mind.

When that old judge look down and smile
He said, "I'll put you on that good road for a while," Lord, Lord
Gotta do my time, gotta do my time
With an aching heart and a worried mind.

You can hear my hammer, you can hear my song
I'm gonna swing it like John Henry all day long, Lord, Lord
Gotta do my time, gotta do my time
With an aching heart and a worried mind.

It won't be long, just a few more days
Till I'll settle down and quit my rowdy ways, Lord, Lord
With that gal of mine, with that gal of mine
She'll be waiting for me when I've done my time.

"In 1953 I saw a movie entitled *Inside the Walls of Folsom Prison.* I wrote the song the following year. It has been requested over the years along with 'I Walk The Line' and a few of the others I've recorded. I think prison songs are popular because most of us are living in one little kind of prison or another, and whether we know it or not the words of a song about someone who is actually in a prison speak for a lot of us who might appear not to be, but really are." —Johnny Cash

FOLSOM PRISON BLUES
by John R. Cash

I hear the train a-comin', it's rollin' round the bend
And I ain't seen the sunshine since I don't know when
I'm stuck in Folsom Prison and time keeps draggin' on
But that train keeps on rollin' down to San Antone.

When I was just a baby, my Mama told me, "Son
Always be a good boy, don't ever play with guns"
But I shot a man in Reno just to watch him die
When I hear the whistle blowin', I hang my head and cry.

I bet there's rich folks eatin' in a fancy dining car
They're probably drinkin' coffee and smokin' big cigars
But I know I had it comin', I know I can't be free
But those people keep a-movin', and that's what tortures me.

Well, if they freed me from this prison, if that railroad train was mine
I bet I'd move it over a little farther down the line
Far from Folsom Prison, that's where I want to stay
And I'd let that lonesome whistle blow my blues away.

(I'M A LONESOME) FUGITIVE

"We were driving home from the country music convention in Nashville, and we had to drive all night through a snow storm. Somewhere near Billings, Montana, on the old Highway 10, we passed a historical marker that described an Indian tribe that had lived near there. It seems that the 'crop' the Indians raised was children, and the white people up there kept hoping that their crops would fail. We stopped the car, got a guitar out of the trunk and wrote the song that same night. 'The Fugitive' was a popular television show at the time, and the fact that we had been on the road so long brought that to mind. Those were the elements that inspired the song."

—Liz and Casey Anderson

(I'M A LONESOME) FUGITIVE

by Liz and Casey Anderson

I raised a lot of cain in my younger days
While Mama used to pray my crops would fail
Now I'm a hunted fugitive with just two ways
Outrun the law or spend my life in jail.

I'd like to settle down, but they won't let me
A fugitive must be a rolling stone
Down every road there's always one more city
I'm on the run, the highway is my home.

I'm lonesome, but I can't afford the luxury
Of having one I love to come along
She'd only slow me down, and they'd catch up with me
For he who travels fastest goes alone.

I WASHED MY HANDS IN MUDDY WATER

"Back in Nebraska where I grew up, our streams and rivers, excluding the Missouri, had sandy bottoms and the water ran clear and blue. We swam in them. When I came to Tennessee, the difference in the character of the rivers of the South was quite noticeable to me, the water being murky, deep, and dark in most cases, and most of all muddy. The thought struck me one day that you could wash all day in water like that and never get clean. It seemed like there was a good parallel to draw here because that is the way it often is in life, especially with people that get into trouble. Sometimes they (or we) seem to want to get clean, but don't because they pursue the wrong solutions. So followed the story of a young man that got off to a bad start and fell into the same troubled life-style his daddy had lived but had warned him about. He ended up just like his father because he did as his daddy did, not what his daddy said."

—Joe Babcock

I WASHED MY HANDS IN MUDDY WATER

by Joe Babcock

I was born in Macon, Georgia
They kept my dad in the Macon jail
My daddy said, "Son, keep your hands clean
And you won't hear those blood hounds on your trail."

I washed my hands in muddy water
I washed my hands, but I didn't get clean
I tried to do like my daddy told me
I must have washed my hands in a muddy stream.

Well, I fell in with bad companions
We robbed a man in Tennessee
The sheriff caught me up in Nashville
They locked me up and threw away the key.

I asked the jailer, "When's my time up?"
He said, "Now, son, we won't forget
And if you try and keep your hands clean
Then we may make a good man of you yet."

I couldn't wait and do my sentence
I broke out of the Nashville jail
Now I just crossed the line of Georgia
And I can hear those blood hounds on my trail.

I'M FREE

"I was writing at the time with Lou Herscher, who wrote the melody. Prison songs were somewhat in vogue in those days, and I fell upon the idea and worked it out to the best of my ability. There was no close tie to my past that brought about the phrase 'free from the chain gang.' I hadn't served time or anything like that. It was just the sort of thing that pops in and out of the air. We submitted about four songs to Jimmie Rodgers, and this was the one he liked." —Saul Klein

I'M FREE (FROM THE CHAIN GANG NOW)

by Saul Klein and Lou Herscher

I've got rid of the shackles that bound me
And the guards who were always around me
Like a bird in the tree, I've found my liberty
And I'm free from the chain gang now.

Long ago I was known and respected
Then one day, I was falsely suspected
And they put me in chains working out in the rains
But I'm free from the chain gang now.

I know my mother's poor heart was broken
'Cause she knew that an untruth was spoken
There were tears on the mail that she sent me in jail
But I'm free from the chain gang now.

All the years I was known by a number
Were just years that I spent without slumber
After long years of shame, I have won back my name
And I'm free from the chain gang now.

Now I'm going back home to another
She's my sweetheart who's waiting with mother
And I'll dry all the tears they've been shedding for years
'Cause I'm free from the chain gang now.

I'M HERE TO GET MY BABY OUT OF JAIL

"Harty Taylor and I were a team, Karl and Harty, and we came to Chicago in June, 1930, to appear on the WLS Barn Dance. Back home in Kentucky we had been an instrumental team, but when we got to Chicago we were supposed to come up with some songs. To make your job more important, you had to sing too. One Sunday I drove the WLS pastor, Bill Vickland, to Madison, Wisconsin. He was the Barn Dance philosopher and said the little blessing at the end of each show. On the way back I was alone, the ride was long and the road was narrow and crooked. I started humming a tune, and two or three times along the way I stopped to write down some lyrics. By the time I got back to my hotel in Chicago I had it completed. Monday morning, Harty and I started rehearsing it and we put it on the air. It drew a lot of mail and later we recorded it on Columbia. We found that sentimental songs always went good with us."

—Karl Davis

I'M HERE TO GET MY BABY OUT OF JAIL

by Karl Davis and Harty Taylor

"I'm not in your town to stay," said a lady old and gray
To the warden of a penitentiary
"I'm not in your town to stay and I'll soon be on my way
I'm just here to get my baby out of jail
Yes, warden, I'm just here to get my baby out of jail."

"I've tried to raise my baby right, I have prayed both day and night
That he'd never follow in the footsteps of his dad
I have searched both far and wide, I had feared that he had died
And at last I find my baby here in jail
Yes, warden, but it's good to find my baby here in jail."

"It is just five years today since my husband passed away
He was found beneath the snow so cold, so white
I made a vow to keep his ring and his gold watch and his chain
But the county laid my husband in the ground
Yes, warden, the county laid my baby's papa in the ground."

"I will pawn you my watch, I will pawn you my chain
I will pawn you my diamond ring
I will wash all your clothes, I will scrub all your floors
If that will get my baby out of jail
Yes, warden, you know I want my darling out of jail."

Then we heard the warden say to this lady old and gray
"I will bring your baby boy to your side"
Two iron gates swung wide apart, she held her darling to her heart
She kissed her baby boy and she died
But smiling, in the arms of her dear boy there she died.

"Regarding Jimmie's revival of those old songs of American ballad fame, such as 'Frankie And Johnny,' 'He's In The Jailhouse Now' and others, reviewers the country over marveled because of his ability to take those old standbys and make engaging novelties out of them. He made them 'come into their own' . . . 'Jailhouse' was for Jimmie such a surprise hit everywhere—even though it had been done for years—that Mr. Ralph Peer urged him to work out an original song along the same lines for a 'Jailhouse Blues Number 2.' Jimmie did—in about twenty minutes; in fact, while we were waiting for breakfast to be sent up in a hotel in Hollywood. He had it ready for recording the next morning, using the portable equipment Mr. Peer had brought to California for him."

—Mrs. Carrie Rodgers
(from *My Husband, Jimmie Rodgers*)

IN THE JAILHOUSE NOW NO. 2
by Jimmie Rodgers

I had a friend named Campbell
He used to rob, steal and gamble
He tried everything that was low-down
He was out tom-cattin' one night
When he started a big fight
Then a big policeman came and knocked him down.

He's in the jailhouse now
He's in the jailhouse now
I told him over again
To quit drinkin' whiskey, lay off of that gin
He's in the jailhouse now.

Campbell broke jail one day
Decided he'd go away
But the police met him at the train
The cop says, "I've come for you"
Campbell says that this won't do
"Because Campbell never was my name."

He's in the jailhouse now
He's in the jailhouse now
Yes, he broke out
All over town the fool walked about
He's in the jailhouse now.

I met his old gal, Sadie
She says, "Have you seen my baby?"

I told her he was downtown in the can
She went down to the jail
Just to go his bail
She says, "I've come down here to get my man."

She's in the jailhouse now
She's in the jailhouse now
So you can understand
Why old kid Sadie's in the can
She's in the jailhouse now.

THE PRISONER'S DREAM

" 'The Prisoner's Dream' was written by Pat McAdory. Harty Taylor and I (Karl & Harty) announced it and put it on the air for the first time on WJJD Chicago."
—Karl Davis

THE PRISONER'S DREAM
by Pat McAdory, Karl Davis, and Harty Taylor

Last night as I lay sleeping, I dreamed a dream so fair
I dreamed about my darling, a rose was in her hair
I dreamed I left this prison, started in life anew
She told me that she loved me, told me her love was true.

It was only a dream, just a prisoner's dream
As I lay on my cold prison bed
My dreams of you can never come true
Dear girl, I wish that I were dead.

I dreamed she called me darling, kissed me and held me tight
I dreamed that we were married, dreamed of a starry night
I dreamed about our children, playing around my knee
They loved and called me Daddy, they thought the world of me.

I dreamed a dream so lovely, heaven on earth it seemed
My wife and little children came to me in my dreams

They threw their arms around me, I was their pride and joy
My little wife, she loved me, I was her darling boy.

THE PRISONER'S SONG

"Guy Massey did not write this song. His brother, Robert Massey, wrote it. Guy always stayed with us when he came to Dallas, and I was with them while my husband sang it and Guy wrote it down. He said he wanted to take it to New York. Well, he did, and he copyrighted it in his own name. Up until the time we were married, Robert traveled around over the country, and he picked up part of it somewhere and put words to it. He was singing it when we were married in 1920. Guy tried to put it on record, but he failed, then their cousin, Vernon Dalhart, recorded it, and it just went like wildfire. In his will, Guy willed it back to my husband, but he never did admit that he didn't write it."

—Novie (Mrs. Robert) Massey

THE PRISONER'S SONG
by Guy Massey

Oh, I wish I had someone to love me
Someone to call me their own
Oh, I wish I had someone to live with
'Cause I'm tired of livin' alone.

Oh, please meet me tonight in the moonlight
Please meet me tonight all alone
For I have a sad story to tell you
It's a story that's never been told.

I'll be carried to the new jail tomorrow
Leaving my poor darling alone
With the cold prison bars all around me
And my head on a pillow of stone.

Now I have a grand ship on the ocean
All mounted with silver and gold
And before my poor darlin' would suffer
Oh, that ship would be anchored and sold.

Now if I had the wings of an angel
Over these prison walls I would fly
And I'd fly to the arms of my poor darlin'
And there I'd be willing to die.

SHACKLES AND CHAINS

"This song was based on a story told to me, though I don't know whether or not it's true. They could have used stones for pillows in those days. It became popular immediately after it was released on one of my records."
—Jimmie Davis

SHACKLES AND CHAINS
by Jimmie Davis

On a long, lonesome journey I'm going
Oh, darling, and please don't you cry
Though in shackles and chains they will take me
In prison to stay till I die
And at night through the bars
I will gaze at the stars
And long for your kisses in vain
A piece of stone I will use as my pillow
While I'm sleeping in shackles and chains.

Put your arms through these bars once, my darling
Let me kiss those sweet lips I love best
In heartache, you're my consolation
In sorrow, my haven of rest
And at night through the bars
I will gaze at the stars
The plans that we made were in vain
A piece of stone I will use as my pillow
While I'm sleeping in shackles and chains.

Bob Miller, one of country music's most prolific and imaginative songwriters, discovered a mother lode in 1930 when he wrote this song. Its instant and overwhelming success inspired a long chain of related answer songs which formed a veritable saga. These included, among others, "The Answer To Twenty-One Years," "New Answer To Twenty-One Years," "Woman's Answer To Twenty-One Years," "After Twenty-One Years," "The End Of Twenty-One Years," "Last Of The Twenty-One Year Prisoner," and, finally, "The Twenty-One Year Prisoner Is Dead." Many of these were successful, and all enjoyed the same tune.

—D. H.

TWENTY-ONE YEARS

by Bob Miller

The judge said "Stand up, boy, and dry up your tears,
You're sentenced to prison for twenty-one years"
So kiss me goodbye, love, and say you'll be mine
For twenty-one years, love, is a mighty long time.

O hear that train blow, love, she'll be here on time
To take me to prison, to serve out my time
So look down that railroad far as you can see
And keep right on waving your farewell to me.

The steam from the whistle, the smoke from the stack
I know you'll be true, love, until I get back
So hold up your head, babe, and dry up your eyes
Best friends must part, so won't you and I.

Go beg the governor, babe, on your sweet soul
If you can't get a pardon, try and get a parole
If I had the governor, well the governor's got me
Before sunrise tomorrow, the governor'd be free.

I've counted the days, love, I've counted the nights
I've counted the minutes, I've counted the lights
I've counted the footsteps, I've counted the stars
I've counted a million of these prison bars.

I've counted on you, babe, to give me a break
I guess you forgot, love, I'm here for your sake
You know who's guilty, you know it so well
But I'll rot in prison, before I will tell.

Come all you young fellows with hearts brave and true
Don't believe any woman you'd meet if you do
Don't trust any woman, no matter what kind,
For twenty-one years, boys, is a mighty long time.

12 | The Working Man

These Hard-Workin' Hands

Country music is poor man's music, working man's music, and it's natural that songs about work should find their way into the body of hillbilly songs. As always, the country songwriter puts his own special brand on these songs, and the music emerges as something unexpected.

As inheritors of a land ravaged by war, leeched by cotton, undernourished and farmed out for generations, the working men might be expected to sing songs of some bitterness, but we find little of it. Laboring in a land of open shops where the company store, the twelve-hour day, and child labor were the rules, they should voice protest, yet protest is the rare exception. Working at hard, physical, boring, and endless tasks, their music could lighten the burden with rhythm and repetition as did black work songs. Yet work songs are few.

Instead, the same values that characterize all country music—the fatalism of an austere Protestantism, the individualism of the pioneer, the stoic acceptance of things as they are—apply to songs about work. Virtually free from class consciousness, the songs that follow are personal, individual reactions to the work experience.

For an idea of what that work experience has been, census figures for the past fifty years are revealing. In 1920, 40 percent of all Americans worked and lived on farms; by 1970 this number had shrunk to 5 percent. So the urbanization and industrialization that began during the last century have accelerated during the period of commercial hillbilly music. The yeoman farmer and the pastoral life remain unifying ideas among this audience, but almost in a mythical sense. Many of those who write and sing hillbilly music, as well as a steadily growing portion of its audience, have never lived on farms or have abandoned rural life long ago.

Leaving the farm, however, didn't necessarily mean leaving the land or the South or a country way of life. Without much capital or education or status, the emigrant from the farm, whether he was forced off or simply left to find a better way, took what jobs were available. In the twentieth century, new opportunities opened up with the oil boom in Texas, the growth of the trucking industry, and industrial expansion in both South and North.

As the base of country music broadened to include these lower-class occupations and spread west and north, the music adapted itself. What had been a rural music of the hill and range with strong folk strains became a blue-collar product, at least in its lyric content. Railroad lore became trucker songs, mill songs evolved into factory songs, and the cowboys of one era became the roughnecks of another.

Trucking songs written since the late thirties could fill a book, and singers like Red Sovine and Dave Dudley carved out careers singing them. Songs about cowboys and railroaders are so numerous they make up separate chapters in this collection. The earliest song in this group, "Cotton Mill Colic," describes conditions in a mill in the thirties; the latest, "Oney," is set in a factory in the seventies. There are four decades of social change between them, but the attitudes—the dignity of labor, the right of a man to speak out, the sense of fairness—are almost identical. This hard-hat pride has been a strong cohesive force in the community and in its music, and helps to explain its continuing vitality.

Yet here again we find only mild protest, an essentially conservative acceptance of the system. These are country songs expressing country values. "These hands ain't the hands of a gentleman," but ". . . these hands brought me happiness."

And that's about all these workers own—their hands. The "Black Land Farmer" obviously has a pretty good piece of land, but more typical of this group is the sharecropper who can't make a living on the "Mississippi Delta Land." Even *he* hasn't given up hope, however—at least for his children. The "Louisiana Man," on the other hand, is a genuine frontiersman, hunting, fishing, and trapping for a living. Like many of these songs, this one is autobiographical, and only the fiddle and voice of Doug Kershaw saved him from a similar life.

The blues, folk or country, are a popular pastime for many of these working men, whether they're roughneck, weaver, trucker, or mule skinner. One selection was derived from a work song (Merle Travis's "Nine Pound Hammer") and another Travis song ("Sixteen Tons") approaches one, but largely they're solid commercial songs which reflect the lives of men who work hard with their hands.

"I was in Korea in the Army, and being a graduate of an auctioneering school myself, felt very strongly about the auctioneering business. I felt that an auctioneering song should be authentic and sound just exactly like the sound you would hear when you walked into a cattle sale barn someplace in the West, Midwest or South—wherever they sell cattle. I was inspired by my boyhood idol, a cousin of mine, a Mr. Ray Sims from Sedalia, Missouri, who is regarded by many authorities in the business as a top auctioneer. The entire lyric is factual except the first line; I couldn't find anything to rhyme with Missouri, so I substituted Arkansas."

—Leroy Van Dyke

AUCTIONEER

by Leroy Van Dyke and Buddy Black

Recitation:

Hey, well, all right, sir, here we go there, and what're ya gonna give for 'em? I'm bid twenty-five, will ya gimme thirty, make it thirty, bid it to buy 'em at thirty dollars on 'er, will ya gimme thirty, now five, who would-a bid it at five, make it five, five bid and now forty dollars on 'er to buy 'em there. . . .

There was a boy in Arkansas
Who wouldn't listen to his ma
When she told him that he should go to school
He'd sneak away in the afternoon
Take a little walk, and pretty soon
You'd find him at the local auction barn.

He'd stand and he'd listen carefully
Then, pretty soon, he began to see
How the auctioneer could talk so rapidly
He said, "Oh, my, it's do or die!
I've got to learn that auction cry
Gotta make my mark and be an auctioneer!"

Twenty . . . thirty . . . thirty . . . thirty
Thirty . . . thirty . . . thirty . . . thirty
Thirty . . . thirty . . . thirty . . . thirty
Thirty . . . thirty . . . bid!

As time went on, he did his best
And all could see he didn't jest
He practised calling bids both night and day
His pop would find him behind the barn

Just working up an awful storm
As he tried to imitate the auctioneer.

Then his pop said, "Son, we just can't stand
To have a mediocre man
Sellin' things at auction using our good name
I'll send you off to auction school
Then you'll be nobody's fool
You can take your place among the best."

Thirty-five dollar bid, and now forty dollar
Will you gimme forty, make it forty
Bidi-di-bom a forty dollar, will you gimme forty
Whoda da bi di da forty dollar bid?
Forty dollar bid and now forty-five
Will you gimme forty-five to make it a forty-five
To bidi-da for forty-five
Who would a-bid it at a forty-five dollar bid?

So from that boy who went to school
There grew a man who played it cool
He came back home a full-fledged auctioneer
Then the people came from miles around
Just to hear him make that rhythmic sound
That fills their hearts with such a happy cheer.

Then his fame spread out from shore to shore
He had all he could do and more
Had to buy a plane to get around
Now he's the tops in all the land
Let's pause to give that man a hand
He's the best hillbilly auctioneer.

Forty . . . fifty . . . fifty . . . fifty
Fifty . . . fifty . . . fifty . . . fifty
Fifty . . . fifty . . . fifty . . . fifty
I sold that hog for a fifty-dollar bid.

Recitation:

Hey, well, all right, sir, open the gate an' let 'em out and walk 'em boys! Here we come with lot number 29 in; what'd ya gonna give for 'em? I'm bid twenty-five, will ya gimme thirty, make it thirty, bid it to buy 'em at thirty dollars on 'er, will you gimme thirty dollars on 'er, now five, thirty-five, an' now the forty dollars on 'er, will you gimme forty, make it forty, now five, forty-five an' now the fifty dollars on 'er, will you gimme fifty, now five, fifty-five, and now the sixty dollars on 'er, will you gimme sixty, make it sixty, now five, who'd bid it at sixty dollars on 'er to buy 'em there . . .

BLACK LAND FARMER

"I didn't grow up on a farm, nor have I ever been a farmer, but I was born and raised in the southern coastal town of Victoria, Texas, where there are many black-land farms. This area supposedly had the best and the deepest black land in the world, good for growing cotton, maize and rice."

—Frankie Miller, Jr.

BLACK LAND FARMER
by Frankie Miller, Jr.

When the Lord made me, He made a simple man
Not much money and not much land
He didn't make no banker or legal charmer
And the Lord made me a black land farmer.

Well, my hands ain't smooth, my face is rough
My heart is warm, and my ways ain't tough
I guess I'm the luckiest man ever born
'Cause the Lord gave me help and a black land farm.

Breakin' up the new ground early in the day
Gonna plant cotton, I'm gonna plant hay
I love to smell the sweet breeze blowin' through the corn
Lord, you sure done me right on my black land farm.

I feel like I'm a-gettin' closer to you, God
A-plantin' the ground and breakin' up the sod
Well, my mind is at ease and I could do no harm
Lord, I owe it all to you and my black land farm.

"When I first wrote 'Busted,' it was about coal miners, but it wound up being about a cotton farmer. I took the coal mining song to Johnny Cash. He liked it, except he said, 'Would you mind if we switched the story around to cotton farmers, because I've picked cotton, but I've never been a coal miner and I'd feel more comfortable doing it about cotton farmers.' Burl Ives was the only person to record the original coal mining version. In my heart when I sing it, I sing the original version, because I have a great sympathy for coal miners. I was born in Kentucky and all my ancestors that I'm aware of are from Kentucky. I have a feeling for coal miners more than I do for cotton farmers." —Harlan Howard

BUSTED
by Harlan Howard

My bills are all due, and the baby needs shoes
But I'm busted
Cotton is down to a quarter a pound
And I'm busted
I got a cow that went dry and a hen that won't lay
A big stack of bills that gets bigger each day
The county's gonna haul my belongings away
'Cause I'm busted.

I went to my brother to ask for a loan
'Cause I was busted
I hate to beg like a dog for a bone
But I'm busted
My brother said, "There ain't a thing I can do
My wife and my kids are all down with the flu
And I was just thinking about callin' on you
'Cause I'm busted."

Well, I am no thief, but a man can go wrong
When he's busted
The food that we canned last summer is gone
And I'm busted
The fields are all bare, and the cotton won't grow
Me and my family got to pack up and go
But I'll make a living, just where I don't know
'Cause I'm busted.

After the Civil War, proponents of an industrial "New South," free from economic colonial dependence on the North, were instrumental in vastly expanding the region's textile industry, particularly in the Carolinas. Southern farmers, however, lured to the factories by the promise of steady pay, often found they had traded rural poverty for industrial poverty. David McCarn was one of these. He left his home in Gastonia, North Carolina, to work in the mills, and soon began composing songs for the amusement of his fellow workers. They proved so popular that Victor recorded six sides during the thirties, and McCarn became a professional country singer. His note of social protest in this song is unusual for a country song.

—D. H.

COTTON MILL COLIC

by David McCarn

When you buy clothes on easy terms
The collector treats you like measley worms
One dollar down and then, Lord knows
If you don't make a payment, they'll take your clothes
When you go to bed, you can't sleep
You owe so much at the end of the week
No use to colic, they're all that way
Pecking at your door till they get your pay
I'm a-gonna starve, everybody will
'Cause you can't make a livin' at a cotton mill.

When you go to work, you work like the devil
At the end of the week you're not on the level
Pay day comes, you pay your rent
When you get through, you've not got a cent
To buy fat back meat and pinto beans
Now and then you get turnip greens
No use to colic, we're all that way
Can't get the money to move away
I'm a-gonna starve, everybody will
'Cause you can't make a livin' at a cotton mill.

Twelve dollars a week is all we get
How in the heck can we live on that?
I've got a wife and fourteen kids
We all have to sleep on two bedsteads
Patches on my britches, holes in my hat
Ain't had a shave since my wife got fat
No use to colic, every day at noon
The kids get to cryin' in a different tune

I'm a-gonna starve, everybody will
'Cause you can't make a livin' in a cotton mill.

They run a few days, and then they stand
Just to keep down the working man
We can't make it, we never will
As long as we stay at a lousy mill
The poor are gettin' poorer, the rich are gettin' rich
If I don't starve, I'm a son of a gun
No use to colic, no use to rave
We'll never rest till we're in our graves
I'm a-gonna starve, everybody will
'Cause you can't make a livin' in a cotton mill.

'LEVEN CENT COTTON, FORTY CENT MEAT

Bob Miller was famous for his social commentaries and topical songs. Though " 'Leven Cent Cotton" was written before the Depression, it became especially relevant during the thirties. Vernon Dalhart and a few others recorded it, but many of its travels were from person to person. Miller was born in Memphis and was no stranger to the rural South.

—D. H.

'LEVEN CENT COTTON, FORTY CENT MEAT

by Bob Miller and Emma Dermer

'Leven cent cotton, forty cent meat
How in the world can a poor man eat?
Pray for the sunshine, 'cause it will rain
Things gettin' worse, drivin' all insane
Built a nice barn, painted it brown
Lightnin' came along and burnt it down
No use talkin', any man's beat
With 'leven cent cotton and forty cent meat.

No corn in the crib, no chicks in the yard
No meat in the smoke house, no tubs full of lard
No cream in the pitcher, no honey in the mug
No butter on the table, no 'lasses in the jug

Things to eat are always high
Every one is selling, no one will buy
We quit kickin', the fault's not our own
We just can't reap where we have sown.

'Leven cent cotton, forty cent meat
How in the world can a poor man eat?
Flour up high, cotton down low
How in the world can we raise the dough?
Our clothes worn out, shoes run down
Old slouch hat with a hole in the crown
Back nearly broken, fingers all wore
Cotton goin' down to rise no more.

'Leven cent cotton, ten dollar pants
Who in the world has got a chance?
We can't buy clothes, we can't buy meat
Got too much cotton, not enough to eat
Can't help each other, what shall we do?
I can't solve the problem, so it's up to you
'Leven cent cotton, forty cent hose
Guess we'll have to do without our clothes.

LOUISIANA MAN

"I had just come out of the Army about two months. I was broke on my ass. I was being kicked out of my apartment, and I was sitting down for the last time, trying to write songs. I wrote six songs and when I got to the seventh, I finally got my head back to when I was a kid, when I was safe. When I wasn't being kicked out, when I had beans on the table. So I just let my head pour out. I never changed a word. I used 'Mack' and 'Ned' instead of 'Rusty' and 'Doug.' But everything else is real names and real facts."

—Doug Kershaw

LOUISIANA MAN
by Doug Kershaw

Well, at birth my Mom and Papa called a little boy Ned
Raised him on the banks of a riverbed

A houseboat tied to a big tall tree
A home for my Papa and my Mama and me.

The clock strikes three, and Papa jumps to his feet
Already Mama's cooking Papa something to eat
At half past, Papa, he's ready to go
Jumps in his pirogue, headed down the bayou.

He's got fishin' lines strung across the Louisiana River
Gotta catch a big fish for us to eat
He's setting traps in the swamp, catching anything he can
He's gotta make a livin', he's a Louisiana man
Gotta make a livin', he's a Louisiana man.

Got muskrat hides hangin' by the dozen
Even got a lady mink, a muskrat's cousin
Get 'em out drying in the hot, hot sun
Tomorrow Papa's gonna turn 'em into 'mon.'

Well, they call my Mama Rita and my Daddy Jack
And little baby brother on the floor, that's Mack
Bren and Lin are the family twins
Big brother Ed, he's on the bayou fishin'.

When the river flows, Papa's great big boat
That's how my papa goes into town
It takes him every bit of a night and day
To even reach a place where people stay.

I can hardly wait until tomorrow comes around
That's the day my Papa takes the furs to town
Papa promised me that I could go
Even let me see a cowboy show.

I saw the cowboys and Indians for the first time then
I told my Pa, "I gotta go again."
Papa said, "Son, we've got lines to run
We'll come back again, but first there's work to be done."

"When I was a child, I used to run away a lot. I lived in Michigan and did a lot of hitchhiking. I hitchhiked one time through the Delta Land down in Mississippi and it made a strong and lasting impression on my mind. I remember walking along these country roads seeing the sharecroppers working out in the fields and these little old shacks they lived in. I have a sympathy for poor people, probably because I was one of them for so many years. I've always realized that these people are just like me; they have the same loves, wants and desires. They don't have much chance for an education or anything else. Their only hope, I guess, is to get out of there and give their kids a better life than they had. I think that the poorer you are and the rougher your conditions, the more important this is to you—to see that your children don't have to do what you've had to do all your life to make a living."
—Harlan Howard

MISSISSIPPI DELTA LAND
by Harlan Howard

Mississippi Delta Land
You robbed me of my youth
And all you gave back was a one-room shack
And a mind that learned the truth
There ain't no future for a man
That works but never owns the land
But now these old hard-working hands
Is leaving for Chicago in the morning.

Mississippi Delta Land
Your riches ain't for me
These kids of mine and me's gonna find
A better place to be
Lord, I hate to leave that old mule behind
Me and him is two of a kind
But he's Mr. Johnson's, not mine
And I'm leaving for Chicago in the morning.

Mississippi Delta Land
My daddy and his daddy, too
Plowed your soil, and for all their toil
They never owned an inch of you
These kids of mine are goin' to school
I may be dumb, but I've learned one rule
The rich is smart and the poor is a fool
And I'm leaving for Chicago in the morning.

"His was a familiar figure in and around 'the yards.' He was known to be the son of a section-foreman on the Mobile & Ohio Railroad: Aaron W. Rodgers' boy—the grinning, hard-working blacks who took Aaron Rodgers' orders made his small son laugh—often. Though small he was white. So, even when they bade him 'bring that water 'round' they were deferential. During the noon dinner-rests, they taught him to plunk melody from banjo and guitar. They taught him darkey songs, moaning chants and crooning lullabies."

—Mrs. Carrie Rodgers
(from *My Husband, Jimmie Rodgers*)

MULE SKINNER BLUES

by Jimmie Rodgers and George Vaughn

Good morning, Captain
Good morning, Shine
Do you need another mule skinner
Out on your new mud line?

I like to work
I'm rolling all the time
I can carve my initials
On a mule's behind.

Hey, little water boy
Bring that water 'round
If you don't like your job
Set that water bucket down.

Workin' on the good road
A dollar and a half a day
My good gal's waitin' on a Saturday night
Just to draw my pay.

I'm goin' to town, honey
What you want me to bring you back?
Bring a pint of booze
And a John B. Stetson hat.

I smell your bread a-burnin'
Turn your damper down
If you ain't got a damper, good gal
Turn your bread around.

"I first heard a version of this song in about 1939 from Texas Ruby. It was on a bus going back to Cincinnati where we were both working at the Boone County Jamboree. I wrote the verse about Harlan and Hazard, which are coal towns in East Kentucky, and a lot of people think I'm from around there. It seems I've spent most of my life telling people I'm from the other end of the state."

—Merle Travis

"Merle Travis' pulsating 'Nine Pound Hammer' has become the standard hammer song in recent country music and bluegrass repertories. The fragment he learned in 1939 was itself part of a long complex originally used by black workers in the post–Civil War South. Tunnel men, railroad right-of-way laborers (tie tampers, track liners, spike drivers), mule-skinners, wheelbarrow haulers, and road builders all developed functional chants to pace their work and husband their strength. In time, various 'hammer' and 'roll' phrases and melodies coalesced into the folksong heard by Travis and extended by him to the coal mining industry."

—Archie Green,
John Edwards Memorial Foundation

NINE POUND HAMMER
by Merle Travis

This nine pound hammer is a little too heavy
For my size, honey, for my size
I'm a-goin' on the mountain, gonna see my baby
But I ain't comin' back, oh, well, I ain't comin' back.

Roll on, buddy, don't you roll so slow
How can I roll when the wheels won't go?
Roll on, buddy, pull a load of coal
How can I pull when the wheels won't go?

It's a long way to Harlan, it's a long way to Hazard
Just to get a little brew, just to get a little brew
When I'm long gone, you can make my tombstone
Out of number nine coal, out of number nine coal.

"I used to work in Florida for the railroad. I had a foreman who stood over me every minute. His name was Frank Oney. In this song I more or less described him and added a few things like retirement. It was one of the few times I had written for a specific artist. I thought Johnny Cash needed a song about a boss standing over a working man and so forth, and the only boss I could think about that I had ever had like that was Frank Oney."

—Jerry Chesnut

ONEY

by Jerry Chesnut

Recitation:

I dedicate this song to the working man, for every man that puts in eight or ten hard hours a day of working toil and sweat he's always got somebody looking down his neck, trying to get more out of him than he really oughta have to put in.

After twenty-nine long years of working
In this shop with Oney standing over me
Today when that old whistle blows
I'll check in all my gear and I'll retire
The superintendent just dropped by and said
They'd planned my little get-together
Then he said I'd never made it
If old Oney hadn't held me to the fire.

I've seen him in my dreams at night
And woke up in the morning feeling tired
And old Oney don't remember when I came here
How he tried to get me fired
With his folded hands behind him
Every morning Oney waited at the gate
Where he'd rant and rave like I committed murder
Clocking in five minutes late.

But today they'll gather round me
Like I've seen 'em do when any man retires
Then old Oney's gonna tell me
From now on I'm free to do what I desire
He'll present me with that little old gold watch
They give a man at times like this
But there's one thing he's not counting on
Today's the day I give old Oney his.

I've been workin', buildin' muscles
Oney's just been standing 'round a-gettin' soft
And today about four-thirty
I'll make up for every good night's sleep I've lost
When I'm gone I'll be remembered
As the workin' man who put his point across
With a right hand full of knuckles
'Cause today I show old Oney who's the boss.

Mmmm, what time is it? Four thirty? Hey Oney! Oney! Ha ha ha ha!

ROUGHNECK BLUES

"The roughneck has been providing the oil industry with the same hard work, determination and color that the cowboy contributed to the settling of the old West. He works long, hard hours under uncomfortable and dangerous conditions, and plays as hard as he works. Instead of riding a horse, he rides a crewboat or helicopter, since more and more drilling for oil is done offshore. Instead of rounding up cattle, he handles drill pipe and mud. He is too important in the development of the America we know not to be written and sung about. In 'Roughneck Blues,' I've tried to tell his story.

—Bob Terry

ROUGHNECK BLUES

by Bob Terry

Ten days out and four days in
And then I'm out ten days again
Four days ain't enough to lose
These low-down roughneck blues.

I'd like to quit, but I don't know how
I guess my blood is crude oil now
I guess I'm never gonna lose
These low-down roughneck blues.

On at midnight, off at noon
My four days off can't come too soon
Make good money, spend it all
When I go on a ball.

Ten days out and four days in
And then I'm out ten days again
Four days ain't enough to lose
The low-down roughneck blues.

I told our driller yesterday
I'm going home, and home I'll stay
But he knows just as well as me
In four days, here I'll be.

SIX DAYS ON THE ROAD

"At the time we wrote this song, we were driving a truck for Robbins Floor Products in Tuscumbia, Alabama, running the East Coast into the Pittsburgh area and down the Eastern Seaboard, just like the song says. We were gone six days almost every week. We'd leave out of here on Sunday and get back on Friday or Saturday, and we were actually on the road six days. We had gone to Pittsburgh this particular trip, and one of us said, 'This would make a good title for a song: 'Six Days On The Road.' So we wrote it riding down that day. The biggest part of the song is actual fact. The part where 'I've got ten forward gears and a Georgia overdrive,' for example: We were in the State of Alabama coming down Highway 67 into Decatur, and there's a long mountain there. We fell off this hill, and knocked it out of gear—that's 'Georgia overdrive'—you get going as fast as you can and you want to go a little faster. A 'Jimmy and a White' is trucker talk for a GMC and a White tractor, and the 'ICC,' of course, is the Interstate Commerce Commission that checks on truck weights. It all stems from the run that we had. We were musicians at the time, working weekends in a little club when we could. The only thing that was fictitious in the song, I guess, was the line: 'I could have a lot of women, but I'm not like some of the guys.' " —Earl Greene

SIX DAYS ON THE ROAD
by Earl Greene and Carl Montgomery

Well, I pulled out of Pittsburgh, a-rollin' down that Eastern Seaboard
I got my diesel wound up, and she's a-runnin' like never before

There's a speed zone ahead, well alright
I don't see a cop in sight
Six days on the road, and I'm gonna make it home tonight.

I got me ten forward gears and a Georgia overdrive
I'm taking little white pills, and my eyes are open wide
I just passed a Jimmy and a White
I've been passing everything in sight
Six days on the road, and I'm gonna make it home tonight.

Well, it seems like a month since I kissed my baby goodbye
I could have a lot of women, but I'm not like some of the guys
I could find one to hold me tight
But I could never make believe it's alright
Six days on the road, and I'm gonna make it home tonight.

The ICC is a-checkin' on down the line
I'm a little overweight, and my log book's way behind
But nothin' bothers me tonight
I can dodge all the scales, alright
Six days on the road, and I'm gonna make it home tonight.

Well, my rig's a little old, but that don't mean she's slow
There's a flame from the stack, and that smoke's a-blowin' black as coal
My home town's a-comin' in sight
If you think I'm happy, you're right
Six days on the road, and I'm gonna make it home tonight.

SIXTEEN TONS

"I had to do an album at Capitol Records, and Cliffie Stone said, 'Do a folksong album.' I said, 'Well, Burl Ives has sung all the folksongs,' and he said, 'Write some.' So that's how I came to write 'Sixteen Tons'—because I had to. There was an old saying around the coal mines in the Depression days. Somebody'd say, 'How you doing?' And he'd say, 'Well, alright, I guess. I can't afford to die, because I owe my soul to the company store.' I just wrote around that." —Merle Travis

SIXTEEN TONS

by Merle Travis

Some people say a man is made out of mud
A poor man's made out of muscle and blood
Muscle and blood and skin and bones
A mind that's weak and a back that's strong.

You load sixteen tons, what do you get?
Another day older and deeper in debt
Saint Peter, don't you call me, 'cause I can't go
I owe my soul to the company store.

I was born one mornin' when the sun didn't shine
I picked up my shovel and I walked to the mine
I loaded sixteen tons of number nine coal
And the straw boss said, "Well bless my soul."

I was born one morning, it was drizzling rain
Fightin' and trouble are my middle name
I was raised in a canebrake by an old mama lion
Can't no high-toned woman make me walk the line.

If you see me comin', better step aside
A lot of men didn't, a lot of men died
One fist of iron, the other of steel
If the right one don't get you, then the left one will.

THESE HANDS

"I wrote 'These Hands' while in the Army in 1955, stationed in El Paso, Texas. One night I drew guard duty, and during my shift, I looked at the wasteland that is West Texas and New Mexico, and a song from the second World War, 'This Is Worth Fighting For,' kept running through my mind. Looking at the barren country around me, my thoughts were, 'Is *this* worth fighting for?' There is a line in that song to the effect, 'Didn't I build that cabin, didn't I raise that corn?' and the idea that these tasks,

along with any other, are done with a man's hands, prompted the song. I didn't plan for it to be a religious or even an inspirational song, but until Johnny Cash put it in its proper perspective, a working man's song, this is how most people took it."
—Eddie Noack

THESE HANDS
by Eddie Noack

These hands ain't the hands of a gentleman
These hands are calloused and old
These hands raised a family; these hands raised a home
Now these hands raise to praise the Lord.

These hands won the heart of my loved one
And with hers they were never alone
If these hands filled their task, then what more could one ask?
For these fingers have worked to the bone.

Now don't try to judge me by what you'd like to be
For my life ain't been much success
While some people have power, but still they grieve
While these hands brought me happiness.

Now I'm tired and I'm old and I ain't got much gold
Maybe things ain't been all that I planned
God above hear my plea, when it's time to judge me
Take a look at these hard-workin' hands.

TRUCK DRIVER'S BLUES

"Late at night, returning from playing dances around the country, we would stop at little roadside cafes. They were popular with the truck drivers, and I noticed that when they came in, they headed for the juke box and put a nickel in or so. I realized that no one had ever written a song about them, and that such a song would have a ready-made audience. So I wrote the first truck drivers song, and it became the top-selling country song of 1939, because truck drivers demanded it all over the nation."
—Ted Daffan

TRUCK DRIVER'S BLUES

by Ted Daffan

Feelin' tired and weary, from my head down to my shoes
Feelin' tired and weary, from my head down to my shoes
Got a low-down feelin', truck driver's blues.

Keep them wheels a-rollin', I ain't got no time to lose
Keep them wheels a-rollin', I ain't got no time to lose
Got a low-down feelin', truck driver's blues.

Ride, ride, ride on in to town
There's a honky-tonk gal a-waitin'
I've got troubles to drown.

Never did have nothin', I got nothin' much to lose
Never did have nothin', I got nothin' much to lose
Got a low-down feelin', truck driver's blues.

WEAVEROOM BLUES

"My Dad wrote this song because he worked in a cotton mill in his home town of Darlington, South Carolina. He worked in the weaveroom. That's a real noisy, dreary place and it's a hard way to make a living. He went to work in this mill when he was twelve years old, and he worked there for about six years . . . and of course they treated kids like slaves. It was during those Hoover days. I guess he had the blues when he wrote that song." —Reverend Dorsey Dixon, Jr.

WEAVEROOM BLUES

by Dorsey Dixon and W. E. Mainer

Working in a weaveroom, fighting for my life
Trying to make a living for my kiddies and my wife
Some are needing clothing, and some are needing shoes
But I'm getting nothing but them weaveroom blues.

I got the blues, I got the blues
I got them awful weaveroom blues.

With your looms a-slamming, shuttles bouncing on the floor
And when you flag your fixer, you can see that he is sore
I'm trying to make a living, but I'm thinking I will lose
For I'm going crazy with them weaveroom blues.

The harness eyes are breaking with the doubles coming through
The devil's in your alley, and he's coming after you
Our hearts are aching, let us take a little booze
For we're going crazy with them weaveroom blues.

Slam-outs, break-outs, knot-ups by the score,
Cloth all rolled back and piled up in the floor
The bats are running ends, the strings are hanging to our shoes
I'm simply dying with them weaveroom blues.

13 | Cowboy Songs

Out on the Texas Plains

As Merle Travis says, "Country and western, they're all cousins—double first cousins."

One may wonder what a selection of modern cowboy songs is doing in an anthology of country lyrics, particularly when the cowboy ballad has been collected, studied, explained, and anthologized at least since 1908, when Nathan Howard ("Jack") Thorp published his *Songs of the Cowboy,* one of the first American folk collections of any kind.

Few of the "western" songs that comprise a large share of country music literature, however, are authentic relics of that celebrated quarter-century following the end of the Civil War when the great cattle drives took place. Many songs which entered the popular cowboy repertory were based on folksongs and popular songs of the last century, but perhaps too much has been made of singing "on nightherd." Song was an effective means of quieting the cattle at night and punctuating the lonely watches on a cattle drive north, but the genuine cowboy of the seventies and eighties probably sang popular songs or ditties more often than ballads. Many "traditional" cowboy ballads, in fact, first appeared as poems in newspapers of those days and were set to popular or home-made tunes.

The songs that follow are, instead, distinctly part of country music, and the similarities between the two styles outweigh what are largely regional differences. They enjoy the same audiences, are based on the same sentiments and values, and often were written and recorded by the same composers and artists. Several are the works of authentic cow-hands, but most fall well within the definition of commercial country music.

An examination of the lyrics of the two forms supports Travis's comment; more than "double first cousins," they are almost identical twins. The roots of western music are somewhat different from those of traditional hillbilly songs, borrowing more heavily on Mexican, Cajun, jazz, and blues experiences than on those of the Southeast, but from the earliest times, the two styles have traded heavily on each other.

Since the image of the cowboy as a strong, self-reliant "man's man" was so much more attractive than that of the ragged, barefoot hillbilly, country musicians from the earliest days adopted a western mystique which included fancy dress, cowboy names, posturing, and many songs.

The cowboy image—the tailored shirt, bright colors, ten-gallon hat and high-heeled boots—was more appealing to the country singer than the costume of the mountaineer or farmer. Many singers who seldom sang cowboy songs gave themselves titles like The Cherokee Cowboy or The Yodeling Ranger, while groups like The Bronco Busters and The Arizona Wranglers sprang up throughout the South and Southwest. "Tex," "Hank," "Hap," and "Slim" became common nicknames, whether a singer was from Macon, Georgia, or Mason City, Iowa.

But this was nothing new.

The romance of the West was firmly implanted in the American consciousness by the turn of the century, and the commercial exploitation of the cowboy image dates back at least to 1883, when Buffalo Bill Cody launched the first of his series of Wild West Shows. The works of Bret Harte and novels like Owen Wister's *The Virginian* and Zane Grey's *Riders of the Purple Sage* did much to popularize the cowhand, and the first western film in recognizable form, *The Great Train Robbery,* was produced in 1903. Nor was the cowboy ignored by the writers of popular song; one of the great Tin Pan Alley hits of 1902 was "Ragtime Cowboy Joe" by Grant Clarke and Lewis Muir.

So it is understandable that, when commercial country music originated in the early twenties, it revealed a western influence. Not only were traditional cowboy songs included in the early country repertory, some of the performers themselves had been working range hands. Men like Charles Nabell, Carl T. Sprague, Goebel Reeves, and Jules Verne Allen not only had authentic western origins (Allen began working cattle in Texas at the age of ten), much of their repertories consisted of authentic cowboy songs. The first cowboy recording was made in 1924 by Nabell and released in 1925, slightly more than a year after the first hillbilly recording. Sprague's 1925 recording of "The Work's All Done This Fall" probably was the first western hit. Other early traditional songs they recorded included "Cow Trail To Mexico," "Zebra Dun," "The Old Chisholm Trail," and "Get Along Little Dogies." Many of these songs remain familiar favorites today.

Even in this period little distinction was made between "hillbilly" and "western" record releases. To the recording executives of the Northeast, both styles were recognized as being rural in origin and appeal

—and with good reason, for many of the settlers of the western range of the southern states (Texas, Oklahoma, and Louisiana) originated in the Southeast and brought with them their values and religion as well as their music. True, these were modified by outside influences unique to the Southwest, but from the beginning, western music preserved a strong and recognizable country strain.

Much of the impact of the strong western theme in country songs during the thirties must be attributed to Jimmie Rodgers. Though there are no Rodgers songs in this chapter, in fact, there were few cowboy songs in his repertory—the Blue Yodler from Meridian, Mississippi, adopted the state of Texas as well as a western flair that we can trace in the country songs of today. Rodgers's yodel and the sentiment of his songs helped to reinforce the western image both in the Southwest and in the Southeast.

Meanwhile, a parallel movement drawing on the same romantic cowboy image was growing up in California with the almost accidental incorporation of cowboy songs into the already well-established action western film. Ken Maynard, the first "singing cowboy" of the movies, introduced four songs in a film called *Songs of the Saddle* in 1930. Maynard's voice was so unremarkable, however, that the film's musical element caused little stir. It was not until 1934, when Gene Autry, a radio cowboy singing star, who copied Rodgers's style in his early years, was cast in a minor role in a Maynard film, *In Old Santa Fe,* that the formula caught on. So great was the audience response to Autry's appearance that Republic styled an entirely new kind of film around him, beginning in 1935 with *Tumbling Tumbleweeds.* Autry teamed up with Smiley Burnett, who provided hillbilly comedy, and the Sons of the Pioneers for choral background and riding companions. He became the most popular cowboy singing star ever and was followed by a long list of country performers, including Merle Travis, Johnny Bond, Roy Rogers, Tex Ritter, and Jimmy Wakely, who balanced six-guns with guitars.

Many performers whose roots were in the Southeast made the pilgrimage to California, even if their only screen role was to sit around a campfire and strum a guitar.

"To work a picture out there was nothing more than working a recording session in Nashville," Travis said. "The phone would ring and they'd say, 'You want to do a picture? Get yourself together three guys that can ride.' "

Johnny Bond, who appeared in about fifty movies, most of them westerns, said that movies and radio were most important in sustaining the cowboy appeal. "The main popularity of the trend sustained itself through the thirties and forties through movies and radio," Bond writes, "but not necessarily records. In 1937 or 1938, Don Law of Columbia Records turned down our Cowboy Trio, explaining that cowboy songs didn't sell and urging us to lean towards honky tonk.

"Cowboys were popular on radio and screen but not on records! That was our rude awakening."

Not only did Tin Pan Alley composers add cowboy songs to their copyright lists, but popular performers often added them to their repertories as program material. "The Last Roundup" was introduced by Joe Morrison at New York's Paramount Theater in 1933, and James Melton was instrumental in making "Carry Me Back To The Lone Prairie" a national favorite.

Without these commercial incentives and the newly emerging media of radio and the movies, many of the songs we revere would never have been written, and many more older ones would have been lost.

Despite the hardiness of songs like "Chisholm Trail" and "Sam Bass," whose origins stubbornly resist investigation, we can say that the western song with its sentimentalized cowboy is a product of not too long ago.

Significantly, the popularity of the cowboy song largely declined with the decline of the singing western movie and the emergence of the so-called adult western in the early fifties. ("High Noon," perhaps the last cowboy song to attain national popularity, was not an integral part of the film, but was written by popular writers Ned Washington and Dimitri Tiomkin and sung by Tex Ritter on the soundtrack.)

The songs that follow are a selection of the popular cowboy songs from that particular era. They are still heard occasionally today, but very few new ones are being written. Some of them were written from actual experience, some to fill the needs of the popular media, but all carry with them an air of authenticity that brings alive the "Old West."

BACK IN THE SADDLE AGAIN

"I received a phone call from my producer at RKO Studios about 5:00 A.M. with news that we could use another song if I could write one before 7:00 A.M., the time of our call to pre-record the music for our current picture. When I hung up, my wife Kay said, 'What was that all about?' I replied, 'I'm back in the saddle again; they need another song.' Then she said, 'You already have the title, "Back In The Saddle Again."' I thanked her and started the song. Within the hour I had completed one verse and the tune. As I left I said, 'I'll put in a Whoopie-ti-yi-yay or something when I get to the studio.' And that is how the song was born. The song reached its popularity through the good offices of my co-writer Gene Autry, who recorded it on Columbia Records. It became his theme song. Without him, it would have been just another song." —Ray Whitley

BACK IN THE SADDLE AGAIN
by Ray Whitley and Gene Autry

I'm back in the saddle again
Out where a friend is a friend
Where the longhorn cattle feed
On the lowly jimson weed
Back in the saddle again.

I'm ridin' the range once more
Totin' my old forty-four
Where you sleep out every night
And the only law is right
Back in the saddle again.

Whoopie-ti-yi-yo, rockin' to and fro
Back in the saddle again
Whoopie-ti-yi-yay, I'm on my way
Back in the saddle again.

BLOOD ON THE SADDLE

"At a rodeo in Florence, Arizona, some time in the fall of 1926, a young bronc rider by the name of Orville Fisher from some place in Oregon was killed by a bucking horse. This song came out of the memory of it. He was riding in the saddle of a brown gelding named Bolshevik when the horse turned a somersault, landing on him and killing him instantly. The whole thing was so tragic and gruesome that the memory of it stayed with me for a long time. The melody came out of my head, as I never knew one note from another, although I did sing some and play chords on the guitar. I started singing it about 1927 at dude ranches and resorts in several states in the West. In 1929, I went to Hollywood to visit George 'Big Boy' Gillespie, a friend who was working in the movies, and he and I got a chance to sing some songs on the radio. Robert Bruce, a producer of 'one-reelers,' heard me sing 'Blood On The Saddle' over the air and asked me to sing it in a short subject called *Cow Camp Ballads,* which was released through Paramount. About a year later, I was in New York, trying to ride broncs at the Madison Square Garden rodeo, but

I didn't find many I could ride. I was better known as a dude wrangler than a rodeo hand. After the rodeo closed, its director Alan Brannon introduced me to Cheryl Crawford who was casting a new Lynn Riggs play for the Theatre Guild called *Green Grow the Lilacs.* I got a part singing 'Blood On The Saddle' on the edge of the stage in what they call the 'interlude.' The play ran 23 weeks in all and played as far west as St. Louis, Chicago and Minneapolis. It was then that I met Tex Ritter and formed a long and lasting friendship with him."

—Everett Cheetham

BLOOD ON THE SADDLE

by Everett Cheetham

There was blood on the saddle and blood all around
And a great big puddle of blood on the ground
A cowboy lay in it, all covered with gore
And he never will ride any broncos no more.

Oh, pity the cowboy, all bloody and red
For the bronco fell on him and mashed in his head
There was blood on the saddle and blood all around
And a great big puddle of blood on the ground.

CARRY ME BACK TO THE LONE PRAIRIE

"This song was written because Carson disputed the old song, 'Bury Me Not On The Lone Prairie.' He could not conceive that a cowboy would want to be buried anywhere but on the prairie. James Melton was directly responsible for starting it off to be a big number. He sang it literally hundreds of times in his programs and concert tours."

—Catherine A. (Mrs. Carson) Robison

CARRY ME BACK TO THE LONE PRAIRIE

by Carson Robison

Oh, carry me back to the lone prairie
Where the coyotes howl and the wind blows free
And when I die, you can bury me
'Neath the western skies on the lone prairie.

I'm a roving cowboy far away from home
Far from the prairie where I used to roam
Where the dogies wander and the wind blows free
Though my heart is yonder on the lone prairie.

CATTLE CALL

"My late husband was a real cowboy, he really rode the range, and at one time he worked for the King Ranch. This is the way I remember him telling how he wrote the song 'Cattle Call': 'I was sitting in the office building on the eleventh floor of the Pickwick Hotel in Kansas City, Missouri, waiting to do a broadcast on KMBC. Snow began falling. Small flakes at first, then big ones, so big they blotted out my view of the buildings through the window. Now, I grew up on a ranch, and I used to do a lot of cattle feeding, and in winter I could never help feeling sorry for the dumb animals out in the wet and cold. Sitting there in the hotel, watching the snow, my sympathy went out to cattle everywhere, and I just wished I could call them all around me and break some corn over a wagon wheel and feed them. That's when the words, "cattle call," came to my mind. I picked up my guitar, and in thirty minutes I had wrote the music and four verses to the song.' " —Maude J. (Mrs. Tex) Owens

CATTLE CALL
by Tex Owens

The cattle are prowlin' and coyotes are howlin'
Way out where the dogies bawl
Where spurs are a-jinglin', a cowboy is singin'
This lonesome cattle call.

Woo-hoo woo-hoo hoo hoo
Woo-hoo woo-hoo hoo hoo
Woo-hoo hoo woo-hoo hoo hoo
Woo-hoo hoo hoo hoo

He rides in the sun, till his day's work is done
And he rounds up the cattle each fall
Woo-hoo hoo woo-hoo hoo hoo
Singin' his cattle call.

For hours he will ride on the range far and wide
When the night wind blows up a squall
His heart is a feather in all kinds of weather
He sings his cattle call.

Woo-hoo woo-hoo hoo hoo
Woo-hoo woo-hoo hoo hoo
Woo-hoo hoo woo-hoo hoo hoo
Woo-hoo hoo hoo hoo
He's brown as a berry from ridin' the prairie
And sings with an ol' western drawl
Woo-hoo hoo woo-hoo hoo hoo
Singin' his cattle call.

CIMARRON

"In 1938, the Jimmy Wakely Trio, of which I was a member, was broadcasting 'live' on Radio Station WKY, Oklahoma City. As was our custom, we always opened our shows with a fast, rollicking, upbeat type of western song, since it was mostly western material that we featured. As time passed, we soon tired of much of the limited selections at our disposal, and the opinion was expressed that we sorely needed a new 'opener.' I had recently viewed the re-release of the movie *Cimarron,* starring Richard Dix and Irene Dunne, in which I noted the absence of a featured number using the popular title. We were well familiar with the Cimarron River which runs through the northern part of Oklahoma, having crossed it many times in our travels. There was a county by that same name as well as several towns throughout the area. With all this in mind, I sat myself down, guitar in hand, with the express purpose of turning out a song which we could use on our shows. In the days of live radio, 'Cimarron' was used by many acts as their opening and closing theme."

—Johnny Bond

CIMARRON (ROLL ON)

by Johnny Bond

Cimarron, roll on
To my lonely song
Carry me away
From the skies of gray
Tho' I'm feelin' blue
I'll roll on with you
To the ocean blue
Cimarron, roll on.

COOL WATER

"The actual story of 'Cool Water' was inspired by the Arizona desert after I came there from the backwoods of Canada. The impact of transition between the northern climate and the desert made me fall in love with the desert. I had made up my mind that I wanted to depict the picture of a mirage in song, and 'Cool Water' was the outcome. The lyrics of 'Cool Water' are my feelings of the desert in words."

—Bob Nolan

COOL WATER

by Bob Nolan

All day I've faced a barren waste
Without the taste of water, cool water
Old Dan and I with throats burnt dry
And souls that cry for water, cool water.

Keep a-movin', Dan, don't you listen to him, Dan
He's a devil, not a man, and he spreads the burning sand with water
Oh Dan, can you see that big, green tree
Where the water's running free and it's waiting there for you and me
Cool, clear water.

The nights are cool and I'm a fool
Each star's a pool of water, cool water
But with the dawn, I'll wake and yawn
And carry on to water, cool water.

The shadows sway and seem to say
"Tonight we pray for water, cool water
And way up there, He'll hear our prayer
And show us where there's water, cool, clear water."

Dan's feet are sore, he's yearning for
Just one thing more than water, cool water
Like me, I guess, he'd like to rest
Where there's no quest for water, cool, clear water.

DUSTY SKIES

"My idea for 'Dusty Skies' came from an old newspaper clipping that I found among some old letters and pictures belonging to my Grandmother Walker. It was a story telling of the terrible hardships the dust storms had brought to the people, the cattle and the land. A story that filled my eyes with tears and my heart with such an ache that the only way I could get it out was to write it out. Not too long afterward, Bob Wills recorded it, Tommy Duncan sang it, and it became my first country and western hit. Bob Wills and the Texas Playboys also sang it in a Columbia motion picture of the same title." —Cindy Walker

DUSTY SKIES
by Cindy Walker

Dusty skies, I can't see nothin' in sight
Good old Dan, you'll have to guide me right
For if we lose our way, the cattle will stray
And we'll lose them all tonight.

With all of the grass and water gone
We'll have to keep the cattle movin' on.

Sand blowin', I just can't breathe in this air
Thought it would soon be clear and fair
But the dust storms played hell with land and folks as well
I've got to be moving somewhere.

I hate to leave the old ranch so bare
But I've got to be movin' somewhere.

So get along dogies, we're moving off of this range
I never thought as how I'd make the change
But the blue skies have failed, we're on our last trail
Underneath these dusty skies.

These ain't tears in my eyes
Just sand from these dusty skies.

I WANT TO BE A COWBOY'S SWEETHEART

"This song was written in 1934 while I was on a tour with Gene Autry on a show called 'The WLS Round-Up' out of Chicago, Illinois. My first song on the WLS National Barn Dance was 'Texas Plains.' I had changed the name of 'Texas' to 'Montana,' as it was a show about different states. This set my pattern and style with the vast WLS audience. After singing the song so many times in all my appearances, I became tired of it. On the round-up show was an act called Mac and Bob. I fell in love with their manager, Paul E. Rose, whom I later married, and am still married to him. He was away from the show for several days and I was a love-sick lonely 'cowgirl.' During a show somewhere in Illinois in my dressing room, I wrote this song. The title was first suggested by Joe Franks, who is now in the Hall of Fame in Nashville, Tennessee. I patterned the song after 'Texas Plains.' I introduced the song on the Barn Dance and it became an instant hit. It was recorded in New York, April, 1935, and I became the first Country and Western girl singer to sell a million records."

—Patsy Montana

I WANT TO BE A COWBOY'S SWEETHEART
by Patsy Montana

I want to be a cowboy's sweetheart
I want to learn to rope and to ride
I want to ride o'er the plains and the desert
Out west of the great divide
I want to hear the coyotes howling
As the sun sinks in the west
I want to be a cowboy's sweetheart
That's the life I love best.

I want to ride Old Paint a-goin' at a run
I want to feel the wind in my face
A thousand miles from all this city life
Goin' a cowhand's pace
I want to pillow my head near the sleeping herd
While the moon shines down from above
I want to play my guitar and yodel
Oh, that's the life that I love.

THE LAST ROUNDUP

" 'Roundup' probably was inspired by a visit to Texas on a ranch during roundup time, according to Nat Vincent who had been a collaborator on one of my father's songs. Quite often a cowboy would be trampled to death if he fell from his horse during a roundup, and my father and Nat had witnessed this happening, standing on a knoll overlooking the plains. Nat said many times the older cowboys going into a roundup would speak of this as perhaps their last roundup, meaning they feared they might not live to the next one."

—Lee Hill Taylor

THE LAST ROUNDUP
by Billy Hill

I'm headin' for the last roundup
Gonna saddle Old Paint for the last time and ride

So long, old pal, it's time your tears were dried
I'm headin' for the last roundup.

Git along little dogie, git along, git along
Git along little dogie, git along
Git along little dogie, git along, git along
Git along little dogie, git along.

I'm headin' for the last roundup
To the far away ranch to the Boss in the sky
Where the strays are counted and branded, there go I
I'm headin' for the last roundup.

I'm headin' for the last roundup
There'll be Buffalo Bill with his long snow white hair
There'll be old Kit Carson and Custer waitin' there
A-ridin' in the last roundup.

I'm headin' for the last roundup
Gonna saddle Old Paint for the last time and ride
So long, old pal, it's time your tears were dried
I'm headin' for the last roundup.

OKLAHOMA HILLS

"Leon (Jack) and I left Oklahoma when we were kids and went to Texas. He loved horses and rode rodeo until he was thrown from a horse and hurt his back. He and Woody teamed up and had a radio show together over KFVD in Los Angeles. In fact I think they used it as their theme song. Leon got a recording contract with Capitol Records and recorded it. He was overseas when it was published and released, and when he came back, Woody sued him for the money he had received. Woody let him know that the money didn't mean anything to him; he just wanted to get his break. They signed a contract, and Leon didn't get any more money until Woody had gotten as much as he did. There is a controversy over who wrote this song, and I really don't know why there should be. It has always been my impression that Woody wrote the words and Leon wrote the music."

—Wava Guthrie Blake

OKLAHOMA HILLS

by Woody and Jack Guthrie

Many months have come and gone since I wandered from my home
In those Oklahoma hills where I was born
Many a page of life has turned, many a lesson I have learned
Yet I feel like in those hills I still belong.

'Way down yonder in the Indian nation
I rode my pony on the reservation
In those Oklahoma hills where I was born
'Way down yonder in the Indian nation
A cowboy's life is my occupation
In those Oklahoma hills where I was born.

But as I sit here today
Many miles I am away
From the place I rode my pony through the draw
Where the oaken black jack trees
Kiss the playful prairie breeze
In those Oklahoma hills where I was born.

As I turn life a page
To the land of the great Osage
To those Oklahoma hills where I was born
Where the black oil rosin flows
And the snow white cotton grows
In those Oklahoma hills where I was born.

THE STRAWBERRY ROAN

"Curley Fletcher was a very famous rodeo rider who also wrote poems, some of which were published in local newspapers in the towns he appeared in. When he broke both arms and legs and could no longer ride, he brought us this poem and offered to sell it for two hundred dollars. I told him I would buy it, but I would also give him credit and a full share of royalties if it ever sold as a song. I broke the poem up into stanzas and wrote a refrain for each one. It was used first in the Ken Maynard movie, *Strawberry Roan,* made by Republic Pictures, and later on by Gene Autry in a Columbia picture using the same title." —Nat Vincent

THE STRAWBERRY ROAN

by Nat Vincent, Curley Fletcher, and Fred Howard

Let me tell you a tale, a good one I own
Of a bucking old bronc, a strawberry roan
I was hanging 'round town, not earning a dime
Being out of a job, just a-spending my time
When a stranger steps up, and he says, "I suppose
You're a bronc-bustin' man from the looks of your clothes."
So I says, "Guess you're right, there's none I can't tame
If it's ridin' wild ponies, that's my middle name."

Oh that strawberry roan, oh that strawberry roan
He says he's a cayuse that's never been rode
The guy that gets on him is bound to be throwed
Throwed off this strawberry roan.

So I gets all het up and asks what he pays
If I rides this old nag a couple of days
Then he offers me ten, says I, "I'm your man
For the bronc never lived yet that I couldn't fan."
So he says, "Come on, Bud, I will give you a chance."
In his buckboard he hops and rides to his ranch
Until morning we stayed, then right after chuck
We go out to see how this old outlaw could buck.

Oh that strawberry roan, oh that strawberry roan
I'll break him to saddle or break my own dome
I'll ride him until he lies down with a groan
Bring on your strawberry roan.

In the corral I looks, and there, all alone
Is this sleepy old nag, this strawberry roan
He's got spavined old legs and small pigeon toes
And a pair of pig eyes and a long Roman nose
He's got little pin ears, they're all split at the tips
In the middle he's lean, but wide at the hips
So I puts on my spurs and coils up my twine
And I says to the stranger, "That ten-spot is mine."

Oh that strawberry roan, oh that strawberry roan
I'll ride him until he lies down with a groan
There's nary a bronco I couldn't bring home
Bring on your strawberry roan.

Then I puts on the blinds, it sure was a fight
Then my saddle comes next; I screws it down tight
Then I piles on his back, and well, I knew then
If I rides this old pony, I'll sure earn my ten
For he bowed his old neck, and he leaped from the ground
Twenty circles he made before he came down
He's the worst buckin' bronc I've seen on the range
He can turn on a nickel and give you some change.

Oh that strawberry roan, oh that strawberry roan
He went toward the East, then came down toward the West
To stay in his middle I'm doing my best
On that old strawberry roan.

There's no foolin', I'll say, this pony can step
But I'm still sittin' tight and earning a rep
When my stirrups I lose, and also my hat
And I starts pullin' leather, as blind as a bat
And he makes one more jump; he is headed up high
Leaves me settin' on air way up in the sky
Guess I turned over twice and comes back to earth
And I starts into cussin' the day of his birth.

Oh that strawberry roan, oh that strawberry roan
That sun-fishin' critter's worth leavin' alone
There's nary a buster from Texas to Nome
Could ride that strawberry roan.

TAKE ME BACK TO MY BOOTS AND SADDLE

"At the time we wrote this song, Billy Hill had had a great success with 'The Last Roundup,' and we were trying to write western songs because they were so popular. We took 'Boots' to several publishers before it was accepted. John Charles Thomas was the first to record it around 1935."
—Leonard Whitcup

TAKE ME BACK TO MY BOOTS AND SADDLE

by Leonard Whitcup, Walter G. Samuels, and Teddy Powell

Take me back to my boots and saddle
Oooooooooh
Let me see that general store
Let me ride the range once more
Give me my boots and saddle.

Let me ramble along the prairie
Oooooooooh
Ropin' steers on Old Bar X
With my buddies, Slim and Tex
Give me my boots and saddle.

Got a hankerin' to be with a banjo on my knee
Strummin' a pretty western tune
There's a gal in Cherokee, and she's waitin' there for me
Waitin' beneath the Texas moon.

Take me back to my boots and saddle
Oooooooooh
Let me greet each blazin' morn
On the ranch where I was born
Give me my boots and saddle.

TEXAS PLAINS

"This is one of the first songs I ever wrote. After I got to California, I started writing it and crying my eyes out. I got so lonesome to hear coyotes at night or a wolf howl that I almost went back to Texas. It was my theme song on radio for twenty-three years."
—Stuart Hamblen (Reprinted with permission from the book *The Birth of a Song* by Stuart Hamblen)

TEXAS PLAINS

by Stuart Hamblen

I wanta drink my java from an old tin can
When the moon goes to shining high
I wanta hear the calls of the whippoorwills
I wanta hear the coyotes whine
I wanta house my saddle horse between my legs
Ridin' him out on the range
Just to kick him in the sides, just to show his step and pride
Out on the Texas plains.

Each night in my dreams, somehow it seems
I'm back where I belong
Just a country hick, way back in the sticks
Back where I belong
Because these city lights and these city ways
Are driving me insane.
Oh, I wanta go back; oh, please take me back
Back to the Texas plains.

I'm tired of subways and forty-story shacks
They're driving me insane
Oh, I wanta go back; oh, please take me back
Back to the Texas plains.

TUMBLING TUMBLEWEEDS

"I originally wrote the song about 'tumbling leaves.' During a period of time, in singing it over the radio with the Sons of the Pioneers, of which I was an original member, the listening audience would request it under the title 'Sing about the tumblin' weeds.' After many such requests, I changed the words to 'Tumbling Tumbleweeds,' changing the tune slightly to accommodate the extra syllables. The Sons of the Pioneers then had an hour on the radio every day, which prompted us to make 'Tumbling Tumbleweeds' our theme song." —Bob Nolan

TUMBLING TUMBLEWEEDS

by Bob Nolan

See them tumbling down
Pledging their love to the ground
Lonely but free I'll be found
Drifting along with the tumbling tumbleweeds.

Cares of the past are behind
Nowhere to go but I'll find
Just where the trail will wind
Drifting along with the tumbling tumbleweeds.

I know when night is gone
That a new world is born at dawn.

But I'll keep rolling along
Deep in my heart is a song
Here on the range I belong
Drifting along with the tumbling tumbleweeds.

I'm a roving cowboy, ridin' all day long
Tumbleweeds around me sing their lonely song
Nights underneath the prairie moon
I ride along and sing a tune.

I'll keep rollin' along
Deep in my heart is a song
Here on the range I belong
Drifting along with the tumbling tumbleweeds.

WHEN THE BLOOM IS ON THE SAGE

"During my vaudeville days, I played the Pantages Circuit, which included the cities of Waco, San Antonio, Houston, Fort Worth and Dallas. While I was in Fort Worth, I was invited out to see a roundup. I never saw a range or meadows with more beautiful flowers, and I got the idea of writing a song about it. In 1926, The Piggly Wiggly Trio on the Blue

Monday Jamboree broke up, and I took the tenor, Harry Morton, copyrighted the name 'Happy Chappies' and continued on that fine program. Several years later, Morton had to return to his home town, and I did a single until I ran into a very fine entertainer, Fred Howard. We blended so nicely in harmony that we soon became the idols of San Francisco. I continued to write and found that Howard could take my ideas and my titles and work them out. A big Texan wired the Blue Monday Jamboree from his hotel offering $250 if we would write a song and sing it during the program. The program director put us on at the beginning of the show and gave us a studio and a piano to see what we could come up with. Here was my chance to write that song about the roundup. Before the program was finished, we wrote a verse and chorus and called it 'When The Bloom Is On The Sage.' It took off like a cyclone."

—Nat "Bubbles" Vincent

WHEN THE BLOOM IS ON THE SAGE
by Nat Vincent and Fred Howard

For most folks, there's a spot that lives forever
Deep down within their fondest memory
Though I have been a rover, I have never
Seen any place where I would rather be.

When it's roundup time in Texas
And the bloom is on the sage
Then I long to be in Texas
Back a-ridin' on the range
Just to smell the bacon fryin'
When it's sizzlin' in the pan
Hear the breakfast horn in the early morn
Drinkin' coffee from a can.

Just a-ridin', rockin', ropin'
Poundin' leather all day long
Just a-swayin', sweatin', swearin'
Listen to a cowhand's song
How it beckons, and I reckon
I would work for any wage
To be free again, just to be again
Where the bloom is on the sage.

When it's roundup time in Texas
And the bloom is on the sage
Then I long to be in Texas
Back a-ridin' on the range

Where the purple hills are callin'
Callin' to me from afar
To come back again to the Rio Grande
And the lonely Texas star.

How I'm longin' to be livin'
Where the prairie flowers grow
I'd be willin' to start walkin'
To the land that I love so
How it beckons, and I reckon
I would work for any wage
To be free again, just to be again
Where the bloom is on the sage.

WHEN THE WORK IS DONE NEXT FALL

"This famed ballad describing the tragic death of a cowpuncher in a night-time stampede evolved from a set of verses written by D. J. O'Malley and published in the Miles City, Montana, *Stock Grower's Journal* for October 6, 1893. O'Malley, an eastern Montana cowboy for nineteen years and a prolific writer of verses about life on the open range, called his poem 'After The Roundup' and modeled it on the 1892 Charles K. Harris waltz-time song hit 'After The Ball,' whose refrain is still popular today."
—John I. White

WHEN THE WORK IS DONE NEXT FALL
by D. J. O'Malley

A group of jolly cowboys discussed their plans at ease
Said one, "I'll tell you something, boys, if you will listen, please
I am an old cowpuncher, and though here I'm dressed in rags
I used to be a tough one and take on great big jags.

I've got a home, boys, a good one you all know
Although I haven't seen it since long, long ago

But I'm going back to Dixie once more to see them all
I'm going to see my mother when the work is done next fall.

After the roundup's over and after the shipping's done
I'm going right straight home, boys, ere all my money's gone
Mother's heart is breaking, it's breaking for me, that's all,
But with God's help I'll see her when the work is done next fall."

That very night this cowboy went out to stand his guard
The weather, it was stormy and raining very hard
The cattle, they got frightened and rushed in wild stampede
The cowboy tried to head them while riding at full speed.

While riding in the darkness so loudly he did shout
Trying his best to head them and turn the herd about
His saddle horse did stumble, on him did fall
And he'll not see his mother when the work is done next fall.

The poor boy was so mangled they thought that he was dead
They picked him up so gently and laid him on his bed
He opened wide his blue eyes and looking all around
He motioned to his comrades to sit near him on the ground.

"Boys, send mother my wages, the wages I have earned
For I am afraid, boys, my last steer I have turned
I'm going to a new range, I hear my Master's call
And I'll not see my mother when the work is done next fall.

Bill, you take my saddle; and George, you take my bed
And Fred, you take my pistol, after I am dead
Think of me kindly as you gaze upon them all
And give my love to mother when the work is done next fall."

Poor Charlie was buried at sunrise, no tombstone at his head
Nothing but a little board, and this is what it said:
"Charlie died at daybreak, he died from a fall
And he'll not see his mother when the work is done next fall."

14 | Traveling Songs

I'm Movin' On

After the Civil War, the railroad penetrated the southern backwoods, crossed its rivers, strung its towns together and created new ones. Unlike the muddy roads, which were fine for going to church or market or to the next town populated by friends and relatives, the shiny steel rails went *somewhere*—somewhere important.

As they came to another town, they brought with them new jobs, new faces—and sometimes took away the old ones. They promised escape, adventure, romance, new opportunities. During hard times, they offered transportation to jobs "on down the line." And if the jobs didn't exist, at least the move gave you something to do.

Then there were the engines themselves—great, dangerous, fiercely masculine beasts on a scale no farm boy had ever dreamed of—the embodiments of purpose and direction. There were the men who tamed them, brave engineers, lonely boomers, steel-driving men. There were wrecks, hundreds of them in all parts of the country, tragic, spectacular. And finally, there were the hobos who rode them in search of work or of the Rock Candy Mountain, who created a new life-style uniquely their own.

Truly, this was the stuff of dreams and legends, and no country songwriter or singer ever missed a chance to identify with a legend. In addition to songs about trains, train wrecks, and heroic feats which, in the words of the folklorist, treat the train as an "artifact," there is a large body of songs that use it as a symbol—of restlessness, of newfound mobility, of loneliness and separation. Taken together, these songs comprise a large category of hillbilly song that has roots both in tradition and in the Tin Pan Alley of the late nineteenth and early twentieth centuries.

The list of country artists who have strongly identified with train songs is long and impressive and includes names like Jimmie Rodgers, Hank Snow, Roy Acuff, Johnny Cash, Hank Williams, and the Delmore Brothers. Spanning the fifty years of recorded country music, these men and others have managed to keep the legend of the train alive and vital, even though the railroad itself is fast passing into the realm of nostalgia. A few recent songs have seen the intrusion of the jet plane as an image, but this cool, sophisticated symbol probably never will replace the train in the hearts of Americans.

The history of railroading in this country goes back at least to 1830, when the Baltimore & Ohio first began regular runs. The train arrived slightly later in the South, but by 1840 there were short lines in Georgia and Alabama, and one road joined Wilmington, North Carolina, and Fredericksburg, Virginia. By the time of the Civil War, the South had about ten thousand miles of railroad, roughly half of what the North could boast, but by 1865 most of it was destroyed or beyond repair. A construction boom followed, however, and by the 1890s the South had almost forty thousand miles of track, most of it quite new.

This, too, was the period that saw the beginning of the great tradition of railroad ballads that included black work songs like "John Henry" and a rash of composed numbers. Railroad songs figured prominently in the early history of both popular and hillbilly recording. In 1910, the Victor Company recorded two Tin Pan Alley favorites for its general audience, "Casey Jones" (copyrighted in 1909 by T. Lawrence Seibert and Eddie Newton) and "Drill, Ye Tarriers, Drill" (published in 1888 and ascribed to Thomas F. Casey).

Virginia textile worker Henry Whitter recorded "The Wreck On The Southern Old 97" in 1923, one of the earliest hillbilly records, and its success was instrumental in Vernon Dalhart's decision to enter country music. Dalhart's Victor record of "The Wreck Of The Old 97," backed by "The Prisoner's Song," became the company's largest seller prior to the introduction of electric recordings in 1925. Estimated sales of this national country hit range anywhere from one to six million records.

"Casey" and "Old 97" immortalized wrecks, of course, and began a tradition of railroad tragedy songs that lasted through the forties. Others of this kind include the Carter Family's "Engine One Forty-Three," commemorating an 1890 accident on the C & O at Hinton, West Virginia; and Blind Alfred Reed's account of a 1927 wreck at Ingleside, West Virginia, called "The Wreck Of The Virginian."

Not all railroaders were heaven-bound engineers, however, and Jimmie Rodgers and others preferred to write about a more humble side of the business, which included boomers, brakemen, and bums. Rodgers was himself a railroad man, in addition to his uncontested title as the Father of Country Music. He was raised on a switchyard and became a brakeman at fourteen, then spent another fourteen years at various railroad jobs including those of callboy, baggagemaster, and flagman. He also knew poverty, struggling to become a musician in the postwar and Depression-ridden South.

"It's good times here, but it's better down the road," sang Rodgers in "The Brakeman's Blues," a line that captured the attitude of many of his songs—optimistic, but eternally restless. Next to the railroads themselves, he loved best the workers, the hobos, and the unemployed he met by the thousands up and down the line in the late twenties. He was always a soft touch for a few dollars, a free meal, or a free ride.

In 1929, he wrote the classic hobo song based on earlier fragments, "Waiting For A Train," which he followed with others like "Train Whistle Blues" and "Hobo's Meditation." Taken together, they paint a plaintive picture of these sons of the road. His influence was strongly felt in most of the "on the bum" songs that followed, from Waldo O'Neal's "Hobo Bill's Last Ride," which follows the carefree tramp to his almost inevitable cold and lonely death; to Bob Nolan's poetic "Way Out There," glorifying the romance of the road.

Another country great who got his start in railroading was Roy Acuff. Acuff was a callboy for the L & N at Knoxville, Tennessee, and it was there that he learned many of the old songs like "Wabash Cannon Ball," which he later was to resurrect with such success. His name will forever remain synonymous with such railroad standards as "Night Train To Memphis," his partner Fred Rose's "Fireball Mail," John Lair's "Freight Train Blues," and his own composition, "Streamlined Cannon Ball."

Hank Snow never worked the roads, but there was seldom a day in his childhood when he didn't go down to the station to see the train come in. "I started loving the old steam trains and the old steam whistles when I was a child," said Snow, who later was to make extensive use of the railroad metaphor in his unrequited love songs, "I'm Movin' On" and "The Golden Rocket." He considers himself a direct descendant of Rodgers through his patron Ernest Tubb, and has been a prominent figure in the many memorials to The Singing Brakeman.

The latest (but certainly not the last) singer in this railroad tradition is Johnny Cash. According to Frederick Danker, a professor at Boston State College, part of Cash's admiration for the train song can be traced back to Rodgers through the songs of Hank Snow: "Cash was influenced by Snow from his youth in Arkansas," wrote Danker *(Journal of American Folklore),* "but he also grew up in the Delta area in the Depression near railroads; they were part of the lifeline of the area and bore some aura of romance. The image of the lonesome, wandering man hopping freights to move on to another town . . . relates to the Depression hobo and poor white, and is a deep part of the folk esthetic surfacing in Cash's work. . . ."

Cash released several railroad albums in the early sixties which included traditional songs like "Rock Island Line" and "Old 97" and his own lyrics on "Hey, Porter," about going home on a southbound train. But his best-known railroad record was a revival of the Ervin Rouse song, "Orange Blossom Special."

There have been many other composers and stylists strongly identified with trains and traveling over the past fifty years—Harry McClintock, Goebel Reeves, "Pop" Stoneman, Carson Robison, Beasley Smith, and John Lair, to name but a few—but each decade has had its giant. As Rodgers dominated the thirties, Acuff held forth in the forties, Snow in the fifties, and Cash in the sixties. All of Rodgers's railroad songs are still available, and Acuff, Snow, and Cash can scarcely escape a personal appearance without performing at least one train song.

What of the seventies? Perhaps Steve Goodman's "City Of New Orleans" ("This train's got the disappearing railroad blues . . .") signals not only the end of the train, but the end of the train song as well. The railroad has yielded to the superhighway and the jet plane, and their images have begun to enter the country consciousness. The ghostly truck driver of "Phantom 309" has replaced the engineer in "Casey Jones," and recent hits like "L. A. International Airport" and "In The Early Morning Rain" make use of the silent and impersonal symbol of the jetliner.

Whatever becomes of the train, the spirit of the hobo undoubtedly will live on. Leon Payne's "Lost Highway" was one of the best, if not the first, highway songs, and symbolically bridged the gap between the hobo songs of the thirties and the rambling songs of the fifties and sixties—songs like "Bumming Around" and "Me And Bobby McGee." Whether he hops a freight, flags down a semi, or buys a youth-fare ticket, the spirit of the young and restless country boy or girl remains the same: "I'm Movin' On."

BRAKEMAN'S BLUES

"His railroad card shows fourteen years of service. During those years he played various roles on many roads; call-boy, flagman, baggagemaster, brakeman . . . But—'I crave to cover distance'—so, as freight brakeman, young Jimmie Rodgers thought he was doing fine. He was going places, seeing things, doing things. Carefree, happy always, when answering a call he reached first for banjo, mandolin or ukelele."

—Mrs. Carrie Rodgers
(from *My Husband, Jimmie Rodgers*)

BRAKEMAN'S BLUES

by Jimmie Rodgers

Portland, Maine, is just the same as sunny Tennessee
Portland, Maine, is just the same as sunny Tennessee
Any old place I hang my hat is home sweet home to me.

I went to the depot and looked up on the board
I went to the depot and looked up on the board
It says it's good times here, but it's better down the road.

I'll eat my breakfast here and my dinner in New Orleans
I'll eat my breakfast here and my dinner in New Orleans
I'm gonna get me a mama I ain't never seen.

Where was you, Mama, when the train left the shed?
Where was you, Mama, when the train left the shed?
Standing in my front door, wishing I was dead.

BUMMING AROUND

"I used to rodeo in and around White Salmon, Washington, and had written a few rodeo songs prior to this. I lifted part of the lyrics from one of my rodeo songs, added a new tune, and came up with this song in 1946. By this time I had a dance band, and the new tune was more danceable. I'm a logger now, and I guess 'Bumming Around' kinda fits my life."

—Pete Graves

BUMMING AROUND

by Pete Graves

Got an old slouch hat, got my roll on my shoulder
I'm as free as the breeze, and I'll do as I please
Just a-bummin' around.

I got a million friends, don't feel any older
I've got nothing to lose, not even the blues
Just a-bummin' around.

Whenever worries start to botherin' me
I grab my coat, my old slouch hat
Hit the trail again, you see.

I ain't got a dime, don't care where I'm goin'
I'm as free as the breeze and I'll do as I please
Just a-bummin' around.

CITY OF NEW ORLEANS

"I got married in February of 1970, and that spring my wife Nancy and I went downstate to Mattoon, Illinois, to see her grandmother who was ninety-something years old so she could say, 'Oh, that's who you married.' We were riding the City of New Orleans on the Illinois Central Line. When I had been a student at the University of Illinois, I had ridden it once all the way to New Orleans. Nancy fell asleep, and I was just looking out the window, writing down everything I saw—junkyards, little towns that didn't even have a sign to say what they were. Just out of Chicago, there was a bunch of old men standing around tin cans, warming themselves and waving, and it was a cold morning in April. It was better journalism than it was songwriting at the time. When I got back to Chicago, I showed it to a friend of mine, and he told me they were going to take the train off the line in six months if the passenger traffic didn't improve—that had been in the newspapers. He said, 'You've got the future of the train and what you saw out the window, now you should describe what happened on the train.' So I sat down and wrote the second verse about the card game and the paper bag. That part about 'Memphis, Tennessee' is strictly from memory, but I figured I couldn't write a song about a train that went 900 miles through the center of the country and stop the song in Mattoon because I was getting off."

—Steve Goodman

CITY OF NEW ORLEANS
by Steve Goodman

Riding on the City of New Orleans
Illinois Central Monday morning rail
Fifteen cars and fifteen restless riders

Three conductors and twenty-five sacks of mail
All out on a southbound odyssey
The train pulls out of Kankakee
And rolls along past houses, farms and fields
Passing towns that have no name
The freight yards full of old black men
And the graveyards of the rusted automobiles.

Good morning, America, how are you?
Don't you know me? I'm your native son
I'm the train they call the City of New Orleans
I'll be gone five hundred miles when the day is done.

Dealing card games with the old men in the club car
Penny a point, ain't no one keepin' score
Pass the paper bag that holds the bottle
Feel the wheels rumblin' 'neath the floor
And the sons of pullman porters
And the sons of engineers
Ride their fathers' magic carpet made of steel
Mothers with their babes asleep
Rocking to the gentle beat
And the rhythm of the rails is all they feel.

Nighttime on the City of New Orleans
Changing cars in Memphis, Tennessee
Halfway home, we'll be there by morning
Through the Mississippi darkness rolling down to the sea
But all the towns and people seem
To fade into a bad dream
And the steel rail still ain't heard the news
The conductor sings his song again
"The Passengers will please refrain . . ."
This train's got the disappearing railroad blues.

"It's a very good number, and it's done very well for me. A lot of the boys are still doing it today. I recorded it in 1943 in the key of A, but when I do it now, I have to do it down a couple of notes. I first thought it was written by a lady who was connected with Mr. Art Satherly, but I found out later, after I recorded it, that Fred wrote it under the name Floyd Jenkins. I didn't know at first who 'Floyd Jenkins' was; it's easy to fool a country boy."

—Roy Acuff

FIREBALL MAIL

by Floyd Jenkins (Fred Rose)

Here she comes, look at her roll
There she goes, eatin' that coal
Watch her fly, look at her sail
Let her by, by, by, it's the Fireball Mail
Watch her go, look at her steam
Hear her blow, whistle and scream
Like a hound, waggin' his tail
Dallas-bound, bound, bound, it's the Fireball Mail.

Engineer, makin' up time
Tracks are clear, look at her climb
See that freight, clearin' the rail
Bet she's late, late, late, it's the Fireball Mail
Watch her swerve, look at her sway
Get that curve out of the way
Watch her fly, look at her sail
Let her by, by, by, it's the Fireball Mail.

FREIGHT TRAIN BLUES

"I just remembered down here in the mountains where I came from that a freight train whistle at night is an awfully lonesome sound. In a quiet country where you don't hear many sounds, if you've ever heard a few trains go through these mountain passes, you never forget them. I wrote this song especially for Red Foley. I took Red to Chicago for the first time and introduced him to radio."

—John Lair

FREIGHT TRAIN BLUES

by John Lair

I was born in Dixie in a boomer shack
Just a little shanty by the railroad track
The humming of the drivers was my lullaby
And a freight train whistle taught me how to cry.

I got the freight train blues
Lawdy, Lawdy, Lawdy
Got them in the bottom of my ramblin' shoes
And when the whistle blows, I gotta go
Oh! Lawdy! Guess I'm never gonna lose the
Freight train blues.

My daddy was a fireman and my mammy dear
Was the only daughter of an engineer
My sweetie is a brakeman and it ain't no joke
It's a shame the way she keeps a good man broke.

Aeroplanes and autos always leave me cold
The moaning of a steamboat never stirs my soul
The only thing that makes me want to navigate
Is a wildcat whistle on a southbound freight.

I know I'm old enough to quit this running 'round
I've tried a hundred times to stop and settle down
But every time I find a place I'd like to stay
I hear a freight train holler, and I'm on my way.

THE GOLDEN ROCKET

"I remember writing most of the lyrics to 'The Golden Rocket' during the night while driving from Chattanooga to some place in North Carolina where we were to appear the next afternoon. I was a lover of the old steam engines and followed them when I was a child by going to the little old country station and watching them come and go. I also gained much experience through reading, and I admired the many songs that were written and recorded about trains by the late Jimmie Rodgers."

—Hank Snow

THE GOLDEN ROCKET

by Hank Snow

From old Montana down to Alabama
I've been before and I'll travel again
You triflin' women can't keep a good man down
You dealt the cards but you missed a play
So hit the road and be on your way
Gonna board the Golden Rocket and leave this town.

I was a good engine, a-runnin' on time
But, baby, I'm switchin' to another line
So, honey, never hang your signal out for me
I'm tired of runnin' on the same old track
Bought a one-way ticket and I won't be back
This Golden Rocket's gonna roll my blues away.

Hear that lonesome whistle blow
That's your cue, and now you know
That I got another true love waitin' in Tennessee
This midnight special is a-burnin' the rail
So, woman, don't try to follow my trail
This Golden Rocket's gonna roll my blues away.

Hear her thunder on through the night
This Golden Rocket is doin' me right
And that sunny Southland sure is a part of me
Now, from your callboard, erase my name
Your fire went out, you done lost your flames
And this Golden Rocket is rollin' my blues away.

That old conductor, he seemed to know
You done me wrong, I was feelin' low
For he yelled aloud, "We're over that Dixon Line!"
The brakeman started singin' a song
Said, "You're worried now, but it won't be long
This Golden Rocket is leavin' your blues behind."

Then the porter yelled with his southern drawl
"Let's rise and shine; good mornin', y'all!"

And I sprang to my feet to greet the newborn day
When I kissed my baby at the station door
That whistle blew like never before
Of the Golden Rocket that rolled my blues away.

HOBO BILL'S LAST RIDE

"When I was a youngster in Clarendon, Texas, we lived 200 yards from a railroad. This was during the Depression. Men couldn't find jobs, and they'd hop a train and go somewhere. I had seen experiences like Hobo Bill's, men that died on the freight trains, unable to find jobs anywhere. Some of these men were respectable, too. I really never rode a freight train except for two or three times in my life and those were special occasions. Another Jimmie Rodgers song, 'Waiting For A Train,' was kind of responsible for 'Hobo Bill's Last Ride.' I sat down and wrote the lyrics to the meter of that song." —Waldo Lafayette O'Neal

HOBO BILL'S LAST RIDE
by Waldo Lafayette O'Neal

Riding on an East-bound freight train, speeding through the night
Hobo Bill, a railroad bum, was fighting for his life
The sadness of his eyes revealed the torture of his soul
He rose a weak and weary hand to brush away the cold.

No warm lights flickered 'round him, no blankets there to hold
Nothing but the howling wind and the driving rain so cold
When he heard a whistle blowing in a dreamy kind of way
The hobo seemed contented, for he smiled there where he lay.

Outside the rain was falling on that lonely boxcar door
But the little form of Hobo Bill lay still upon the floor
While the train sped through the darkness and the raging storm outside
No one knew that Hobo Bill was taking his last ride.

It was early in the morning when they raised the hobo's head
The smile still lingered on his face, but Hobo Bill was dead

There was no mother's longing to soothe his weary soul
For he was just a railroad bum who died out in the cold.

HOBO'S MEDITATION

"I think this song probably was from an experience of Daddy's. Between jobs on the railroad, before he started singing, he didn't have much money. He probably slept in some boxcars himself to get out of the rain and cold. He knew everything about railroads and railroad people—and that included a good many hobos, especially during the Depression. Daddy was a religious man, and he went to church when he could; of course, he couldn't go regularly, being on the road and all. Very few people know this, but he sang in churches and prisons all over the South."

—Anita Rodgers Court

HOBO'S MEDITATION

by Jimmie Rodgers

Tonight as I lay on a boxcar
Just waiting for a train to pass by
What will become of the hobos
Whenever their time comes to die?

Has the Master up yonder in heaven
Got a place that we might call our home?
Will we have to work for a living
Or can we continue to roam?

Will there be any freight trains in heaven?
Any boxcars in which we might hide?
Will there be any tough cops and brakemen?
Will they tell us that we cannot ride?

Will the hobo chum with the rich man?
Will he always have money to spare?

Will they have respect for a hobo
In the land that lies hidden up there?

I'M MOVIN' ON

" 'I'm Movin' On' was written about four years before it was ever recorded. On my first session, which was held by RCA in Chicago in 1949, the song was turned down flat by Steve Sholes, recording director. Later on, in the spring of 1950, in Nashville, Mr. Sholes had not remembered the song, so I recorded it. This song, by the way, has been recorded by between 50 and 60 artists around the world." —Hank Snow

I'M MOVIN' ON

by Hank Snow

That big eight-wheeler rollin' down the track
Means your true lovin' daddy ain't coming back
I'm movin' on, I'll soon be gone
You were flyin' too high for my little old sky
So I'm movin' on.

That big loud whistle as it blew and blew
Said "Hello Alabama, we're comin' to you"
We're movin' on; oh, hear my song
You had the laugh on me, so I've set you free
And I'm movin' on.

Mister engineer, take that throttle in hand
This rattler's the fastest in the southern land
Keep movin' on, keep rollin' on
You're gonna ease my mind, so put me there on time
Keep rollin' on.

I warned you, baby, from time to time
But you just wouldn't listen or pay me no mind
I'm movin' on, I'm rollin' on
You have broken your vow and it's all over now
So I'm movin' on.

But someday, baby, when you've had your play
You're gonna want your daddy, but your daddy will say

"Keep movin' on, you stayed away too long
I'm through with you; too bad you are blue
So keep movin' on."

LOST HIGHWAY

"In the early days of Leon's career, he hitchhiked from one place to another, finding jobs wherever he could. Once he was in California hitchhiking to Alba, Texas, to visit his sick mother. He was unable to get a ride and finally got help from the Salvation Army. It was while he was waiting for help that he wrote this song." —Myrtie (Mrs. Leon) Payne

LOST HIGHWAY
by Leon Payne

I'm a rolling stone, all alone and lost
For a life of sin, I have paid the cost
When I pass by, all the people say
"Just another guy on the lost highway."

Just a deck of cards and a jug of wine
And a woman's lies make a life like mine
Oh, the day we met, I went astray
I started rollin' down that lost highway.

I was just a lad, nearly twenty-two
Neither good nor bad, just a kid like you
And now I'm lost, too late to pray
Lord, I've paid the cost on the lost highway.

Now, boys, don't start your ramblin' round
On this road of sin or you're sorrow bound
Take my advice or you'll curse the day
You started rollin' down that lost highway.

"I had just gone to work for Combine Music. Fred Foster, the owner, called me and said, 'I've got a title for you: Me And Bobby McKee.' Bobby was a secretary in Boudleaux Bryant's office, but I thought he said 'McGee.' He said, 'How's that grab you?' I said, 'How's what grab me?' He said, 'The song title. Go write it.' I thought there was no way I could ever write that, and it took me months of hiding from him, because I can't write on assignment. But it must have stuck in the back of my head. One day I was driving between Morgan City and New Orleans. It was raining and the windshield wipers were going, I started coming out with Baton Rouge and the places I was working at the time. I took an old experience with another girl in another country. I had it finished by the time I got to Nashville. That song probably turned over more audience to me than any song I ever had."

—Kris Kristofferson

ME AND BOBBY MCGEE

by Kris Kristofferson and Fred Foster

Busted flat in Baton Rouge, headin' for the trains
Feelin' nearly faded as my jeans
Bobby thumbed a diesel down just before it rained
Took us all the way to New Orleans.

I took my harpoon out of my dirty red bandana
And was blowin' sad while Bobby sang the blues
With them windshield wipers slappin' time and Bobby clappin' hands
We fin'ly sang up ev'ry song that driver knew.

Freedom's just another word for nothin' left to lose
And nothin' ain't worth nothin' but it's free
Feelin' good was easy, Lord, when Bobby sang the blues
Good enough for me and Bobby McGee.

From the coal mines of Kentucky to the California sun
Bobby shared the secrets of my soul
Standing right beside me, Lord, through everything I done
And every night she kept me from the cold.

Then somewhere near Salinas, Lord, I let her slip away
Lookin' for the home I hope she'll find
And I'd trade all of my tomorrows for a single yesterday
Holdin' Bobby's body close to mine.

Freedom's just another word for nothin' left to lose
And nothin' left is all she left for me

Feelin' good was easy, Lord, when Bobby sang the blues
Good enough for me and Bobby McGee.

NIGHT TRAIN TO MEMPHIS

"Owen Bradley, Beasley Smith and I had a company at the time and we pooled our material. Beasley Smith came up with this idea about a 'Night Train To Memphis' and I simply added to it. There was a night train from Nashville to Memphis at that time. Of course, there were a lot of trains everywhere at all times of day. Now they've all faded out."

—Marvin Hughes

" 'Night Train To Memphis' was written about a train called The City Of Memphis. It ran on the Nashville, Chattanooga and St. Louis line. The engine was called The Blue Goose. The train was built completely in Nashville at Radnor Yards. It was the first streamlined train in this part of the country."

—Rosalind Smith Minton

NIGHT TRAIN TO MEMPHIS

by Marvin Hughes, Beasley Smith, and Owen Bradley

Take that night train to Memphis, take that night train to Memphis
And when you arrive at the station
I'll be right there to meet you, I'll be right there to greet you
So don't turn down my invitation.

Hallelujah! Hallelujah!
I'll be shoutin' hallelujah all the day
Oh we'll have a jubilee down in Memphis, Tennessee
And I'll shout hallelujah all the day.

Take that night train to Memphis, take that night train to Memphis
You know how I'm longing to see you
Leave at three-fifty-seven and arrive at eleven
Then I'll be shoutin' "Hallelujah!"

Take that night train to Memphis, take that night train to Memphis
Tell that engineer to pull the throttle open

Keep that engine stack a-smokin', I'm not kiddin', I'm not jokin'
And I'll soon be with my girl, I'm hopin'.

ORANGE BLOSSOM SPECIAL

"About 1936 or 1937 we played a little ol' fiddlin' piece we thought was a little crazy—me and my brothers Gordie and Earl. Our manager, Lloyd Smith, from Cosemie, Florida, named our fiddlin' piece. We came out at the christening of the Orange Blossom Special at the Seaboard Railroad Station in Miami, and it was him that named it. We got our copyright back in 1938. Later on, I was riding around Lake Okeechobee and wrote the lyrics before me and my brother Gordie went to New York and recorded it for RCA Victor in 1939. I never rode the Special, and I'm so sorry to say I didn't because our train from Miami to New York I've been told by engineers was without doubt the most powerful train in the entire world."

—Ervin T. Rouse

ORANGE BLOSSOM SPECIAL

by Ervin T. Rouse

Look a-yonder comin'
Comin' down that railroad track
Look a-yonder comin'
Comin' down that railroad track
It's the Orange Blossom Special
Bringing my baby back.

I'm going down to Florida
And get some sand in my shoes
Or maybe California
And get some sand in my shoes
I'll ride that Orange Blossom Special
And lose those New York blues.

Talk about a-travelin'
She's the fastest train on the Line
Talk about a-travelin'

She's the fastest train on the Line
It's that Orange Blossom Special
Rollin' down the Seaboard Line.

THE POOR TRAMP HAS TO LIVE

"When Ralph Peer left Okeh in 1926 to join the Victor Talking Machine Company as A & R man, he took Daddy with him. This was one of Victor's first electrical recordings. Daddy loved the railroad. He worked as a mail clerk and as a section hand. We were poor folks, extremely poor, and we always somehow ended up living by a railroad track. A great many railroad bums would come to our house, and we would always manage to feed them somehow. I remember one day a bum came to our house and asked for food, and we just plain told him we had none. We hadn't eaten ourselves in a couple of days. He went away, and later on in the afternoon, he came back with a couple of cans of canned milk and a loaf of bread for us young'uns. He had gone down the street to a store and worked to get food for us. Daddy understood bums. He knew them and knew about them."

—Pattie Stoneman

THE POOR TRAMP HAS TO LIVE

by Ernest V. Stoneman

I'm a poor old railroad man, once a helping section hand
And old age is slowly creeping on the way
Now hard times are coming on, and my last gold dollar is gone
And this song is what I'm made to sing and play.

Now you ofttimes see the stamp of the poor unfortunate tramp
Who has no home and has no place to fill
As you see him pass along and he sings his little song
Please remember that the poor tramp has to live.

My health broke down out on the track, heavy loads upon my back
Now I have to make my way the best I can
We never know when we are young what may be our future doom
These words are from a broke down section hand.

Yes, my health is broken down and I tramp from town to town
Sing and play and take whatever you may give
While I try to sing and play, just divide your little change
And remember that the poor tramp has to live.

STREAMLINED CANNON BALL

"I wrote 'Streamlined Cannon Ball' when they had begun to do away with the steam engine and were beginning to streamline trains."

—Roy Acuff

STREAMLINED CANNON BALL

by Roy Acuff

A long steel rail, a short cross-tie
I'm on my way back home
I'm on a train, the king of them all
The Streamlined Cannon Ball.

She moves along like a cannon ball
Like a star in its heavenly flight
This lonesome sound from the whistle you love
As she travels through the night.

Her head light gleams out in the night
The fire box flash you see
The blinds I ride, the life that I love
It's home, sweet home to me.

I can see the smile of the engineer
Although he's old and gray
A contented heart, he waits the call
Of the Streamlined Cannon Ball.

" 'Tennessee Central Number Nine' was the first song my father ever wrote. Roy Acuff's recording of it sold over half a million copies. Number Nine was the engine number of a train that ran from Nashville to Harriman, Tennessee, on the Tennessee Central Line."

—Rosalind Smith Minton

TENNESSEE CENTRAL NUMBER NINE

by Beasley Smith

Oh, that big, black engine comes a-puffin' 'round the bend
Puffin' 'round the bend, puffin' 'round the bend
Oh, that big, black engine comes a-puffin' 'round the bend
It's the Tennessee Central Number Nine.

With her smoke stack blazin', she's a-burnin' up the wind
Burnin' up the wind, burnin' up the wind
With her smoke stack blazin', she's a-burnin' up the wind
It's the Tennessee Central Number Nine.

Oh, that ol' TC, it's good enough for me
Let the flagman give the engineer the sign
Get a feelin' I must go when I hear that whistle blow
On that Tennessee Central Number Nine.

All aboard, good people
Can't you hear that bell a-ringin'?
Hear that bell a-ringin'? Dongin' and a-ringin'?
It's the Tennessee Central Number Nine.

Gonna hit that mountain, just a rockin' and a-reelin'
Rockin' and a-reelin', moanin' and a-squealin'
Gonna hit that mountain, just a-rockin' and a-reelin'
On that Tennessee Central Number Nine.

When we leave the station, she'll be pantin' and a-blowin'
Pantin' and a-blowin', gettin' and a-goin'
When we leave the station, she'll be pantin' and a-blowin'
It's the Tennessee Central Number Nine.

We'll roll into Knoxville, just a-shoutin' and a-singin'
Just a-shoutin' and a-singin', swayin' and a-singin'
We'll roll into Knoxville, a-shoutin' and a-singin'
On that Tennessee Central Number Nine.

TRAIN WHISTLE BLUES

". . . the Jimmie who was a brakeman, a happy-go-lucky youngster forever strumming and singing—when he wasn't 'going high' on box cars; caring little whether he had a job or not—but loving the old smokies, silver rails and the hollow whistles from 'that old smokestack.' Whistles? Pretty train whistles? . . . He'd jump up from the table, leaving a delicious, nourishing hot meal to grow cold and tasteless—while he rushed outside where he could hear better, to—listen; just listen to some old smokie in the distance—'whoo-o-o—'."

—Mrs. Carrie Rodgers
(from *My Husband, Jimmie Rodgers*)

TRAIN WHISTLE BLUES
by Jimmie Rodgers

When a woman gets the blues, she hangs her head and cries
When a woman gets the blues, she hangs her head and cries
But when a man gets the blues, he grabs a train and rides.

Every time I see that lonesome railroad train
Every time I see that lonesome railroad train
It makes me wish I was going home again.

Look a-yonder coming, coming down that railroad track
Look a-yonder coming, coming down that railroad track
With the black smoke rolling, rolling from that old smoke stack.

I've got the blues so bad till the whole round world looks blue
I've got the blues so bad till the whole round world looks blue
I ain't got a dime, I don't know what to do.

I'm weary now, I want to leave this town
I'm weary now and I want to leave this town
I can't find a job, I'm tired of hanging around.

WABASH CANNON BALL

"The earliest record of a passenger train by the famous name Wabash Cannon Ball dates to 1885 . . . when the old Wabash Railroad applied the term to its Chicago to Kansas City run."

—C. R. Fountain, Norfolk & Western Railway Co.
(quoted in the *Champaign-Urbana Courier*)

"The first published version of 'Wabash Cannon Ball' was written by William Kindt in 1905. Kindt must have based his text on an earlier song entitled 'The Great Rock Island Route!,' which was published by 1882, words and music by J. A. Roff. The earliest recordings on disc were in 1929 . . . however, the recordings that were most responsible for the widespread popularity of the song were those by Roy Acuff in 1936 and 1947. It is interesting to note the extent to which Roy Acuff's 1936 version has driven out earlier versions. Acuff's earlier text was essentially the same as the one recorded by Hugh Cross in 1929."

—Norm Cohen, Executive Secretary,
John Edwards Memorial Foundation

"I learned the 'Wabash Cannon Ball' when I was a very young boy living in East Tennessee near Knoxville. I sing the song in exactly the same way I found it. I never changed a word. The fact that there's a reference to a Daddy Claxton in the last verse, which also happens to be my middle name, is a coincidence. My father named me after Dr. P. T. Claxton, a prominent teacher and lecturer at Auston Peay College in Clarksville, Tennessee. On the day I was born he had given a lecture in our town. My father was so impressed, he named me after him."

—Roy Acuff

WABASH CANNON BALL
by A. P. Carter

From the great Atlantic Ocean to the wide Pacific shore
From the queen of flowing mountains to the south bell by the shore

She's mighty tall and handsome and known quite well by all
She's the combination on the Wabash Cannon Ball.

She came down from Birmingham one cold December day
As she rolled into the station, you could hear all the people say
"There's a girl from Tennessee, she's long and she's tall
She came down from Birmingham on the Wabash Cannon Ball."

Our Eastern states are dandy, so the people always say
From New York to Saint Louis and Chicago, by the way
From the hills of Minnesota where the rippling waters fall
No changes can be taken on the Wabash Cannon Ball.

Here's to Daddy Claxton, may his name forever stand
And always be remembered 'round the courts of Alabam'
His earthly race is over, and the curtains 'round him fall
We'll carry him home to victory on the Wabash Cannon Ball.

Listen to the jingle, the rumble and the roar
As she glides along the woodland through the hills and by the shore
Hear the mighty rush of the engine, hear the lonesome hobo's squall
We're traveling through the jungles on the Wabash Cannon Ball.

WAITING FOR A TRAIN

"Most people on the railroads would put hobos off the train and tell them, 'This is no free ride.' They wouldn't put them in jail, they would just tell them to be on the way, whereas Daddy would let them go ahead and ride. I remember Mother telling me that he'd just close the doors and make out like he didn't even see them. Daddy would pick up hobos—that's what my mother called them—and buy them food and clothing and even luggage. I remember one time he brought one home whose name was 'Sides.' He just kept staying and staying until Mother finally told Daddy it was time he went on down the way. 'We're not running a hotel here, Jimmie.' But that was just like him; every time we turned around he was picking up somebody. He would give you the shirt off his back."

—Anita Rodgers Court

WAITING FOR A TRAIN

by Jimmie Rodgers

All around the water tank, waiting for a train
A thousand miles away from home, sleeping in the rain
I walked up to a brakeman to give him a line of talk
He said "If you've got money, I'll see that you don't walk"
"I haven't got a nickel, not a penny can I show"
He said "Get off, you railroad bum," and slammed the boxcar door.

He put me off in Texas, a place I surely love
Wide open spaces all around me, the moon and stars above
Nobody seems to want me or lend me a helping hand
I'm on my way from 'Frisco, goin' back to Dixieland
My pocketbook is empty, and my heart is filled with pain
I'm a thousand miles away from home, just waiting for a train.

WAY OUT THERE

"This was my very first tune. There was something about the lure of the road and the knights of the road that prompted me to join them. For approximately four years, my young life was spent in riding the rails and enjoying the 'romance of the Road.' I traveled everywhere in this country, moving along on a capricious thought. I actually composed 'Way Out There' when I was enjoying the freedom of boyhood travel."

—Bob Nolan

WAY OUT THERE

by Bob Nolan

A lonely spot I know where no man will go
Where the shadows have all the room
I was ridin' free on the old SP
Softly humming a southern tune
When a man came along, made me hush my song
Kicked me off away out there.

As she pulled out of sight, I turned to my right
The left and everywhere
But all I could see was a cactus tree
And a prairie dog playing there
Saw the prairie dog feed on the tumbling weed
That's his home away out there.

So I threw down my load in the desert road
And rested my weary legs
Watched the sinking sun make the tall shadows run
Out across the barren plain
Then I hummed a tune to the rising moon
He gets lonesome 'way out there.

And then I closed my eyes to the starlit skies
And I lost myself in dreams
Dreamt the desert sand was a milk-and-honey land
Then I woke up with a start
There's a train coming back on that one-way track
Gonna take me 'way from there.

As she was passing by, caught her on the fly
I climbed in an open door
Then I turned around to that desert ground
Saw the spot I will see no more
And as I rode away, heard the pale moon say
"Farewell, pal, it gets lonesome here."

THE WRECK OF NUMBER NINE

" 'The Wreck Of Number Nine' was written at a time when there seemed to be a rash of tragedy songs ending up in a sort of moral. Carson's comments on this song read: 'Good piece of railroad story material (fictional).' There has been consistent use of this number over the years, and it seems to have revived recently."

—Catherine (Mrs. Carson) Robison

THE WRECK OF NUMBER NINE

by Carson Robison

On a cold and stormy night, not a star was in sight
And the cold north wind came howling down the line
With his sweetheart so dear, stood a brave engineer
With his orders to pull old Number Nine.

She kissed him goodbye with a tear in her eye
For the joy in her heart she would not hide
For the whole world seemed right when she told him that night
That tomorrow she'd be his blushing bride.

Oh, the wheels rolled along, and the train hummed a song
And the black smoke came pouring from the stack
His headlight a-gleam seemed to brighten his dream
For tomorrow he'd be a-comin' back.

He spun around the hill, and his brave heart stood still
For a headlight was shining in his face
He whispered a prayer as he threw on the air
For he knew this would be his final race.

In the wreckage he was found lying there on the ground
And he asked them to lift his weary head
As his breath slowly went was the message he sent
To the maiden he thought he was to wed:

"There's a little white house that I bought for our own
And I thought we'd be happy by and by
But I'll leave it to you, for I know you'll be true
Till we meet at that Golden Gate; goodbye."

WRECK OF THE OLD '97

"On September 27, 1903, Number 97, the Southern Railway's fast mail train between Washington and Atlanta, reached Monroe, Virginia, about an hour late. There, a change of crew put engineer Joseph A. Broady at the throttle. Known as something of a daredevil, Broady was trying to make up lost time when he hit Stillhouse Trestle, a wooden bridge across Cherrystone Creek, too fast to make the descending curve, and locomotive and five cars flew off the rails into the ravine below. Several local musicians put together ballads about the accident, modeling their compositions after Henry Clay Work's popular 1865 song, 'The Ship That Never Return'd.' In 1923, it was recorded by one of country music's first recording artists, Henry Whitter. Vernon Dalhart copied Whitter's recording for the Victor Talking Machine Company. 'Old 97,' having made musical history, went on to make legal history, as the battle over the composer's royalties for the million-seller occupied the courts off and on until 1940. Folklorist Robert W. Gordon proved that Fred Lewey and Charles W. Noell of North Carolina had a hand in writing the ballad; who else did, we are still uncertain."

—Norman Cohen, Executive Secretary,
John Edwards Memorial Foundation

WRECK OF THE OLD '97*

On one cloudless morning, I stood on the mountain
Just watching the smoke from below
It was coming from a tall, slim smokestack
'Way down on the Southern Railroad.

It was Ninety-Seven, the fastest train
Ever run on the Southern Line
All the freight trains and pass'gers take the side for Ninety-Seven
For she's bound to be at stations on time.

They gave him his orders at Monroe, Virginia
Saying "Stevie, you're away behind time
This is not Thirty-Eight, but it's Old Ninety-Seven
You must put her into Spencer on time."

He looked around and said to his black, greasy fireman
"Just shovel in a little more coal
And when I cross that ole White Oak Mountain
You can just watch Old Ninety-Seven roll."

It's a mighty rough road from Lynchburg to Danville
And the line is on a three-mile grade

*Text transcribed from the contemporary Kelly Harrell recording (Okeh 7010) which used a more complete version than either the Whitter or Dalhart records.

It was on that grade that he lost his average
And you see what a jump that he made.

He was going down grade, making ninety miles an hour
When his whistle began to scream
He was found in the wreck with his hand on the throttle
He was scalded to death with the steam.

Did she ever pull in? No, she never pulled in.
And at one forty-five he was due
For hours and hours there's a switchman been waiting
For that fast mail that never pulled through.

Did she ever pull in? No, she never pulled in.
And that poor boy, he must be dead
Oh, yonder he lays on that railroad track
With the car wheels over his head.

Ninety-Seven, she was the fastest train
That the South had ever seen
But she run so fast on that Sunday morning
That the death score was numbered fourteen.

Now, ladies, you must take warning
From this time now and on
Never speak hard words to your true, loving husband
He may leave you and never return.

---

15 | Story Songs

I Will Tell You My Story, Kind Mister

Much has been written of the contribution of ballads and broadsides to early country music, and undoubtedly there was a strong carryover in the early repertory. But the forces which Josiah Combs describes as "the impact of civilization and commerce" *(Folk-Songs of the Southern United States)* had by the early thirties considerably reduced the role of traditional song in recorded hillbilly music.

Although most folklorists bemoan this decline and reject the great body of commercial song that followed, it should be pointed out that the oral tradition of the South did not diminish—instead, the process was accelerated. The rural southerner did not reject the songs of his ancestry; many are being recorded and are still current today. But the lure of the new and the novel, widely available for the first time through the electronic transmission of radio and recordings, provided an attractive alternative to the older songs. The conscious composition of new material became an economic necessity, as well as a major impetus to the commercial hillbilly tradition.

Many of these early compositions copied the style and even borrowed the tunes of earlier songs, evolving into a series of "event" songs such as "Amelia Earhart's Last Flight" and "The Death Of Floyd Collins" which, because of their generally tragic themes, are covered elsewhere in this book. These event songs were similar in certain respects to the eighteenth-century ballads printed on broadside sheets and hawked on street corners in both England and in the American colonies.

A far stronger and more enduring influence on the modern story song was that of the "parlor song" of the late nineteenth century, whose influence can be traced in the songs in this chapter. Parlor songs were the popular, commercial products of Tin Pan Alley that were kept alive in the rural South long after they were forgotten in the cities.

Unlike the event song, which seized on a brief moment in history, or the ballad, which can go on verse after verse almost indefinitely, these parlor songs were more akin to the vaudeville playlets of the 1890s or the more modern short story. The characteristics of brevity, a simple plot, frequent use of irony or morality, and broad effects of either humor or sadness are recognizable in most parlor songs, and in their more modern offspring.

Story songs are self-contained. They tell a whole story, describe a complete character, or re-create an emotion or mood. Many of them use a dramatic twist or punchline to pay off their humor. Originally limited by the playing time of a 78-rpm record, they served as a kind of oral literature for backwoods society.

Many of the early songs pointed strong morals, as did at least two songs made famous by Jimmie Rodgers, "Mother Was A Lady," a true parlor ballad written in 1896 and revived by Rodgers in the twenties, and "Mother, The Queen Of My Heart," co-written with Hoyt Bryant in the thirties. Both seem quaint and even a little ludicrous to many people today, but they remain very much alive in the country repertory.

Hillbilly songwriters continued to create story songs through the forties and early fifties, often with tragic love themes as in the Morris Brothers' "Tragic Romance," Guthrie's "Philadelphia Lawyer," and Hank Williams's and Fred Rose's "Kaw-liga."

The real renaissance of the story song, however, came in 1958 and 1959, principally as an outgrowth of the blossoming folksong revival which created such pop hits as "Tom Dooley." Jimmie Driftwood's "The Battle Of New Orleans" became a number-one song for Johnny Horton, and Driftwood quickly followed it with "Tennessee Stud," based partly on his family history. It, too, was a hit, this time for Eddy Arnold.

The year 1959 also saw the creation of "The Long Black Veil," which co-writer Danny Dill humorously refers to as an "instant folksong," and Marty Robbins's authentic-sounding western ballad "El Paso." This song, which is pure fiction despite the existence of a real Rosa's cantina outside El Paso, illustrates the importance of a complete narrative line in the modern story song. The complete recording is well over four minutes, unusually long for country material oriented to single-record sales.

Two major songs of 1961 followed the story song tradition: "Big Bad John," a modern mining epic, and "The Blizzard," about a man who freezes to death rather than leave his lame pony. "Leona," written in 1962, is another straightforward tragedy, this time including cheating, retribution, and the wild side of life.

With "Saginaw, Michigan," story songs took on a strong ironic slant which, in songs like "Carroll County Accident" and "Ballad Of Forty Dollars," became an almost acid point of view.

From the gentle morality tales of the 1890s to the sophisticated perspectives of the 1970s, the songs that follow show the evolution of country music perhaps better than any other category. A strong oral tradition persists in the South today, in spite of industrialization and the rise of large cities, and the story song remains a lively art—as witness such recent hits as "Country Bumpkin."

BALLAD OF FORTY DOLLARS

"At a young age, 13 or 14, I had worked in a graveyard as a summer-time job. I helped dig the graves and carry the chairs and mow the grass and keep everything straight. So I saw a number of funerals, and having the kind of mind I had, I would sit and contemplate them. It dawned on me then, and later was even more significant, how much hypocrisy there was involved. Yesterday, the guy was a son of a bitch, and today, he was a great old guy who really meant well." —Tom T. Hall

BALLAD OF FORTY DOLLARS

by Tom T. Hall

The man who preached the funeral said it really was a simple way to die
He lay down to rest one afternoon and never opened his eyes
They hired me and Fred and Joe to dig the grave and carry up some chairs
It took us seven hours, and I guess we must've drunk a case of beer.

I guess I ought to go and watch them put him down, but I don't own a suit
And anyway when they start talking about the fire and hell, well, I get spooked
So I'll just sit here in my truck and act like I don't know him when they pass
Anyway, when they're all through, I've got to go to work and mow the grass.

Well, here they come and who's that riding in that big old shiny limousine?
Hm, look at all that chrome, I do believe that's the sharpest thing I've seen
That must belong to his great uncle; someone said he owned a big old farm
When they get parked, I'll mosey down and look it over; that won't do no harm.

Well, that must be the widow in the car, and would you take a look at that?
That sure is a pretty dress; you know some women do look good in black
Well, he's not even in the ground, and they say that his truck is up for sale
They say she took it pretty hard, but you can't tell too much behind the veil.

Well, listen, ain't that pretty when the bugler plays the military taps?
I think that when you's in the war, they're always hired to play a song like that
Well, here I am, and there they go, and I guess you could call it my bad luck
I hope he rests in peace, the trouble is the devil owes me forty bucks.

BIG BAD JOHN

"While appearing in summer stock in 'Destry Rides Again,' I became acquainted with an actor by the name of John. He was six-feet-five and built like a football player. He was the only guy in the group I had to look up to, so I started calling him 'Big John.' Then, while flying to a recording session in Nashville, and needing a fourth side to record, I started writing this song that had been going round in my mind. I always thought that 'Big John' had a powerful ring to it, so, in an hour and a half, I had put 'Big John' in a mine and killed him. And there you have 'Big Bad John.' "

—Jimmy Dean

BIG BAD JOHN

by Jimmy Dean

Every morning at the mine you could see him arrive
He stood six-foot-six and weighed two-forty-five
Kind of broad at the shoulder and narrow at the hip
And everybody knew you didn't give no lip to Big John!

Big John, Big John, Big Bad John, Big John!

Nobody seemed to know where John called home
He just drifted into town and stayed all alone

He didn't say much, a-kinda quiet and shy
And if you spoke at all, you just said "Hi" to Big John!
Somebody said he came from New Orleans
Where he got in a fight over a cajun queen
And a crashing blow from a huge right hand
Sent a Louisiana fellow to the promised land, Big John!

Then came the day at the bottom of the mine
When a timber cracked and the men started crying
Miners were praying and hearts beat fast,
And everybody thought that they'd breathed their last 'cept John
Through the dust and the smoke of this man-made hell
Walked a giant of a man that the miners knew well
Grabbed a sagging timber and gave out with a groan
And like a giant oak tree, just stood there alone, Big John!

And with all of his strength, he gave a mighty shove
Then a miner yelled out, "There's a light up above!"
And twenty men scrambled from a would-be grave
And now there's only one left down there to save—Big John!
With jacks and timbers they started back down
Then came that rumble way down in the ground
And smoke and gas belched out of that mine
Everybody knew it was the end of the line for Big John!

Now they never re-opened that worthless pit
They just placed a marble stand in front of it
These few words are written on that stand
"At the bottom of this mine lies a big, big man, Big John!"

THE BLIZZARD

" 'The Blizzard' is about my favorite song. I was sitting around years ago, wanting to write something different. I wrote down this title, 'The Blizzard,' and then I went kind of into a fog or trance or something, and when I came back to my senses, there it was in my handwriting, and it had six (what I thought) beautiful verses. It kind of carried me along and was spiritualistic the way the song kind of wrote itself. Almost always I've

known what was going to happen at the end. But this time I didn't. I've always had a love for the elements. I realize they're the boss and we're not. I've always had a love for the West. I traveled out there quite a bit, read lots of stories. I remember some about the terrific blizzards out in West Texas, people following fence lines, trying to get back home. I've never been a cowboy, but I have a feel for those people. Old cowboys love their women. They want to get home to their women just like we do on our freeways."
—Harlan Howard

THE BLIZZARD
by Harlan Howard

There's a blizzard comin' on and I'm wishing I was home
For my pony's lame and he can hardly stand
Listen to that Norther sigh; if we don't get home we'll die
But it's only seven miles to Mary Anne.
It's only seven miles to Mary Anne.

You can bet we're on her mind, for it's nearly suppertime
And I'll bet there's hot biscuits in the pan
Lord, my hands feel like they're froze, and there's numbness in my toes
But it's only five more miles to Mary Anne
It's only five more miles to Mary Anne.

That wind's howlin' and it seems mighty like a woman's screams
And we best be movin' faster if we can
Dan, just think about that barn and that hay so soft and warm
For it's only three more miles to Mary Anne
It's only three more miles to Mary Anne.

Dan, git up, you on'ry cuss, or you'll be the death of us
I'm so weary, but I'll help you if I can
Alright Dan, perhaps it's best that we stop awhile and rest
For it's still a hundred yards to Mary Anne.
It's still a hundred yards to Mary Anne.

Late that night the storm was gone, and they found him there at dawn
He'd have made it, but he couldn't leave old Dan
Yes, they found him on the plains, his hands froze to the reins
He was just a hundred yards from Mary Anne.
He was just a hundred yards from Mary Anne.

"I was driving through Tennessee on my way to Mississippi when I passed an interstate sign that said 'Carroll County,' and I said to myself, 'If I don't slow down, I'll be the Carroll County accident,' and then I thought, 'If that isn't a song title, I've never heard one.' As I drove through Mississippi, I passed into another Carroll County and thought, 'There's an omen.' By the time I completed the trip, the song was practically written. I've since learned there are no fewer than thirteen counties by that name in the United States."
—Bob Ferguson

CARROLL COUNTY ACCIDENT
by Bob Ferguson

Carroll County's pointed out as kinda square
The biggest thing that happens is the county fair
I guess that's why it seemed like such a big event
What we all call the Carroll County accident.

It happened on the highway just inside the line
Walter Browning lost his life and for a time
It seemed that Mary Ellen Jones would surely die
But she lived long enough for her to testify.

Walter Browning was a happy married man
He wore a golden wedding ring upon his hand
But it was gone, nobody knew just where it went
He lost it in the Carroll County accident.

Mary Ellen testified he thumbed her down
Said he was sick and could she drive him into town?
Well, no one even doubted what she said was true
'Cause she was well respected in the county, too.

I went down to see the wreck like all the rest
The bloody seats, the broken glass, the tangled mess
But I found something no one else had even seen
Behind the dash in Mary's crumpled-up machine.

A little match box circled by a rubber band
And inside was the ring from Walter Browning's hand
And it took a while before I knew just what it meant
The truth about the Carroll County accident.

By dark of night I dropped the ring into a well
And took a sacred oath that I would never tell

The secret of the Carroll County accident
'Cause the county ordered Dad a marble monument.

Yes, I lost him in the Carroll County accident.

COAT OF MANY COLORS

"This is a true story, and means more to me than any other song I've ever recorded. There were twelve children in our family, and we were real poor. We had food to eat, because we raised it, but as far as money to buy clothes, all we had was what Mama made. I was about eight years old, and it was my first year in a big public school. Before that, I went to school over 'in the holler' where we lived in the foothills of Webb Mountain. The original reason Mama made the coat was because I didn't have one and to have something to have my picture taken in. Somebody had sent her a box of scraps to make quilts out of, and she took them and made me a little coat out of it. This was the first time I was ever going to have my picture taken. That's why it hurt me so bad when the kids laughed, because I was so proud of it. I especially liked the bright colors, and I thought I was the prettiest thing in school." —Dolly Parton

COAT OF MANY COLORS
by Dolly Parton

Back through the years I go wandering once again
Back to the seasons of my youth
And I recall a box of rags that someone gave us
And how my Mama put the rags to use.

There were rags of many colors, but every piece was small
And I didn't have a coat, and it was away down in the fall
Mama sewed the rags together, she sewed every stitch with love
And made my coat of many colors that I was so proud of.

And as she sewed, she told a story from the Bible that she'd read
About a coat of many colors that Joseph wore
And then she said, "This coat will bring you good luck and happiness"
And I just couldn't wait to wear it, and she blessed it with a kiss.

My coat of many colors that my Mama made for me
Made only from rags, but I wore it so proudly
And, although we had no money, I was rich as I could be
With my coat of many colors that my Mama made for me.

So, with patches in my britches and holes in both my shoes
In my coat of many colors, I hurried off to school
Just to find the children laughing and making fun of me
In my coat of many colors that my Mama made for me.

And I couldn't understand it, for I felt that I was rich
And I told them of the love that Mama sewed in every stitch
And I told them all the story Mama told me as she sewed
And how my coat of many colors was worth more than all their
clothes.

But they didn't understand it, and I tried to make them see
That one is only poor, only if they choose to be
I know we had no money, I was rich as I could be
In my coat of many colors that my Mama made for me.

EL PASO

"I always wanted to write a song about El Paso, because traditionally that is where the West begins. Western stories that I had read and stories my grandfather told me inspired me to write it. I went through El Paso three times before I ever wrote the song. I wrote it on Christmas vacation on my way to Phoenix. Had I been born a little sooner, the cowboy life is the kind of life I'd like to have lived."

—Marty Robbins

EL PASO

by Marty Robbins

Out in the West Texas town of El Paso
I fell in love with a Mexican girl
Nighttime would find me in Rosa's cantina
Music would play, and Felina would whirl.

Blacker than night were the eyes of Felina
Wicked and evil while casting a spell
My love was deep for this Mexican maiden
I was in love, but in vain, I could tell.

One night a wild young cowboy came in
Wild as the West Texas wind
Dashing and daring, a drink he was sharing
With wicked Felina, the girl that I loved.

So, in anger I challenged his right for the love of this maiden
Down went his hand for the gun that he wore
My challenge was answered in less than a heartbeat
The handsome young stranger lay dead on the floor.

Just for a moment, I stood there in silence
Shocked by the foul, evil deed I had done
Many thoughts raced through my mind as I stood there
I had but one chance, and that was to run.

Out through the back door of Rosa's I ran
Out where the horses were tied
I caught a good one, it looked like it could run
Up on its back, and away I did ride.

Just as fast as I could from the West Texas town of El Paso
Out to the badlands of New Mexico.

Back in El Paso, my life would be worthless
Everything's gone in life, nothing is left
It's been so long since I've seen the young maiden
My love is stronger than my fear of death.

I saddled up, and away I did go
Riding alone in the dark
Maybe tomorrow, a bullet may find me
Tonight, nothing's worse than this pain in my heart.

And at last here I am on the hill overlooking El Paso
I can see Rosa's cantina below
My love is strong, and it pushes me onward
Down off the hill to Felina I go.

Off to my right I see five mounted cowboys
Off to my left ride a dozen or more

Shouting and shooting, I can't let them catch me
I have to make it to Rosa's back door.

Something is dreadfully wrong, for I feel
A deep, burning pain in my side
Though I am trying to stay in the saddle
I'm getting weary, unable to ride.

But my love for Felina is strong, and I rise where I've fallen
Though I am weary, I can't stop to rest
I see the white puff of smoke from the rifle
I feel the bullet go deep in my chest.

From out of nowhere, Felina has found me
Kissing my cheek as she kneels by my side
Cradled by two loving arms that I'll die for
One little kiss, then, Felina, goodbye.

KAW-LIGA

"Hank stayed at a fishing lodge in South Alabama called Lake Kowaliga. The name struck 'Pappy' as a good Indian name and also as a good title for a song."
—Wesley Rose

KAW-LIGA
by Hank Williams and Fred Rose

Kaw-liga was a wooden Indian standing by the door
He fell in love with an Indian maiden over in the antique store
Kaw-liga just stood there and never let it show
So she could never answer "yes" or "no."

Poor ol' Kaw-liga, he never got a kiss
Poor ol' Kaw-liga, he don't know what he missed
Is it any wonder that his face is red?
Kaw-liga, that poor ol' wooden head.

He always wore his Sunday feathers and held a tomahawk
The maiden wore her beads and braids and hoped some day he'd talk

Kaw-liga, too stubborn to ever show a sign
Because his heart was made of knotty pine.

Kaw-liga was a lonely Indian, never went nowhere
His heart was set on the Indian maid with the coal black hair
Kaw-liga just stood there and never let it show
So she could never answer "yes" or "no."

And then one day a wealthy customer bought the Indian maid
And took her, oh, so far away but ol' Kaw-liga stayed
Kaw-liga just stands there as lonely as can be
And wishes he was still an old pine tree.

LEONA

" 'Leona' was not based on a true incident known to me. It was written for Stonewall Jackson. He likes and sings the story type song so well I simply tried to write a little fiction story in song that might have happened or could have happened somewhere, someplace or sometime."

—Cindy Walker

LEONA
by Cindy Walker

Leona, Leona, you tell him you're through
You tell him, Leona, about me and you
You tell him we're married with a baby of two
You tell him, Leona, you tell him you're through.

You laughed as I pleaded and walked out the door
To meet him, to kiss him, to shame me once more
I knew where to find you, just follow the sign
"Dancing and Dining, Cocktails and Wine."

The sidewalk was crowded in front of the bar
I heard the sirens, the black police car
Two bodies lay crumpled, a woman, a man
His wife stood there by you, a gun in her hand.

Leona, Leona, it's over and through
The baby is crying and calling for you
For me there's no difference, I've known for so long
That someday you'd leave me and now you are gone.

LONG BLACK LIMOUSINE

"My son Bobby went into the Air Force in 1954 and was stationed in Germany for a couple of years. While he was there, he studied German, and he either knew or had heard of a couple living there. According to Bobby, they were ordinary working people, but the woman had always wanted to be rich. She would tell her husband that one day she'd be riding in a long black limousine. And she did. She was later killed in an automobile accident, and they brought her body back to him in a black funeral car. Bobby and Vern Stoval wrote the song less than a year after he got out of service."
—Mrs. Bessie George

LONG BLACK LIMOUSINE
by Bobby George and Vern Stoval

There's a long line of mourners driving down our little street
Their fancy cars are such a sight to see
They are all your rich friends who knew you in the city
And now they finally brought you home to me.

The papers told how you lost your life
The party and the fatal crash that night
The rock on the highway, the curve you didn't see
And now you're in that long black limousine.

When you left you told me some day you'd be returning
In a fancy car for all the world to see
Now everyone is watching; you finally got your dream
You're riding in a long black limousine.

Through tear-dimmed eyes I watch as you ride by
A chauffeur at the wheel dressed so fine

I'll never love another, my heart and all my dreams
Go with you in that long black limousine.

THE LONG BLACK VEIL

"I got on a kick with Burl Ives songs—those old songs—but I didn't know any, and I had no way to find any at the time, or was too lazy to look. So I said, 'I'll write me a folksong'—an instant folksong, if you will. So I worked on it for months, and then it all came to me. There's three incidents I've read about in my life that really please me. There was a Catholic priest killed in New Jersey many years ago under a town hall light, and there was no less than 50 witnesses. They never found a motive. They never found the man. Until this day, it's an unsolved murder. That always intrigued me, so that's 'under the town hall light.' Then the Rudolf Valentino story's always impressed me—about the woman that always used to visit his grave. She always wore a long black veil—now there's the title for the song. And the third component was Red Foley's 'God Walks These Hills With Me.' I always thought that was a great song, so I got that in there, too. I just scrambled it all up, and that's what came out."

—Danny Dill

THE LONG BLACK VEIL
by Danny Dill and Marijohn Wilkin

Ten years ago, on a cold, dark night
Someone was killed 'neath the town hall light
There were few at the scene, but they all agreed
That the slayer who ran looked a lot like me.

She walks these hills in a long, black veil
She visits my grave when the night winds wail
Nobody knows, nobody sees, nobody knows but me.

The judge said, "Son, what is your alibi?
If you were somewhere else, then you won't have to die."
I spoke not a word, although it meant my life
For I had been in the arms of my best friend's wife.

The scaffold was high and eternity near
She stood in the crowd and shed not a tear
But sometimes at night, when the cold wind moans
In a long black veil, she cries o'er my bones.

MAY I SLEEP IN YOUR BARN TONIGHT, MISTER?

This song probably dates from around 1890–1900. Written to the tune of "Red River Valley," it was one of the most popular songs recorded by Charlie Poole and the North Carolina Ramblers. It has recently been revived as "May I Sleep In Your Arms Tonight, Mister?" —D. H.

MAY I SLEEP IN YOUR BARN TONIGHT, MISTER?

One night it was dark and it was storming
When along came a tramp in the rain
He was making his way to some station
To catch a long distance train.

"May I sleep in your barn tonight, Mister?
It is cold lying out on the ground
And the cold North wind is whistling
And I have no place to lie down.

"Oh, I have no tobacco or matches
And I'm sure that I'll do you no harm
I will tell you my story, kind mister
For it runs through my heart like a storm.

"It was three years ago last summer
I shall never forget that sad day
When a stranger came out from the city
And said that he wanted to stay.

"Now, the stranger was fair, tall and pleasant
And he looked like a man who had wealth
In his eyes there, a sad look was present
Said he wanted to stay for his health.

"Now, my wife thought his board and his lodging
Could afford to keep us a home
So we took in that tall, handsome stranger
Who later did break up our home.

"One night, as I came from my workshop
I was whistling and singing with joy
I expected a kind-hearted welcome
From my sweet, loving wife and my boy.

"But what did I find but a letter?
It was placed in a room on the stand
And the moment my eyes fell upon it
I picked it right up in my hand.

"Now, this note said my wife and the stranger
They had left and had taken my son
Oh, I wonder if God up in heaven
Only knows what this stranger has done?"

MOTHER, THE QUEEN OF MY HEART

"When I was just a kid, I was sitting in a restaurant and overheard a conversation between two guys who were evidently both gamblers. One of the guys was telling a story very similar to the story in this song, and he said that it had actually happened to him. I remembered the story, dressed it up and changed it around to make it into a song. The first line originally was 'I had a home out in Georgia.' Jimmie Rodgers changed it to 'I had a home out in Texas,' since he was living in Texas at the time."

—Thomas Hoyt (Slim) Bryant

MOTHER, THE QUEEN OF MY HEART

by Hoyt Bryant and Jimmie Rodgers

I had a home out in Texas, down where the blue bonnets grew
I had the kindest old mother; how happy we were, just we two
Till one day the angels called her, that debt we all have to pay
She called me close to her bedside, these last few words to say:

"Son, don't start drinking and gambling, promise you'll always go straight"

Ten years have passed since that parting, that promise I've broke, I must say
I started in gambling for pastime, at last I was just like them all
I bet my clothes and my money, not dreaming that I'd ever fall.

One night I bet all my money, nothing was left to be seen
All that I needed to break them was one card, and that was a queen
The cards were dealt all 'round the table, each man took a card on the draw
I drew the one that would beat them; I turned it and here's what I saw:

I saw my mother's picture, and somehow she seemed to say,
"Son, you have broken your promise," so I tossed the cards away
My winnings I gave to a newsboy, I knew I was wrong from the start;
And I'll ne'er forget that promise, to mother, the queen of my heart.

MOTHER WAS A LADY

"We were in a restaurant when we conceived our next sensation. It was a German restaurant on Twenty-First Street [in New York in 1896] and some of the customers were joshing a new waitress ('joshing' was a popular word then). The girl, a comely, simple sort with a great bun of taffy-colored hair, burst into tears. 'No one would dare insult me,' she said, 'if my brother Jack was only here.' And she added, 'My mother was a lady.' Meyer Cohen, known as 'The California Tenor,' a favorite ballad singer, was at our table and suggested the possibilities of this line as a song title. Stern and I wrote it that afternoon, and Meyer introduced it at Pastor's the next day." —Edward Marks *(They All Sang)*

MOTHER WAS A LADY (OR, IF JACK WERE ONLY HERE)
by Edward Marks and Joseph Stern

Two drummers, they were seated in a grand hotel one day
While dining, they were chatting in a jovial sort of way
There came a pretty waitress to bring a tray of food
They spoke to her familiarly in a manner rather rude.

At first, she did not notice or make the least reply
But one remark was made to her, brought teardrops to her eyes
She turned on her tormentors, her cheeks were blushing red
Approaching as a picture, this is what she said:

"My mother was a lady, like yours, you would allow
And you may have a sister who needs protection now
I've come to this great city to find a brother dear
And you wouldn't dare insult me, sir, if Jack were only here."

The two sat there in silence, their heads hung down in shame
"Forgive me, miss, we meant no harm; pray tell me, what is your name?"
She told him, and he cried aloud, "I know your brother, too!
We've been friends for many, many years, and he often speaks of you.

"Come, go with me when I go back, and if you'll only wed
I'll take you to him as my bride, for I love you since you said:"

ODE TO BILLY JOE

"I think perhaps the question most asked about my composition, 'Ode To Billy Joe,' has been the inevitable, 'What was thrown off the Tallahatchie Bridge?' The question is of secondary importance in my mind. The story of Billy Joe has two more interesting underlying themes. First, the illustration of a group of people's reactions to the life and death of Billy Joe, and its subsequent effect on their lives, is made. Second, the obvious generation gap between the girl and her mother is shown when both women experience a common loss (first, Billy Joe and later, Papa), and yet Mama and the girl are unable to recognize their mutual loss or share their grief."

—Bobbie Gentry

ODE TO BILLY JOE

by Bobbie Gentry

It was the third of June, another sleepy, dusty Delta day
I was out choppin' cotton, and my brother was balin' hay
And at dinner time, we stopped and went back to the house to eat
And Mama hollered at the back door, "Y'all remember to wipe your feet"
And then she said, "I got some news this mornin' from Choctaw Ridge
Today Billy Joe McAllister jumped off the Tallahatchie Bridge."

Papa said to Mama as she passed around the black-eyed peas
"Well, Billy Joe never had a lick of sense; pass the biscuits, please
There's five more acres in the lower forty I got to plow"
And Mama said, "It was a shame about Billy Joe, anyhow
Seems like nothin' ever comes to no good up on Choctaw Ridge
And now Billy Joe McAllister's jumped off the Tallahatchie Bridge."

Brother said he recollected when he and Tom and Billy Joe
Put a frog down my back at the Carroll County picture show
And wasn't I talkin' to him at the church last Sunday night?
"I'll have another piece of apple pie; you know, it don't seem right
I saw him at the sawmill yesterday up on Choctaw Ridge
And now you tell me Billy Joe's jumped off the Tallahatchie Bridge."

And Mama said to me, "Child, what's happened to your appetite?
I've been cookin' all morning, and you haven't touched a single bite
That nice young preacher Brother Taylor brought by today
Said he'd be pleased to have dinner on Sunday; oh, by the way
He said he saw a girl who looked a lot like you up on Choctaw Ridge
And she and Billy Joe was throwin' somethin' off the Tallahatchie Bridge."

A year has come and gone since we heard the news about Billy Joe
Brother married Becky Thompson; they bought a store in Tupelo
There was a virus going 'round, Papa caught it, and he died last spring
And now Mama doesn't seem to wanta do much of anything
And me, I spend a lot of time pickin' flowers up on Choctaw Ridge
And drop them into the muddy water off the Tallahatchie Bridge.

PHILADELPHIA LAWYER

"Woody Guthrie was a writer of hundreds of songs; however, he composed very little music. His style was to parody folksongs, and 'Philadelphia Lawyer' is one of his best known parodies, which was based on the folk ballad 'The Jealous Lover.' Woody wrote the lyrics sometime around August, 1937, while he was singing over KFVD in Los Angeles. He first titled it 'Reno Blues.' Woody apparently heard 'The Jealous Lover' when he grew up in Okemah, Oklahoma, but when and where he learned the song is pure speculation, for 'The Jealous Lover' is the most popular native American murder ballad to be sung. In its structure it refers to no specific time or place or person; it is a generalized ballad about a lover murdering his sweetheart because she refuses to marry him. However, as it traveled from community to community, it has on occasion assumed specific identity within some regions. Woody took the melody and put new words with a light humorous touch to it. It is possible that when it was sung over KFVD, that someone wrote it down and that it eventually was brought to the attention of Rose Maddox who recorded it. Her words are identical to Woody's version; only the title was changed from 'Reno Blues' to 'Philadelphia Lawyer.' "

—Guy Logsden, University of Tulsa

PHILADELPHIA LAWYER
by Woody Guthrie

Way out in Reno, Nevada
Where romance blooms and fades
A great Philadelphia lawyer
Was in love with a Hollywood maid
"Come, love, and we will wander
Out where the lights are bright
I'll win you a divorce from your husband
And we can get married tonight."

Now Bill was a gun-totin' cowboy
Ten notches were carved on his gun
And all the boys around Reno
Left Wild Bill's maiden alone
One night when he was returning
From riding the range in the cold
He dreamed of his Hollywood maiden
Her love was as lasting as gold.

As he drew near her window
A shadow he saw on the shade
'Twas the great Philadelphia lawyer
Makin' love to his Hollywood maid
The night was as still as the desert
The moon was bright overhead
Bill listened awhile to the lawyer
He could hear ev'ry word that he said.

"Your hands are so pretty and lovely
Your form so rare and divine

Come go with me to the city
And leave this wild cowboy behind."
Now back in old Pennsylvania
Among those beautiful pines
There's one less Philadelphia lawyer
In old Philadelphia tonight.

SAGINAW, MICHIGAN

"At the time, city songs were going pretty good. 'Detroit City' was a big one. I've always been hung up on Indian sounds and Indian names—the rhythmic flow of Indian names. Prior to becoming a full-time songwriter, I was a tool and die maker. One of my basic tools in this trade were Lufkin depth micrometers made in Saginaw, Michigan. This was printed on the box they came in, and I would look at that on my tool bench five and six days a week. I had heard weather forecasts about Saginaw, Michigan, and I loved the sound of it. All I had to start with was the name, so I decided I would write the song about people and just have it happen in Saginaw, Michigan. I got it what I thought was finished and took it to Tree Publishing. Bill Anderson liked it, but felt it needed a little different twist, so he finished it."

—Don Wayne

SAGINAW, MICHIGAN

by Don Wayne and Bill Anderson

I was born in Saginaw, Michigan
I grew up in a house on Saginaw Bay
My dad was a poor, hard-working Saginaw fisherman
Too many times he came home with too little pay.

I loved a girl in Saginaw, Michigan
The daughter of a wealthy, wealthy man
But he called me "that son of a Saginaw fisherman,"
Not good enough to claim his daughter's hand.

Now I'm up here in Alaska, looking around for gold
Like a crazy fool, I'm diggin' in this frozen ground so cold
But with each new day I pray I'll strike it rich, and then
I'll go back home and claim my love in Saginaw, Michigan.

I wrote my love in Saginaw, Michigan
I said, "Honey, I'm coming home, please wait for me
And you can tell your dad I'm coming home a richer man
I hit the biggest strike in Klondike history."

Her dad met me in Saginaw, Michigan
He gave me a great big party with champagne
Then he said, "Son, you're a wise, young, ambitious man,
Will you sell your father-in-law your Klondike claim?"

Now he's up there in Alaska, diggin' in the cold, cold ground
The greedy fool is looking for the gold I never found
It serves him right, and no one here is missing him
Least of all the newlyweds of Saginaw, Michigan.

THE SON OF HICKORY HOLLER'S TRAMP

"Of all the songs I've written, this is my favorite. I like to say that this is a story about a mother's love for her children." —Dallas Frazier

THE SON OF HICKORY HOLLER'S TRAMP
by Dallas Frazier

The corn was dry, the weeds were high when Daddy took to drinkin'
Then him and Liz Walker, they took up and went away
Mama cried a tear and then she promised fourteen children
"I'll swear you'll never see a hungry day."

But Mama sacrificed her pride, and neighbors started talking
But I was much too young to understand the things they said
The things that mattered most of all was Mama's chicken dumplings
And a kiss goodnight before we went to bed.

Oh, the path was deep and wide from footsteps leading to our cabin
Above the door there burned a scarlet lamp
And late at night a hand would knock and there would be a stranger
Yes, I'm the son of Hickory Holler's tramp.

When Daddy left and destitution came upon our cabin
Not one neighbor volunteered to lend a helping hand
So let 'em gossip all they want; she loved us and she raised us
The proof is standing here, a full grown man.

Last summer Mama passed away and left the ones who loved her
Each and every one is more than grateful for his birth
Each Sunday she receives a fresh bouquet of fourteen roses
And a card that reads, "The greatest Mom on earth."

STREETS OF BALTIMORE

"It was about '62 or '63 when I started thinking along that line. Free love was becoming acceptable, and religion was relaxing some of its restraints. I noticed around the Opry and around larger cities I played there were a lot of young married couples looking very distraught. I had this feeling that they were probably married before they knew it and caught up in something they could have been trying out without being married. I saw one little girl visiting the Grand Ole Opry with her boyfriend. He had a lot of grease under his fingernails, and he could hardly afford to get her there. She was dressed in all her finery. All the guys were giving her a three or four-time go-over. The poor ole boy was so tired, he could hardly drive home. She looked like she was ready to fly with anybody that could get her the hell out of there. This ole boy falls in love with that little ole pretty chick, marries her. She's got higher ambitions than he's got. She's going to use him as a stepping stone to get on, and that's what she does. So he sells the farm. This couple and many like them were pretty much the average small town, rural Americans, members of the silent majority. This sort of thing happened a lot back then. I don't think it does anymore. It was a very important thing in a lot of people's lives when rural America discovered how the jet set was living."
—Tompall Glaser

STREETS OF BALTIMORE
by Tompall Glaser and Harlan Howard

I sold the farm to take my woman where she longed to be
We left our kin and all our friends back there in Tennessee

I bought the one-way tickets she had often begged me for
And they took us to the streets of Baltimore.

Her heart was filled with laughter when she saw those city lights
She said the prettiest place on earth was Baltimore at night
Well, a man feels proud to give his woman what she's longing for
And I kind of liked the streets of Baltimore.

I got myself a factory job, I ran an old machine
Bought a little cottage in a neighborhood serene
But every night when I came home with every muscle sore
She would drag me through the streets of Baltimore.

Eventually our little home began to lose its glow
The night life and the wine had changed the girl I used to know
And when I tried to talk to her she'd leave and slam the door
As she headed for the streets of Baltimore.

Well, I did my best to bring her back to what she used to be
But I soon learned she loved those bright lights more than she loved me
Now I'm going back on that same train that brought me here before
While my baby walks the streets of Baltimore.

TENNESSEE STUD

"This is actually the story of two generations of my wife's family—John Merriman, her great grandfather, and Jess Goodman, her grandfather—rolled into one. John Merriman settled in Tennessee, not Arkansas, in about 1820 or 1825, and a lot of the incidents in the song describe his exploits. Jess Goodman was a soldier in the Union Army in the Civil War and got home to Tennessee only to find it overrun with "Jayhawkers" [desperados]. Since he was a Union soldier in predominantly Confederate territory, he decided he had better head West. Jess settled in the trading territory of a Frenchman named Timbeaux and founded the town of Timbo, Arkansas. He raised horses and raced them for money until the legislature outlawed it. When he went back to Tennessee, he found a girl, 'whupped her brother and whupped her pa,' and brought her back to Arkansas. And when they got back home, it wasn't long before there was a pretty little horse colt in the yard and a little baby."

—Jimmie Driftwood

TENNESSEE STUD

by Jimmie Driftwood

Along about 1825
I left Tennessee very much alive
Never would have made it through the Arkansas mud
If I hadn't been a-riding on the Tennessee Stud.

Tennessee Stud was long and lean
The color of the sun, and his eyes were green
He had the nerve, and he had the blood
And there never was a horse like the Tennessee Stud.

One day I was riding in a beautiful land
I run smack into an Indian band
They jumped their knives with a whoop and a yell
And I rode away like a bat out of hell.

I circled their camp for a time or two
Just to show what the Tennessee horse can do
The red-skinned boys couldn't get my blood
'Cause I was a-riding on the Tennessee Stud.

Rode on down across No Man's Land
Across the river from the Rio Grande
Raced my horse with a Spaniard's pole
Till I got me a skinful of silver and gold.

Me and a gambler, we couldn't agree
We got in a fight over Tennessee
We jerked our guns, he fell with a thud
And I got away on the Tennessee Stud.

Rode on back across Arkansas
Whupped her brother and I whupped her pa
I found that girl with the golden hair
And she was a-riding on a Tennessee mare.

Stirrup to stirrup, and side by side
Across the mountains and the valleys wide

Yonder Big Muddy and the foot of the flood
On a Tennessee mare and the Tennessee Stud.

Pretty little baby on the cabin floor
Little horse colt playing 'round the door
I love the girl with the golden hair
And the Tennessee Stud wed the Tennessee mare.

THE YEAR THAT CLAYTON DELANEY DIED

"Clayton Delaney was a real person, though that wasn't his real name. He lived in Eastern Kentucky, and as a young man of 18, he moved to Ohio. It was right after the second world war, during the boom, when the G.I.s were all coming home, and there was money to spend, and people were drinking beer and dancing. Hank Williams was happening. Jim Reeves was happening. Ernest Tubb was still very popular. And Clayton was a great country music picker. He worked in Ohio for awhile in nightclubs and saloons, and then his health failed him, and he came back home to Kentucky. He died of either cancer of the lung or TB, but they never knew which. I remember he used to say, 'Boy, Tom, you should have seen us then! We all had the shirts just alike.' He didn't pick like the records, though, and this was really how I got into the music business. Because, at seven or eight, I thought that songs just came from somewhere—they were all hits, because they didn't play the ones that weren't. But Clayton would take the hit records and sing them the way he wanted to sing them. At first, I was a little bit insulted, but then I was very much entertained. He would change the tempo, play different licks. Everybody else I'd heard play guitar and sing wanted to do it as close to the record as they could get, but Clayton wanted to do it the way Clayton did it. And I said, 'Hey! That's an idea. If a guy can do that, probably you could get some new songs and start all over and have a whole new style.' Which is where Tom T. Hall came from."

—Tom T. Hall

THE YEAR THAT CLAYTON DELANEY DIED
by Tom T. Hall

I remember the year that Clayton Delaney died
They said for the last two weeks that he suffered and cried

It made a big impression on me, although I was a barefoot kid
They said he got religion at the end, and I'm glad that he did.

Clayton was the best guitar-picker in our town
I thought he was a hero, and I used to follow Clayton around
I often wondered why Clayton, who seemed so good to me
Never took his guitar and made it down in Tennessee.

Well, Daddy said he drank a lot, but I could never understand
I knew he used to pick up in Ohio with a five-piece band
Clayton used to tell me, "Son, you'd better put that old guitar away
Ain't no money in it; it'll lead you to an early grave."

I guess if I'd admit it, Clayton taught me how to drink booze
I can see him, half-stoned, a-pickin' up on "Lovesick Blues"
When Clayton died, I made him a promise I was gonna carry on
  somehow
I'd give a hundred dollars if he could only see me now.

I remember the year that Clayton Delaney died
Nobody ever knew it, but I went out in the woods and I cried
I know there's a lot of big preachers that know a lot more than I do
But it could be that the good Lord likes a little pickin', too.

Bibliography

PRIMARY SOURCES, (ANNOTATIONS)

Acuff, Roy ("Fireball Mail," "Great Speckled Bird," "The Old Age Pension Check," "Pins And Needles," "The Precious Jewel," "Streamlined Cannon Ball," "Stuck Up Blues," "Wabash Cannon Ball"). Interview, Nashville, Tennessee, September 8, 1973. Letter from Miss Dean May quoting Mr. Acuff, November 16, 1973.

Allison, Joe ("He'll Have To Go"). Interview, Nashville, Tennessee, September 5, 1973.

Anderson, Bill ("Bright Lights And Country Music," "City Lights," "Po' Folks," "Saginaw, Michigan," "Where Have All Our Heroes Gone?"). Interview, Nashville, Tennessee, September 1, 1973.

Anderson, Casey and Liz ("[I'm A Lonesome] Fugitive"). Interview, Nashville, Tennessee, July 18, 1973.

Arnold, Eddy ("I'll Hold You In My Heart," "Molly Darling"). Telephone interview, September 20, 1973.

Autry, Gene ("That Silver-Haired Daddy Of Mine"). Letter, October 19, 1973.

Babcock, Joe ("I Washed My Hands In Muddy Water"). Letter, May 7, 1973.

Bailes, Walter ("Dust On The Bible"). Letter, March 17, 1973.

Barlow, Harold ("I've Got Tears In My Ears From Lying On My Back In My Bed While I Cry Over You"). Telephone interview, March 22, 1974.

Barnes, Howard Lee ("I Really Don't Want To Know"). Letter, July 14, 1973.

Bartlett, Gene (E. M. Bartlett's "Take An Old Cold Tater [And Wait]"). Letter, April 9, 1973.

Baxter, Dick (Stuart Hamblen's "But I'll Go Chasin' Women," "It Is No Secret," "My Mary," "Remember Me, I'm The One Who Loves You," "Texas Plains," "This Ole House"). Letter, May 8, 1973, dictated by Stuart Hamblen.

Bennard, Hannah (Mrs. George) (Rev. George Bennard's "The Old Rugged Cross"). Letter, June 22, 1973. Telephone interview, July 3, 1973.

Berbert, Edith (Ed Burt [pseud.]) ("Silver Dew On The Blue Grass Tonight"). Telephone interview, December 7, 1973. Letter, December 14, 1973.

Blair, Hal ("Please Help Me, I'm Falling [In Love With You]," "One Has My Name, The Other Has My Heart"). Letters, April 6, 1973; August 6, 1973.

Blake, Wava Guthrie (Jack Guthrie's "Oklahoma Hills"). Letter, November 1, 1973.

Bond, Johnny ("Cimarron," "I Wonder Where You Are Tonight"). Letter, September 2, 1972.

Brumley, Albert E. ("I'll Fly Away," "Turn Your Radio On"). Letter, January 10, 1973.

Bryant, Boudleaux ("Out Behind The Barn"). Interview, Nashville, Tennessee, June 1, 1973.

Bryant, Felice ("We Could"). Telephone interview, June 1, 1973.

Bryant, Thomas Hoyt (Slim) ("Mother, The Queen Of My Heart"). Letter, November 7, 1973.

Butcher, Dwight ("When Jimmie Rodgers Said Goodbye"). Letter, February 8, 1974.

Cardwell, Jack ("The Death Of Hank Williams"). Telephone interview, January 20, 1974.

Carlisle, Bill ("Too Old To Cut The Mustard"). Interview, Nashville, Tennessee, June 10, 1973.

Carter, Maybelle ("Keep On The Sunny Side Of Life," "Bury Me Beneath The Willow," A. P. Carter's "Wildwood Flower," "You Are My Flower"). Interview, Nashville, Tennessee, September 6, 1973.

Carter, Sara (A. P. Carter's "I'm Thinking Tonight Of My Blue Eyes"). Telephone interview, September 5, 1973.

Cash, Johnny ("Folsom Prison Blues," "I Walk The Line"). Telephone interview, November 6, 1973.

Chapin (MacDonald), Elizabeth ("The Convict And The Rose"). Telephone interview, January 17, 1974.

Cheetham, Everett ("Blood On The Saddle"). Letter, January 2, 1974.

Chesnut, Jerry ("Oney"). Interview, Nashville, Tennessee, October 17, 1973.

Clements, Zeke ("Smoke On The Water"). Telephone interview, May 13, 1973.

Coben, Cy ("How To Catch A Man"). Telephone interview, August 1, 1973.

Cohen, Norm ("Wabash Cannon Ball," "Wreck Of The Old 97"). Letter, May 21, 1974.

Court, Anita Rodgers (Jimmie Rodgers's "Hobo's Meditation," "Waiting For A Train"). Letter, January 10, 1974.

Cummins, Betty Foley (Red Foley's "Old Shep"). Telephone interview, May 19, 1973.

Daffan, Ted ("Born To Lose," "Headin' Down The Wrong Highway," "I'm A Fool To Care," "Truck Driver's Blues," "Worried Mind"). Letter, December 12, 1972.

Danoff, Bill and Taffy ("Take Me Home, Country Roads"). Letter, August 27, 1973.

Davidson, Ken (Billy Cox's "Sparkling Brown Eyes"). Telephone interview, May 23, 1974.

Davis, Karl ("Kentucky," "I'm Here To Get My Baby Out Of Jail," "The Prisoner's Dream"). Telephone interview, August 1, 1973.

Dean, Jimmy ("Big Bad John"). Letter, July 16, 1973.
Dexter, Al ("Pistol Packin' Mama"). Letter, March 9, 1973.
Dill, Danny ("Detroit City," "The Long Black Veil"). Interview, Nashville, Tennessee, June 2, 1973.
Dixon, Dorsey, Jr. (Dorsey Dixon's "Weaveroom Blues," "Wreck On The Highway"). Taped interview, June 20, 1973.
Dorsey, Thomas A. ("Take My Hand, Precious Lord," "There'll Be Peace In The Valley For Me"). Telephone interview, August 10, 1973.
Driftwood, Jimmie ("The Battle Of New Orleans," "Tennessee Stud"). Telephone interview, April 14, 1973.
Duff, Arleigh ("Y'All Come"). Letter, March 5, 1973.
Ferguson, Bob ("Carroll County Accident," "Wings Of A Dove"). Letter, January 4, 1972.
Foree, Mel ("No One Will Ever Know"). Letter, March 12, 1973.
Franks, Donald (B. L. Shook's "Cabin On The Hill"). Letter, June 11, 1973.
Frazier, Dallas ("The Son Of Hickory Holler's Tramp," "There Goes My Everything"). Interview, Nashville, Tennessee, October 19, 1973.
Friend, Cliff ("Lovesick Blues"). Letter, April 9, 1973.
Frizzell, Lefty ("If You've Got The Money, I've Got The Time," "Mom And Dad's Waltz"). Interview, Nashville, Tennessee, May 30, 1973.
Gaston, Lyle ("Blackboard Of My Heart"). Telephone interview, November 14, 1973.
Gentry, Bobbie ("Ode To Billy Joe"). Letter, November 15, 1973.
George, Bessie (Bobby George's "Long Black Limousine"). Telephone interview, February 21, 1974.
Gibson, Don ("I Can't Stop Loving You," "[I'd Be] A Legend In My Time," "Oh, Lonesome Me"). Interview, Nashville, Tennessee, September 7, 1973.
Glaser, Tompall ("Streets Of Baltimore"). Interview, Nashville, Tennessee, June 7, 1973.
Goodman, Steve ("City Of New Orleans"). Telephone interview, May 23, 1974.
Graves, Pete ("Bumming Around"). Telephone interview, March 15, 1973.
Greene, Earl ("Six Days On The Road"). Telephone interview, May 14, 1973.
Hamblen, Stuart—*see* Baxter, Dick.
Hall, Tom T. ("Ballad Of Forty Dollars," "Harper Valley PTA," "Homecoming," "Margie's At The Lincoln Park Inn," "The Year That Clayton Delaney Died"). Interview, Nashville, Tennessee, September 1, 1973.
Harris, Ted ("Crystal Chandeliers"). Interview, Nashville, Tennessee, June 4, 1972.
Hartford, John ("Gentle On My Mind"). Telephone interview, June 21, 1973.
Hausey, Howard ("Honky Tonk Man"). Telephone interview, July 27, 1973.
Heath, Rose (Hy Heath's "Take These Chains From My Heart"). Letter, April 11, 1973.
Horton, Billie Jean (Hank Williams's "Your Cheatin' Heart"). Letter, June 3, 1974.
Horton, Vaughn ("Address Unknown," "Mockin' Bird Hill"). Telephone interview, September 2, 1973.
Houser, Hazel ("Wait A Little Longer, Please, Jesus"). Telephone interview, July 20, 1973.
Howard, Harlan ("Busted," "Heartaches By The Number," "The Blizzard,"

"Mississippi Delta Land," "Pick Me Up On Your Way Down," "Sunday Morning Christian," "Yours Love"). Interview, Nashville, Tennessee, June 1, 1973.

Hughes, Marvin ("Night Train To Memphis"). Telephone interview, May 11, 1973.

Jacobs, Edythe (Bob Nolan's "Cool Water," "The Touch Of God's Hand," "Tumbling Tumbleweeds," "Way Out There"). Letter, November 29, 1973. quoting Bob Nolan.

Jay, Penny ("Don't Let Me Cross Over"). Telephone interview, July 3, 1973.

Jones, Louis Marshall (Grandpa) ("Eight More Miles To Louisville"). Telephone interview, June 5, 1973.

Karliski, Steve ("Molly"). Interview, New York City, July 10, 1973.

Kershaw, Doug ("Louisiana Man"). Interview, Nashville, Tennessee, June 1, 1973.

King, Pee Wee ("Tennessee Waltz"). Letter, February 1, 1973.

Klein, Saul ("I'm Free [From The Chain Gang Now]"). Telephone interview, August 4, 1973.

Kristofferson, Kris ("Me And Bobby McGee"). Interview, Nashville, Tennessee, June 7, 1973.

Lair, John ("Freight Train Blues," "Only One Step More," "Take Me Back To Renfro Valley"). Interview, Renfro Valley, Kentucky, August 22, 1973.

Latham, Dwight ("I'm My Own Grandpaw"). Letter, March 4, 1973.

Lee, Dickey ("She Thinks I Still Care"). Interview, Nashville, Tennessee, October 18, 1973.

Loesser, Lynn (Frank Loesser's "Have I Stayed Away Too Long?"). Letter, January 10, 1974.

Logsden, Guy (Woody Guthrie's "Philadelphia Lawyer"). Letter, March 8, 1974.

Loudermilk, John D. ("Tobacco Road"). Interview, Nashville, Tennessee, May 28, 1972.

Louvin, Charlie ("Alabama," "I Take The Chance"). Telephone interview, October 19, 1972.

Lynch, Juanita (Clayton McMichen's "Peach Pickin' Time In Georgia"). Letter containing a statement from Mrs. McMichen, September 28, 1973.

Lynn, Loretta ("Coal Miner's Daughter," "Dear Uncle Sam," "Don't Come Home A-Drinkin'," "You Ain't Woman Enough"). Interview, Nashville, Tennessee, May 30, 1973.

McAlpin, Vic ("God Walks These Hills With Me"). Interview, Nashville, Tennessee, May 10, 1972.

McCarty, Nora (E. C. McCarty's "Preachin', Prayin', Singin' "). Telephone interview, June 24, 1973.

McCoy, Faith ("Mommy, Please Stay Home With Me"). Telephone dictation of information furnished by Wallace Fowler, September 10, 1973.

McEnery, Dave ("Amelia Earhart's Last Flight"). Letter, April 17, 1973.

McGee, Sam ("When The Wagon Was New"). Interview, Franklin, Tennessee, April 20, 1973.

McMichen, Mrs. Clayton (McMichen's "Peach Pickin' Time In Georgia"). Letter, September 28, 1973.

McWilliams, Elsie ("Daddy And Home"). Letter, March 18, 1973.

Maphis, Joe ("Dim Lights, Thick Smoke [And Loud, Loud Music]"). Telephone interview, June 27, 1973.

Massey, Novie (Guy Massey's "The Prisoner's Song"). Telephone interview, January 21, 1974.

Merritt, Neal ("May The Bird Of Paradise Fly Up Your Nose"). Telephone interview, December 13, 1973.

Miller, Eddie ("Release Me"). Telephone interview, June 19, 1973.

Miller, Frankie, Jr. ("Black Land Farmer"). Telephone interview, August 1, 1973.

Miller, J. D. ("It Wasn't God Who Made Honky Tonk Angels"). Letter, May 24, 1973.

Minton, Rosalind Smith (Beasley Smith's "Night Train To Memphis," "Tennessee Central Number Nine"). Letter, October 25, 1973.

Montana, Patsy ("I Want To Be A Cowboy's Sweetheart"). Letter, May 14, 1973.

Moody, Clyde ("Shenandoah Waltz"). Interview, Nashville, Tennessee, October 22, 1973.

Mooney, Ralph ("Crazy Arms"). Letter, March 22, 1973.

Moore, Marvin ("Four Walls"). Letter, August 23, 1973.

Moore, Robin, Jr. ("The Ballad Of The Green Berets"). Telephone interview, January 9, 1973.

Morgan, George ("Candy Kisses"). Telephone interview, May 23, 1973.

Morris, W. R. (Guy Drake's "Welfare Cadilac"). Letter, January 28, 1974.

Mullins, John ("Company's Comin' "). Letter, March 10, 1973.

Nelson, Steve ("Bouquet Of Roses"). Letter, August 3, 1973.

Nelson, Willie ("Funny How Time Slips Away"). Interview, New York City, May 17, 1973.

Noack, Eddie ("These Hands"). Letter, March 9, 1973.

Nolan, Bob—*see* Jacobs, Edythe.

Null, Cecil ("I Forgot More Than You'll Ever Know"). Interview, Nashville, Tennessee, June 5, 1973.

O'Neal, Waldo Lafayette ("Hobo Bill's Last Ride"). Telephone interview, February 14, 1973.

Owens, Maude Jewel (Tex Owens's "Cattle Call"). Letter, April 30, 1973.

Parton, Dolly ("Coat Of Many Colors," "In The Good Old Days [When Times Were Bad]"). Telephone interview, September 1, 1973.

Payne, Myrtie (Leon Payne's "I Love You Because," "Lost Highway," "They'll Never Take Her Love From Me"). Telephone interview, December 20, 1972.

Perry, Betty Sue ("The Other Woman"). Letter, June 3, 1973. Telephone interview, July 14, 1973.

Pierce, Webb (Audrey Grisham [pseud.] ("There Stands The Glass"). Interview, Nashville, Tennessee, September 6, 1973.

Putman, Curley, Jr. ("Green, Green Grass Of Home"). Letter, March 21, 1973.

Raney, Wayne ("Blues Stay Away From Me," "Why Don't You Haul Off And Love Me?"). Telephone interview, August 3, 1973.

Rector, Johnny ("Married By The Bible, Divorced By The Law"). Letter, March 24, 1973.

Rice, Alan ("When It's Prayer Meetin' Time In The Hollow"). Letter, October 4, 1973.

Rice, Bill ("Wonder Could I Live There Anymore"). Letter, July 11, 1973.

Robbins, Marty ("El Paso," "My Woman, My Woman, My Wife"). Interview, Nashville, Tennessee, June 5, 1973.

Robison, Catherine (Carson Robison's "Carry Me Back To The Lone Prairie," "Carry Me Back To The Mountains," "Life Gits Tee-jus, Don't It?," "The Wreck Of Number Nine"). Letter, August 7, 1973.

Rose, Wesley (Fred Rose's "Kaw-liga"). Interview, Nashville, Tennessee, June 4, 1973.

Rouse, Ervin T. ("Orange Blossom Special," "Sweeter Than The Flowers"). Interview, New York City, April 26, 1973.

Rule, Jimmie (Hank Williams's "I'm So Lonesome I Could Cry"). Telephone interview, March 2, 1974.

Seitz, Charles L. ("Before I Met You"). Telephone interview, June 1, 1973.

Skinner, Jimmie ("Doin' My Time"). Letter, March 19, 1973.

Smartt, Rosemary Rollins (Don Rollins's "The Other Woman [In My Life]," "The Race Is On"). Letter, October 25, 1973.

Smith, Dorothy Griffin (Rex Griffin's "The Last Letter"). Letter, December 11, 1973.

Snow, Hank ("The Golden Rocket," "I'm Movin' On"). Letter, April 4, 1973.

Southern, Hal ("I Dreamed Of A Hillbilly Heaven"). Letter, September 12, 1973.

Spain (Futrelle), Irene ("The Death Of Floyd Collins," "God Put A Rainbow In The Cloud," Rev. Andrew Jenkins's "A Drunkard's Child"). Letter, July 6, 1973.

Spencer, Hal (Tim Spencer's "Cigareetes, Whusky And Wild, Wild Women"). Telephone interview, September 8, 1973.

Stanphill, Ira ("Supper Time"). Letter, February 14, 1973.

Stewart, Redd ("Soldier's Last Letter"). Letter, June 29, 1973.

Stoneman, Ernest "Pop" ("The Sinking Of The Titanic"). Interview, February 17, 1967.

Stoneman, Pattie (Ernest Stoneman's "The Poor Tramp Has To Live"). Interview, Nashville, Tennessee, October 19, 1973.

Sullivan, Gene ("When My Blue Moon Turns To Gold Again"). Telephone interview, July 20, 1973.

Talley, Lewis ("Dear John Letter"). Interview, New York City, April 5, 1974.

Taylor, Lee Hill (Billy Hill's "Have You Ever Been Lonely [Have You Ever Been Blue]?," "The Last Roundup"). Letter, January 17, 1974.

Templet, C. M. (Jimmie Davis's "Nobody's Darlin' But Mine," "Shackles And Chains," "Where The Old Red River Flows," "You Are My Sunshine"). Letter, October 11, 1973, quoting Jimmie Davis.

Terry, Bob ("Roughneck Blues"). Letter, December 11, 1972.

Tillis, Mel ("Ruby, Don't Take Your Love To Town"). Telephone interview, June 19, 1973.

Tillman, Floyd ("Each Night At Nine," "I Love You So Much It Hurts," "I'll Never Slip Around Again," "It Makes No Difference Now," "Slipping Around"). Letter, November 15, 1972.

Travis, Merle ("Dark As A Dungeon," "I Am A Pilgrim," "Nine Pound Hammer," "No Vacancy," "Sixteen Tons," "Smoke, Smoke, Smoke [That Cigarette]"). Interview, Nashville, Tennessee, July 8, 1973. Telephone interview, September 7, 1973.

Tubb, Ernest ("Our Baby's Book," "Soldier's Last Letter," "Walking The Floor Over You"). Interview, Nashville, Tennessee, October 17, 1971. Letter, February 28, 1973.

Tubb, Glenn D. ("Skip A Rope"). Letter, March 16, 1973.
Van Dyke, LeRoy ("Auctioneer"). Interview, Nashville, Tennessee, June 6, 1972.
Van Ness, Clarke ("Filipino Baby"). Telephone interview, January 10, 1974.
Vincent, Nat ("The Strawberry Roan," "When The Bloom Is On The Sage"). Letter, August 6, 1973.
Wakely, Jimmy ("Too Late"). Telephone interview, May 8, 1973.
Walker, Cindy ("Bubbles In My Beer," "Dusty Skies," "Leona," "Warm Red Wine"). Letter, December 11, 1972.
Walker, Wayne P. ("All The Time"). Interview, Nashville, Tennessee, June 4, 1973.
Wallace, Billy ("Back Street Affair"). Letter, March 10, 1973.
Warren, William ("The Wild Side Of Life"). Telephone interview, December 13, 1973.
Wayne, Don ("Saginaw, Michigan"). Telephone interview, September 6, 1973.
Wheeler, Billy Edd ("Ode To The Little Brown Shack Out Back"). Letter, February 9, 1973.
White, John (D. J. O'Malley's "When The Work Is Done Next Fall"). Letter, December 27, 1973.
Whitley, Ray ("Back In The Saddle Again"). Letter, July 30, 1973.
Williams, Audrey (Hank Williams's "Cold, Cold Heart," "I Saw The Light," "Jambalaya," "A Mansion On The Hill"). Interview, Nashville, Tennessee, June 18, 1971.
Williams, Bill (Bill Monroe's "Blue Moon Of Kentucky," "Kentucky Waltz"). Telephone interview, January 18, 1974, quoting Bill Monroe.
Williams, Doc ("Willie Roy, The Crippled Boy"). Letter, April 5, 1973.
Williams, Lawton ("Fraulein"). Telephone interview, July 18, 1973.
Williams, Louise (Curley Williams's "Half As Much"). Telephone interview, November 8, 1973.
Wills, Betty (Bob Wills's "Faded Love," "[New] San Antonio Rose," "Take Me Back To Tulsa"). Letter, September 20, 1973, dictated by Bob Wills.
Wilson, Happy ("A-Sleepin' At The Foot Of The Bed"). Interview, Nashville, Tennessee, October 20, 1973.
Wiseman, Scott ("Have I Told You Lately That I Love You?," "Mountain Dew," "Remember Me When The Candlelights Are Gleaming," "That Crazy War"). Letters, April 8, 1973; August 8, 1973.

SECONDARY SOURCES (ANNOTATIONS)

Antrim, Doron K. "Whoop-and-Holler Opera." *Colliers* magazine 117 (1946): 18. (Bob Miller's "There's A Star-Spangled Banner Waving Somewhere").
Kerr, Phil. *Music In Evangelism.* Glendale, California: Gospel Music Publishers, 1944. (Ada Blenkhorn's "Keep On The Sunny Side Of Life," Charles Tillman's "Life's Railway To Heaven").
Mare, Frank. Taped interview with Ernest V. Stoneman, February 17, 1967. ("The Sinking Of The Titanic").
Marks, Edward B. *They All Sang.* New York: The Viking Press, 1934. ("Mother Was A Lady").
Monroe, Bill. "Bill Monroe's 'Uncle Pen' " (album notes). Decca DL 7 5348 (1972). ("Uncle Pen").

"The Red Hayes Story." *Country Music People.* Kent, England: Country Music Press, Ltd., July 1973. (J. H. Hayes's "A Satisfied Mind").

Rodgers, Carrie. *My Husband, Jimmie Rodgers.* San Antonio: Southern Literary Institute, 1935. ("Brakeman's Blues," "In The Jailhouse Now No. 2," "Mule Skinner Blues," "The Soldier's Sweetheart," "T For Texas," "Train Whistle Blues").

Sanville, George W. *Forty Gospel Hymn Stories.* Winona Lake, Indiana: The Rodeheaver-Hall Mack Company, 1943. (Virgil Brock's "Beyond The Sunset," Rev. George Bennard's "The Old Rugged Cross").

Stone, Roy Maxwell. *Our Hymns And Gospel Songs.* New York: Carlton Press, Inc., 1972. (J. B. F. Wright's "Precious Memories").

" 'Wabash Cannon Ball' Not The One In Song," Champaign-Urbana, Illinois, *Courier,* March 28, 1969, p. 7.

PRIMARY SOURCES (TEXT)

Johnny Bond. Letter, March 29, 1973.

Jack Cardwell. Telephone interview, January 20, 1974.

Ted Harris. Interview, Nashville, Tennessee, June 4, 1972.

Bill C. Malone. Interview, New Orleans, Louisiana, June 8, 1972. Letters, May 10, 1972; March 24, 1974; May 15, 1974.

Webb Pierce. Interview, Nashville, Tennessee, October 21, 1971.

Hank Snow. Tape-recorded interview. April 15, 1974.

Merle Travis. Interview, Nashville, Tennessee, June 19, 1972.

Wayne Walker. Interview, Nashville, Tennessee, June 4, 1973.

SECONDARY SOURCES (TEXT)

Allen, Frederick Lewis. *Since Yesterday.* New York: Harper & Brothers, 1940.

Baxter, Mrs. J. R. (Ma), and Polk, Videt. *Gospel Song Writers Biography.* Dallas: Stamps-Baxter Music & Printing Co., 1971.

Berliner, Oliver. "Gran'pa's Talking Machine." *High Fidelity,* December 1973.

Cash, W. J. *The Mind of the South.* New York: Alfred A. Knopf, 1941.

Combs, Josiah H. and Wilgus, D. K. eds. *Folk-Songs of the United States.* Austin: The University of Texas Press, 1967.

Danker, Frederick E. "The Repertory and Style of a Country Singer: Johnny Cash." *Journal of American Folklore* 85 (1972), p. 309.

Everson, William K. *A Pictorial History of the Western Film.* New York: The Citadel Press, 1969.

Feather, Leonard. *The Book of Jazz From Then Till Now.* New York: Horizon Press, 1957.

Foote, Henry Wilder. *Three Centuries of American Hymnody.* Cambridge: Harvard University Press, 1940.

Gentry, Linnell. *A History of Country, Western and Gospel Music.* Nashville: Claremont Corporation, 1969.

Goldston, Robert. *The Great Depression.* Greenwich, Connecticut: Fawcett Publications, Inc., 1968.

Green, Archie. "Hillbilly Music: Source and Symbol." *Journal of American Folklore* (1965), pp. 204–28.

______. *Only A Miner.* Urbana: University of Illinois Press, 1972.

Hemphill, Paul. *The Nashville Sound: Bright Lights and Country Music.* New York: Simon and Schuster, 1970.

Jackson, George Pullen. *White and Negro Spirituals.* Locust Valley, New York: J. J. Augustin, 1943.

______. *White Spirituals in the Southern Uplands.* Chapel Hill: University of North Carolina Press, 1933.

The Jukebox Story. Chicago: Music Operators of America, 1973.

Kerr, Phil. *Music in Evangelism.* Glendale, California: Gospel Music Publishers, 1944.

Laws, G. Malcolm, Jr. *Native American Balladry,* rev. ed. Philadelphia: American Folklore Society, 1964.

McLean, Albert F., Jr. *American Vaudeville as Ritual.* Lexington: University of Kentucky Press, 1965.

Malone, Bill C. *Country Music U.S.A.* Austin: The University of Texas Press, 1968.

Marks, Edward B. *They All Sang.* New York: The Viking Press, 1934.

Moore, Thurston, ed. *The 1970 Country Music Who's Who.* New York: Record World Publishing Company, Inc., 1970.

Neese, Chuck, ed. *The 1972 Country Music Who's Who.* New York: Record World Publishing Company, Inc., 1972.

Randolph, Vance. *Ozark Folksongs.* 4 vols. Columbia, Missouri: The State Historical Society of Missouri, 1950.

Spaeth, Sigmund. *A History Of Popular Music In America.* New York: Random House, 1948.

______. *Read 'Em and Weep.* New York: Doubleday, Page & Co., 1926.

______. *Weep Some More, My Lady.* Garden City, New York: Doubleday, Page & Co., 1927.

Stambler, Irwin, and Grelun Landon. *Encyclopedia of Folk, Country and Western Music.* New York: St. Martin's Press, 1969.

Stone, Roy Maxwell. *Our Hymns and Gospel Songs.* New York: Carlton Press, Inc., 1972.

Williams, J. Paul. *What Americans Believe and How They Worship.* rev. ed. New York: Harper & Row, 1962.

Williams, Roger M. *Sing A Sad Song.* New York: Ballantine Books, Inc., 1973.

Williams, T. Harry, Richard N. Current, and Frank Friedel. *A History of the United States to 1877.* 3rd ed. New York: Alfred A. Knopf, 1969.

______. *A History of the United States Since 1865.* 3rd ed. New York: Alfred A. Knopf, 1969.

Woodward, C. Vann. *The Burden of Southern History,* rev. ed. Baton Rouge: Louisiana State University Press, 1968.

Discography

NOTE: All the listings below are 33-1/3 long-playing records unless noted, and are commercially available at this writing. Those designated "out of print" can often be located on older records and may be reissued in the future; check with your record dealer.

SONGS OF HOME

"Alabama." Charlie Louvin, *I'll Remember Always,* Capitol T 2689.
"Cabin On The Hill." Lester Flatt, *Foggy Mountain Breakdown,* RCA LSP 4789.
"Carry Me Back To The Mountains." Roy Acuff, Hickory 45K 1627s (45 rpm).
"Coal Miner's Daughter." Loretta Lynn, *Coal Miner's Daughter,* MCA 10. Norma Jean, *Norma Jean,* RCA LSP 4510.
"Daddy and Home." Jimmie Rodgers, *Never No Mo' Blues,* RCA LPM 1232.
"Detroit City." Bobby Bare, *Best of Bobby Bare,* RCA LSP 3479. Mel Tillis and the Statesiders, *Live at Sam Houston Coliseum,* MGM 4788.
"Eight More Miles To Louisville." The Osborne Brothers, *The Osborne Bros: Bobby & Sonny,* MCA DL 5356. Grandpa Jones, *Grandpa Jones Sings Songs From Hee Haw,* Monument S-18131.
"Green, Green Grass Of Home." George Hamilton IV, *International Ambassador of Country Music,* RCA LSP 4826. Johnny Cash, *Johnny Cash at Folsom Prison,* Columbia CS 9639.
"Homecoming." Tom T. Hall, *Tom T. Hall's Greatest Hits,* Mercury SR 61369.
"In The Good Old Days (When Times Were Bad)." Skeeter Davis, *Skeeter Sings Dolly,* RCA LSP 4732. Dolly Parton, *My Tennessee Home,* RCA APLI 0033.
"Kentucky." Everly Brothers, *End of An Era,* Barnaby BBYZG 30260. Chet Atkins, *Guitar Country,* RCA LSP 2783.
"Little Old Cabin In The Lane, The." Roy Clark, *Roy Clark's Family Album,* Dot DOS 26018. Stoneman Family, *California Blues,* RCA LSP 4431.
"Mockin' Bird Hill." Elton Britt, *The Best of Elton Britt,* Vol. II, RCA LSP 4822 (e).

"Mom and Dad's Waltz." George Jones, *Nothing Ever Hurt Me,* Epic KE 32412. Lefty Frizzell, *Lefty Frizzell's Greatest Hits,* Columbia CS 9288.

"Peach Pickin' Time In Georgia." Hank Snow, *Snow In All Seasons,* RCA Stereo LSP 4122. Jimmie Rodgers, *My Rough and Rowdy Ways,* RCA LPM 2112.

"Take Me Back To Renfro Valley." Renfro Valley Cast, *The Renfro Valley Gatherin',* Renfro Valley Records RVLP 111.

"Take Me Home, Country Roads." Tennessee Ernie Ford, *Mr. Words & Music,* Capitol ST 11001. Statler Bros., *Innerview,* Mercury SR 61358. Carter Family, *Traveling Minstrel Band,* Columbia KC 31454.

"That Silver-Haired Daddy of Mine." Gene Autry, *Gene Autry's Country Music Hall of Fame Album,* Columbia CS 1035.

"This Ole House." Jimmy Dean, *The Jimmy Dean Show,* RCA LSP 3890.

"Tobacco Road." John D. Loudermilk, *Vol. I—Elloree,* Warner Bros. WB-1922. Bobbie Gentry, *Tobacco Road,* Capitol STBB 704.

"Uncle Pen." Bill Monroe, *Bill Monroe's Greatest Hits,* MCA-17. Roy Acuff, *Famous Opry Favorites,* Hickory 139.

"When It's Prayer Meetin' Time In The Hollow." (Out of print.)

"When The Wagon Was New." Sam McGee, *Flat Top Pickin' Sam McGee,* MBA LP MBA 60 6S.

"Where The Old Red River Flows." Red Smiley, *Red Smiley and the Tennessee Cutups,* Rural Rhythm RRRS 211.

"Wonder Could I Live There Anymore." Patsy Sledd, *Yours Sincerely,* Mega S 1020. Charley Pride, *From Me To You,* RCA LSP 4468.

RELIGIOUS SONGS

"Beyond The Sunset." Bill Anderson, *Jan Howard, For Loving You,* Decca 74959. Webb Pierce, *Road Show,* Decca 75280.

"Can The Circle Be Unbroken?" Mac Wiseman, *Concert Favorites,* RCA LSP 4845. Sam & Kirk McGee, *Pillars Of The Grand Ole Opry,* MBA Records, 607(S).

"Dust On The Bible." Kitty Wells, *Dust On The Bible,* Decca 78858. Pat Boone, *Family Who Prays,* Lamb & Lion 1006.

"Farther Along." Bill Monroe, *I'll Meet You In Church Sunday Morning,* Decca 73437. Wanda Jackson, *Country Gospel,* Word Records, 8614.

"God Put A Rainbow In The Cloud." Kitty Wells/Johnny Wright, *Kitty Wells & Johnny Wright Sing Heartwarming Gospel Songs,* Decca DL 75325. Anita Kerr Quartette, *Sunday Serenade,* Decca DL 5325.

"God Walks These Hills With Me." Red Foley, *The Red Foley Story,* Decca DXSB 7177. Rex Allen, *The Touch Of God's Hand,* Decca DL 75205.

"Great Speckled Bird." Roy Acuff, *Country Music Hall Of Fame's Roy Acuff And His Smoky Mountain Boys,* Capitol DT 1870. David Rogers, *Farewell To The Ryman,* Atlantic 7283.

"How Great Thou Art." Connie Smith, *Love Is The Look You're Looking For,* RCA LSP 4840. Leona Williams, *The Best Of Leona Williams,* Hickory LPS 165.

"I Am A Pilgrim." Chet Atkins, *Down Home,* RCA LSP 2450. Doc Watson, *Doc On Stage,* Vanguard VSD 9110.

"If I Could Hear My Mother Pray Again." Country Johnny Mathis, *He Keeps Me Singing,* Little Darlin' LD 4007. Jimmie Davis, *Old Baptizing Creek,* Decca 75273.

"I'll Fly Away." Charley Pride, *Did You Think To Pray,* RCA LSP 4513. Al Brumley, Jr., *Al Brumley Sings, Albert E. Brumley,* American Artists AAS 1020.

"I Saw The Light." Hank Williams, *Hank Williams On Stage Vol. 2,* MGM SE 4109. Hank Williams Jr., *Live,* MGM 4644.

"It Is No Secret." Stuart Hamblen, *Cowboy Church,* Word Records 8504.

"Just A Closer Walk With Thee." Red Foley/Anita Kerr Singers, *Beyond The Sunset,* MCA 147. Roy Clark, *The Entertainer Of The Year,* Capitol SABB 11264.

"Keep On The Sunny Side Of Life." Carter Family, *'Mid The Green Fields Of Virginia,* RCA LPM 2772. A. L. Phipps Family, *Most Requested Sacred Songs Of The Carter Family,* Pine Mountain PMR 139.

"Life's Railway To Heaven." Susan Raye, *Hymns By Susan Raye,* Capitol ST 11255. Leverett Bros., *Lonesome Mandolin,* Birch 1947.

"Old Rugged Cross, The." Stuart Hamblen, *In The Garden,* RCA Camden CAS 973 (E). Wilf Carter, *Let's Go Back To The Bible,* RCA Camden CAL 814.

"Only One Step More." Renfro Valley Cast, *The Renfro Valley Gatherin',* Renfro Valley Records RVLP 111.

"Preachin', Prayin', Singin'." Lester Flatt/Earl Scruggs, *Country Music,* Mercury MG 20358.

"Precious Memories." Rex Allen, *The Touch Of God's Hand,* Decca DL 75205. Susan Raye, *Hymns By Susan Raye,* Capitol ST 11255.

"Supper Time." Jimmie Davis, *Greatest Hits,* Decca DL 74978.

"Take My Hand, Precious Lord." Connie Eaton, *Young Gospel Country,* Chart 1046. Jim Reeves, *We Thank Thee,* RCA LSP 2552.

"The Touch Of God's Hand." Rex Allen, *The Touch Of God's Hand,* Decca DL 75205.

"There'll Be Peace In The Valley For Me." Red Foley, *Beyond The Sunset,* MCA 147. Loretta Lynn, *Hymns,* MCA 5.

"Tramp On The Street, The." Wilma Lee/Stoney Cooper, *There's A Big Wheel,* Hickory H 100. Hank Williams, *Hank Williams On Stage Vol. 2,* MGM SE 4109.

"Turn Your Radio On." Roy Acuff, *I Saw The Light,* Hickory 158. Tennessee Ernie Ford, *Mr. Words And Music,* Capitol ST 11001.

"Wait A Little Longer, Please, Jesus." Doug Green/Vic Jordan, *In God's Eyes,* State Fair Records LPSF 801. Carl Smith, *Country Hymns,* Columbia 45346. Porter Wagoner, *Grand Old Gospel,* RCA LSP 3488.

"Where Could I Go?" Ferlin Husky, *Memories Of Home,* Capitol ST 1633. Jimmie Davis, *Sweet Hour Of Prayer,* Decca 74087.

"Wings Of A Dove." Ferlin Husky, *The Best Of Ferlin Husky,* Capitol (S) SKAO 43. Porter Wagoner/Blackwood Brothers, *Gospel Country,* RCA LSP 4034.

SONGS OF DEATH AND SORROW

"Amelia Earhart's Last Flight." Dickey Lee, *Sparklin' Brown Eyes,* RCA APLI 0311.

"Baggage Coach Ahead." Mac Wiseman, *Golden Hits of Mac Wiseman,* Dot, DLP 25896.

"Death Of Floyd Collins, The." Vernon Dalhart, *Native American Ballads, Vintage Series,* RCA LPV 548.

"Death Of Hank Williams, The." (Out of print.)

"Death Of Little Kathy Fiscus, The." Jimmy Osborne, *Eighteen King-Size Country Hits,* Columbia CS 9468.

"Don't Make Me Go To Bed And I'll Be Good." Roy Acuff, *All Time Greatest Hits,* Hickory 109. Elton Britt, *Sixteen Great Country Performances,* ABC S 744.

"Drunkard's Child, A." Jimmie Rodgers, *The Short But Brilliant Life Of Jimmie Rodgers,* RCA LPM 2634.

"I Dreamed Of A Hillbilly Heaven." Tex Ritter, *An American Legend,* Capitol SKC 11241.

"Mommy Please Stay Home With Me." Roy Acuff, *Living Legend,* Hickory 145.

"Nobody's Darlin' But Mine." Jimmie Davis, *You Are My Sunshine,* MCA DL 78896. Stoneman Family, *White Lightning,* Starday 393.

"Old Shep." Red Foley, *The Red Foley Story,* Decca DXSB7 177. Kenny Price, *Red Foley Songbook,* RCA LSP 4469.

"Our Baby's Book." Ernest Tubb, *Let's Turn Back The Years,* Decca D 175114.

"Precious Jewel, The." Roy Acuff, *Roy Acuff And The Smoky Mountain Boys,* Capitol DT 1870. Carl Smith, *Tribute To Roy Acuff,* Columbia 9870.

"Put My Little Shoes Away." Mac Wiseman, *Concert Favorites,* RCA LSP 4845. Bill Monroe, *Bill Monroe's Country Music Hall Of Fame,* Decca 75281.

"Sinking Of The Titanic, The." Roy Acuff, *Roy Acuff And The Smoky Mountain Boys,* Capitol DT 1870. Stoneman Family, *White Lightning,* Starday SLP 393.

"Sweeter Than The Flowers." Moon Mulligan, *Eighteen King-Size Country Hits,* Columbia CS 9468.

"We Sat Beneath The Maple On The Hill." Carter Family, *Carter Family Album,* Liberty 7230. J. E. Mainer's Mountaineers, *Old Time Country Favorites,* Rural Rhythm CAS 898.

"When Jimmie Rodgers Said Goodbye." (Out of print.)

"Willie Roy, The Crippled Boy." Howard Vokes, *Song,* Starday SLP 258.

"Wreck On The Highway, The." Roy Acuff, *Roy Acuff And The Smoky Mountain Boys,* Capitol DT 1870. Carl Smith, *Tribute To Roy Acuff,* Columbia CS 9870.

COMIC AND NOVELTY SONGS

"A-Sleepin' At The Foot Of The Bed." Jimmy Dickens, *Jimmy Dickens' Greatest Hits,* Decca DL 75133.

"Cigareettes, Whusky And Wild, Wild Women." Buck Owens/Buddy Alan, *Too Old To Cut The Mustard,* Capitol ST 874.

"Company's Comin'." Porter Wagoner, *The Best Of Porter Wagoner,* RCA LSP 3560.

"How To Catch A Man." Minnie Pearl, *Stars Of The Grand Ole Opry,* RCA LPM 6015.

"I Won't Go Huntin' With You, Jake (But I'll Go Chasin' Women)." (Out of print.)

"I'm My Own Grandpaw." Lonzo & Oscar, *Country's Greatest Hits,* Columbia GP 9.

"I've Got Tears In My Ears From Lying On My Back In My Bed While I Cry Over You." (Out of print.)

"Jambalaya." Hank Williams, *The Very Best Of Hank Williams,* MGM SE 4168. Conway Twitty, *Here's Twitty,* Decca 74990.

"Johnson's Old Gray Mule." J. E. Mainer, *Great Mountain Music From North Carolina,* Rural Rhythm RRJE 185.

"Life Gits Tee-jus, Don't It?" Ben Colder, *Have One On Colder,* MGM 4629. Hank Williams, Jr., *Luke The Drifter Jr.* MGM 4632.

"May The Bird Of Paradise Fly Up Your Nose." Jimmy Dickens, *Country's Greatest Hits,* Columbia GP 9.

"Mountain Dew." Mother Maybelle, *Mother Maybelle Carter,* Columbia KG 32436.

"Ode To The Little Brown Shack Out Back." Billy Ed Wheeler, *Ode To The Little Brown Shack Out Back,* Kapp KL 1425.

"Original Talking Blues." Robert Lunn, *Country Music Memorial,* Starday SLP 9 451.

"Out Behind The Barn." Jimmy Dickens, *Jimmy Dickens' Greatest Hits,* Decca DL 75133.

"Pistol Packin' Mama." Al Dexter, *Country Hits Of The '40's,* Capitol ST 884.

"Race Is On, The." George Jones, *The Best Of George Jones, Vol. I,* RCA LSP 4716.

"Smoke, Smoke, Smoke (That Cigarette)." Tex Williams, *Country Hits Of The '40's,* Capitol ST 884.

"Take An Old Cold Tater And Wait." Jimmy Dickens, *Jimmy Dickens' Greatest Hits,* Decca DL 75133.

"Take Me Back To Tulsa." Bob Wills, *The Bob Wills Anthology,* Columbia KG 32416. Hank Thompson, *Hank Thompson Salutes Oklahoma,* Dot DLP 25971.

"Too Old To Cut The Mustard." Bill Carlisle, *The Best Of Bill Carlisle,* Hickory LPS 129. Buck Owens/Buddy Alan, *Too Old To Cut The Mustard,* Capitol ST 874.

"Y'all Come." Bill Monroe, *Bill Monroe's Greatest Hits,* MCA 17. Sam & Kirk McGee, *Sam And Kirk McGee, Pillars Of The Grand Ole Opry,* MBA Records LPMBA 607 (S).

WINNING LOVE SONGS

"All The Time." Bobby Lewis, *The Best Of Bobby Lewis, Vol. I,* United Artists UAS 6760. Marion Worth, *A Woman Needs Love,* Decca DL 74936.

"Before I Met You." Porter Wagoner/Dolly Parton, *Just Between You And Me,* RCA LSP 3926. Charley Pride, *Country Charley Pride,* RCA LSP 3645.

"Gentle On My Mind." Glen Campbell, *Country Hits Of The '60's,* Capitol ST 886. Tompall & Glaser Brothers, *Great Hits From Two Decades,* MGM SE 4888.

"Have I Told You Lately That I Love You?" Tex Ritter, *An American Legend,* Capitol SKC 11241. Gene Autry, *Gene Autry's Country Music Hall Of Fame Album,* Columbia CS 1035.

"I'll Hold You In My Heart." Eddy Arnold, *The Best Of Eddy Arnold,* RCA, LSP 3565. Freddie Hart, *Freddie Hart's Greatest Hits,* MCA 67.

"I Love You Because." Leon Payne, *Country Hits Of The '40's,* Capitol ST 884. Gene Autry, *Gene Autry's Country Music Hall Of Fame Album,* Columbia CS 1035.

"I Love You So Much It Hurts." Floyd Tillman, *Portraits Of Floyd Tillman,* Bagatelle LP 92827. Patsy Cline, *Showcase,* Decca DL 74202.

"(Remember Me) I'm The One Who Loves You." Johnny Cash, *Sunday Down South,* Sun 119.

"I Really Don't Want To Know." Eddy Arnold, *The Best Of Eddy Arnold,* RCA LSP 3565. Johnny Rodriguez, *All I Ever Meant To Do Was Sing,* Mercury SRM 1 686.

"I Walk The Line." Johnny Cash, *I Walk The Line,* Columbia CS 8990. David Rogers, *Farewell To The Ryman,* Atlantic SP 7283.

"Molly Darling." Eddy Arnold, *Anytime,* RCA LSP 1224. Lester McFarland and Robert Gardner, *Mac and Bob,* Birch 1944.

"My Mary." Jimmie Davis, *You Are My Sunshine,* MCA DL 78896.

"My Woman, My Woman, My Wife." Marty Robbins, *Marty Robbins' All Time Greatest Hits,* Columbia KG 31361. George Morgan, *Real George,* Stop 1018.

"Shenandoah Waltz." Jimmy Martin And The Sunny Mountain Boys, *Sunny Side Of The Mountain,* Decca DL 74643. Stanley Brothers, *Stanley Bros. Sing Everybody's Country Favorites,* King 690 (S).

"Sparkling Brown Eyes." Dickey Lee, *Ashes Of Love,* RCA LPS 4715.

"We Could." Kitty Wells, *Singing 'Em Country,* Decca DL 75221. Roy Clark, *The Entertainer Of The Year,* Capitol SABB 11264.

"Why Don't You Haul Off And Love Me?" Wayne Raney, *18 King-Size Country Hits,* Columbia 9468. Porter Wagoner/Dolly Parton, *Always, Always,* RCA LSP 4186.

"You Are My Flower." Lester Flatt/Earl Scruggs, *Flatt and Scruggs' Greatest Hits,* CS 9370.

"Yours Love." Waylon Jennings, *Ruby, Don't Take Your Love To Town,* CAS 2608 RCA. Porter Wagoner/Dolly Parton, *Always, Always,* RCA LSP 4186.

SONGS OF LOST AND UNREQUITED LOVE

"Address Unknown." Hank Snow, Big Country Hits (*Songs I Hadn't Recorded Till Now*), RCA LSP 2458.

"Blackboard Of My Heart." Hank Thompson, *The Best Of Hank Thompson,* Capitol DT 1878.

"Blue Moon Of Kentucky." Bill Monroe, *Sixteen All-Time Greatest Hits With The Blue-Grass Boys,* Columbia CS 1065. David Rogers, *Farewell To The Ryman,* Atlantic SD 7283.

"Blues, Stay Away From Me." Willis Brothers, *The Best Of The Willis Brothers,* Starday SLP 466.

"Born To Lose." Ray Price, *The Other Woman,* Columbia CS 9182; *Danny Boy,* Columbia CS 9477. Sonny James, *Number One,* Capitol ST 629.

"Bouquet Of Roses." Eddy Arnold, *Anytime,* RCA LSP 1224 (e).

"Bury Me Beneath The Willow." Carter Family, *'Mid The Green Fields Of Virginia,* RCA LPM 2772.

"Candy Kisses." George Morgan, *Country's Greatest Hits, Volume 2,* Columbia GP 19. Roy Rogers, *Take A Little Love (And Pass It On),* Capitol ST 11020.

"Cold, Cold Heart." Hank Williams, *The Very Best Of Hank Williams,* MGM SE 4168. Don Gibson, *Hank Williams As Sung By Don Gibson,* Hickory LPS 157.

"Crazy Arms." Ray Price, *Ray Price's All Time Greatest Hits,* Columbia KG 31364. Skeeter Davis, *The Hillbilly Singer,* RCA LSP 4818.

"Faded Love." Bob Wills/Mel Tillis, *King Of Western Swing,* Kapp 3523. Roy Clark, *The Entertainer Of The Year,* Capitol SABB 11264.

"Funny How Time Slips Away." Ray Price, *The Other Woman,* Columbia CS 9182.

"Half As Much." Hank Williams, *The Very Best Of Hank Williams,* MGM SE 4168. Patsy Cline, *Showcase,* Decca DL 74202.

"Have You Ever Been Lonely (Have You Ever Been Blue)?" Jim Reeves, *A Touch of Velvet,* RCA Victor LSP 248. Patsy Cline, *Showcase,* Decca DL 74202.

"Heartaches By The Number." Ray Price, *Ray Price's Greatest Hits,* Columbia CS 8866.

"He'll Have To Go." Jim Reeves, *He'll Have To Go & Other Favorites,* RCA LSP 2223. Roy Rogers, *Take A Little Love (And Pass It On).* Capitol ST 11020.

"I Can't Stop Loving You." Don Gibson, *The Best Of Don Gibson,* RCA LSP 3376. Kenny Price, *Sea Of Heartbreak,* RCA LSP 4839.

"I Forgot More Than You'll Ever Know." Skeeter Davis, *The Best Of Skeeter Davis,* RCA LSP 3374. Jerry Lee Lewis, *There Must Be More To Love Than This,* Mercury SR 61323.

"I Wonder Where You Are Tonight." Johnny Bond, *The Best Of Johnny Bond,* Starday S1P 444. Johnny Rodriguez, *Introducing Johnny Rodriguez,* Mercury SR 61378.

"I'm A Fool To Care." Jim Reeves, *A Touch Of Velvet,* RCA LSP 2487.

"I'm So Lonesome I Could Cry." Hank Williams, *The Very Best Of Hank Williams,* MGM SE 4168. Tanya Tucker, *Delta Dawn,* Columbia KC 31742.

"I'm Thinking Tonight Of My Blue Eyes." Jimmy Martin, *Jimmy Martin,* Decca 74536. Doc Watson, *Good Deal,* Vanguard 79276.

"It Makes No Difference Now." Gene Autry, *Gene Autry's Greatest Hits,* Columbia CL 1575. Jimmie Davis, *You Are My Sunshine,* MCA D 178896.

"Kentucky Waltz." Elton Britt, *Sixteen Great Country Performances,* ABC S744. Cal Smith, *Cal Smith Sings Bluegrass,* Columbia 30548.

"Last Letter, The." Ernest Tubb, *I've Got All The Heartaches I Can Handle,* MCA 341. George Jones, *George Jones,* Epic KE 31321.

"(I'd Be) A Legend In My Time." Don Gibson, *Country Green,* Hickory LPS 160. Hank Snow, *Big Country Hits (Songs I Hadn't Recorded Till Now),* RCA LSP 2458.

"Lovesick Blues." Hank Williams, *The Very Best Of Hank Williams,* MGM SE 4168. Charley Pride, *Charley Pride In Person,* RCA LSP 4094.

"Mansion On The Hill, A." Hank Williams, *The Very Best Of Hank Williams,* MGM SE 4168. Don Gibson, *Hank Williams As Sung By Don Gibson,* Hickory LPS 157.

"No One Will Ever Know." Statler Brothers, *Country Music, Then And Now,* Mercury SR-6-1367.

"Oh, Lonesome Me." Kenny Price, *Sea Of Heartbreak,* RCA LSP 4839. Don Gibson, *The Best Of Don Gibson,* RCA LSP 3376.

"Pick Me Up On Your Way Down." Charlie Walker, *Charlie Walker's Greatest Hits,* Columbia BN 26343. Mel Tillis, *Greatest Hits,* Kapp 3653.

"Release Me." Ray Price, *Ray Price's Greatest Hits,* Columbia CS 8866. Lefty Frizzell, *Lefty Frizzell's Greatest Hits,* Columbia CS 9288.

"Remember Me (When The Candle Lights Are Gleaming)." T. Texas Tyler, *The Hits Of T. Texas Tyler,* Capitol ST 2344. LuLu Belle and Scott Wiseman, *LuLu Belle and Scotty,* Starday 206.

"San Antonio Rose." Bob Wills, *The Bob Wills Anthology,* Columbia KG 32416. Patsy Cline, *Showcase,* Decca DL 74202.

"She Thinks I Still Care." Dickey Lee, *Ashes Of Love,* RCA LSP 4715. George Jones, *Poor Man's Riches,* RCA LSP 4725.

"T For Texas." Jimmie Rodgers, *My Rough And Rowdy Ways,* RCA LPM 2112.

"Take These Chains From My Heart." Hank Williams, *Greatest Hits,* MGM E 3918. Webb Pierce, *I'm Gonna Be A Swinger,* MCA DL 75393.

"Tennessee Waltz." Pee Wee King/Redd Stewart (Single, 45 RPM) Starday 8019. Sue Thompson, *This Is Sue Thompson Country,* Hickory LPS 148.

"There Goes My Everything." Jack Greene, *There Goes My Everything,* Decca 74843. Tammy Wynette, *First Songs Of The First Lady,* Epic KEG 30358.

"They'll Never Take Her Love From Me." Hank Williams, *The Very Best Of Hank Williams, Vol. 2,* MGM SE 4227.

"Too Late." (Out of print.)

"Walking The Floor Over You." Ernest Tubb, *The Ernest Tubb Story,* MCA 16. David Rogers, *Farewell To The Ryman,* Atlantic SP 7283.

"When My Blue Moon Turns To Gold Again." Slim Whitman, *Guess Who,* United Artists UAS 6783. Lester Flatt/Mac Wiseman, *Over The Hills To The Poorhouse,* RCA APL 10309.

"Wildwood Flower." Mother Maybelle, *Mother Maybelle Carter,* Columbia KG 32436. Johnny Cash, *Orange Blossom Special,* Columbia CS 1909.

"Worried Mind." Jimmie Davis, *You Are My Sunshine,* Decca DL 78896.

"You Are My Sunshine." Jimmie Davis, *You Are My Sunshine,* Decca DL 78896. Gene Autry, *Gene Autry's Country Music Hall Of Fame Album,* Columbia CS 1035.

CHEATIN' SONGS

"Back Street Affair." Webb Pierce, *Without You,* MCA Coral CB 20025.

"Don't Let Me Cross Over." Carl and Pearl Butler, *Temptation Keeps Twisting Her Arm,* Chart CHS 1051. George Jones, *Love Bug,* Mercury 3088.

"I'll Never Slip Around Again." (Out of print.)

"I Take The Chance." Charlie Louvin, *I'll Remember Always,* Capitol T 2689. Ernie Ashworth, *The Best Of Ernie Ashworth,* Hickory LPS 146.

"Margie's At The Lincoln Park Inn." Tom T. Hall, *Homecoming,* Mercury SR 61247. Cal Smith, *Cal Smith Sings,* Kapp KS 3608.

"One Has My Name, The Other Has My Heart." Jimmy Wakely, *Country Hits Of The '40's,* Capitol ST 884. Jerry Lee Lewis, *The Best Of Jerry Lee Lewis,* Smash 67131.

"The Other Woman." Loretta Lynn, *Loretta Lynn's Greatest Hits,* MCA 1 Decca DL 7 5000.

"The Other Woman (In My Life)." Ray Price, Columbia CS 9182. Conway Twitty, *Conway Twitty Sings,* Decca 74724.

"Please Help Me, I'm Falling (In Love With You)." Hank Locklin, *The Best Of Hank Locklin,* RCA LSP 3559. Wanda Jackson, *Please Help Me, I'm Falling,* Hilltop JS 6058.

"Ruby, Don't Take Your Love To Town." Waylon Jennings, *Ruby, Don't Take Your Love To Town,* RCA CAS 2608. Faron Young, *The Best Of Faron Young,* Mercury SR 61267.

"Slipping Around." Floyd Tillman, *Portraits Of Floyd Tillman,* Bagatelle LP 92827. Margaret Whiting/Jimmy Wakely, *Country Hits Of The '40's,* Capitol ST 884.

"You Ain't Woman Enough." Loretta Lynn, *Loretta Lynn's Greatest Hits,* MCA 1. Peggy Little, *Little Bit Of Peggy,* Dot 25948.

"Your Cheatin' Heart." Hank Williams, *The Very Best Of Hank Williams,* MGM S/SE 4168. George Jones, *My Favorites Of Hank Williams,* United Artists LA 149 (F).

HONKY-TONK SONGS

"Bright Lights And Country Music." Bill Anderson, *Bill Anderson's Greatest Hits, Vol. 1,* MCA 13.

"Bubbles In My Beer." Bob Wills and Tommy Duncan, *Bob Wills Hall Of Fame,* United Artists UAS 9962. Ernest Tubb, *Baby, Its So Hard To Be Good,* Decca DL 7 5388.

"City Lights." Ray Price, *Ray Price's Greatest Hits,* Columbia CS 8866. Bill Anderson, *The Bill Anderson Story,* Decca DXSB 7198.

"Dim Lights, Thick Smoke (And Loud, Loud Music)." Conway Twitty, *Here's Twitty,* Decca 74990.

"Don't Come Home A-Drinkin'." Loretta Lynn, *Loretta Lynn's Greatest Hits,* MCA 1 Decca DL 7 5000. Tammy Wynette, *The First Songs Of The First Lady,* Epic KEG 30358.

"Four Walls." Jim Reeves, *The Best Of Jim Reeves,* RCA LSP 2890. Bill Monroe, *Bill Monroe's Greatest Hits,* MCA 17.

"Headin' Down The Wrong Highway." Lawton Williams, *Between Truck Stops,* Mega 1004.

"Honky Tonk Man." Johnny Horton, *Honky Tonk Man,* Columbia CS 8779. Bob Luman, *Bob Luman's Greatest Hits,* Epic KE 32759.

"If You've Got The Money, I've Got The Time." Lefty Frizzell, *Lefty Frizzell's Greatest Hits,* Columbia CS 9288. Boots Randolph, *Yakety Sax,* Monument 18002.

"It Wasn't God Who Made Honky Tonk Angels." Kitty Wells, *Kitty Wells' Greatest Hits,* Decca 75001. Skeeter Davis, *The Hillbilly Singer,* RCA LSP 4818.

"There Stands The Glass." Webb Pierce, *Webb Pierce's Greatest Hits,* MCA 120. Johnny Bush, *Whiskey River/There Stands The Glass,* RCA LSP 4817.

"Warm Red Wine." Ernest Tubb, *Ernest Tubb's Greatest Hits, Vol. 2,* MCA DL 7 5252. George Jones, *George Jones,* United Artists WXS 85.

"Wild Side Of Life, The." Hank Thompson, *The Best Of Hank Thompson,* Capitol DT 1878. Conway Twitty, *Look Into My Teardrops,* MCA 112.

SOCIAL COMMENTARY

"Crystal Chandeliers." Charley Pride, *Charley Pride In Person,* RCA LSP 4094. Nat Stuckey, *Nat Stuckey,* RCA APDI 0080.

"Dark As A Dungeon." Johnny Cash, *Johnny Cash At Folsom Prison,* Columbia CS 9639.

"Harper Valley PTA." Jeannie C. Riley, *Jeannie C., Greatest Hits,* Plantation (S) 13. Loretta Lynn, *Your Squaw Is On The Warpath,* Decca 75084.

"Married By The Bible, Divorced By The Law." Hank Snow, *The One And Only Hank Snow,* RCA Camden CAS 722.

"No Vacancy." Rick Nelson, *Rick Nelson Country,* MCA 2—4004.

"Old Age Pension Check." Roy Acuff, *All Time Greatest Hits,* Hickory LP 109.

"Po' Folks." Bill Anderson, *The Bill Anderson Story,* Decca DXSB 7198. Norma Jean, *I Guess That Comes From Being Poor,* RCA LSP 4745.

"Rockin' Alone In An Old Rockin' Chair." Eddy Arnold, *Anytime,* RCA LSP 1224. LuLu Belle and Scott Wiseman, *LuLu Belle and Scotty,* Starday 351.

"Satisfied Mind, A." Porter Wagoner, *The Best Of Porter Wagoner,* RCA LSP 3560. Jean Sheppard, *Country Hits Of The '50's,* Capitol ST 885.

"Skip A Rope." Don Cherry, *The World Of Don Cherry,* Monument (S) KZG 32334. Conway Twitty, *Here's Twitty,* Decca 74990.

"Stuck Up Blues." (Out of print.)

"Sunday Morning Christian." Harlan Howard, *To The Silent Majority,* Nugget NRLP 105 Stereo.

"Welfare Cadilac." Guy Drake, *Welfare Cadilac,* Royal American RES 1001. Ernie

Ashworth, *On The Road With Grand Ole Opry Star Ernie Ashworth,* Three Star Records.

"Where Have All Our Heroes Gone?" Bill Anderson, *Where Have All Our Heroes Gone,* Decca DL 75254.

SONGS OF WAR AND PATRIOTISM

"Ballad Of The Green Berets, The." S/Sgt. Barry Sadler, *Ballad Of The Green Berets,* RCA LSP 3547.

"Battle Of New Orleans, The." Johnny Horton, *Johnny Horton's Greatest Hits,* Columbia CL 8396. Doug Kershaw, *Doug Kershaw,* Warner Bros. WS 1906.

"Dear John Letter, A." Jean Shepard and Ferlin Husky, *Country Hits Of The '50's,* Capitol ST 885. Skeeter Davis/Bobby Bare, *Tunes For Two,* RCA LSP 3336.

"Dear Uncle Sam." Loretta Lynn, *Loretta Lynn's Greatest Hits,* MCA 1.

"Each Night At Nine." Slim Whitman, *Guess Who,* United Artists UAS 6783.

"Filipino Baby." Ernest Tubb, *The Ernest Tubb Story,* MCA DXSB 7159. Cowboy Copas, *The Best Of Cowboy Copas,* Starday SL P 458.

"Fraulein." Freddie Hart, *The World Of Freddie Hart,* Columbia G 31550. Hank Snow, *Big Country Hits; Songs I Hadn't Recorded Till Now,* RCA LSP 2458.

"Have I Stayed Away Too Long?" Tex Ritter, *Hillbilly Heaven,* Capitol ST 1623. Sammi Smith, *Toast Of '45,* Mega 1021.

"I'll Be With You When The Roses Bloom Again." Don Reno/Bill Harrell, *Don Reno and Bill Harrell and The Tennessee Cutups,* Rural Rhythm, DR 171. Lester McFarland and Robert Gardner, *Mac and Bob,* Birch 1944.

"Molly." Bill Anderson, *Still,* Decca 74427.

"Silver Dew On The Bluegrass Tonight." Cal Smith, *The Best Of Cal Smith,* MCA 70.

"Smoke On The Water." Red Foley, *Red Foley's Golden Favorites,* Decca DL 4107.

"Soldier's Last Letter." Merle Haggard, *Hag,* Capitol ST 753. Stonewall Jackson, *The Great Old Songs,* Columbia CS 9708.

"Soldier's Sweetheart, The." Jimmie Rodgers, *Country Music Hall Of Fame,* RCA LPM 2531.

"That Crazy War." Stringbean, *Stringbean,* Starday.

"There's A Star-Spangled Banner Waving Somewhere." Elton Britt, *Sixteen Great Country Performances,* ABC Records ABCS S 744. Hank Snow, *Songs Of Tragedy,* RCA LSP 2901.

PRISON SONGS

"Convict And The Rose, The." Porter Wagoner, *Soul Of A Convict And Other Great Prison Songs,* RCA LSP 3683. Bob Wills/Tommy Duncan, *Living Legend,* Liberty S 7182.

"Doin' My Time." Johnny Cash, *Original Golden Hits,* Sun S 127. Lester Flatt/Earl Scruggs, *Flatt & Scruggs,* Everest EVR 259.

"Folsom Prison Blues." Johnny Cash, *Johnny Cash At Folsom Prison,* Columbia CS 9639. Jerry Reed, *Lord Mr. Ford,* RCA APL 10238.

"I Washed My Hands In Muddy Water." Stonewall Jackson, *The World Of Stonewall Jackson,* Columbia KG3 1411. Hank Snow, *Hello Love,* RCA APL 10441.

"(I'm A Lonesome) Fugitive." Merle Haggard, *I'm A Lonesome Fugitive,* Capitol ST 2702. Charley Pride, *Just Plain Charley,* RCA LSP 4290.
"I'm Free (From The Chain Gang Now)." Jimmie Rodgers, *Country Music Hall Of Fame,* RCA LPM 2531.
"I'm Here To Get My Baby Out Of Jail." Stonewall Jackson, *The Great Old Songs,* Columbia CS 9708. Porter Wagoner, *Soul Of A Convict,* RCA LSP 3683.
"In The Jailhouse Now #2." Jimmie Rodgers, *My Rough And Rowdy Ways,* RCA LPM 2112.
"The Prisoner's Dream." Hank Snow, *Songs of Tragedy,* RCA LSP 2901.
"The Prisoner's Song." Hank Snow, *Songs Of Tragedy,* RCA LSP 2901.
"Shackles And Chains." Stanley Brothers, *Stanley Brothers Sing Everybody's Country Favorites,* King 690. Stonewall Jackson, *The Great Old Songs,* Columbia CS 9708.
"Twenty-One Years." Lester McFarland and Robert Gardner, *Mac and Bob,* Birch 1944.

THE WORKING MAN

"Auctioneer." LeRoy Van Dyke, *LeRoy Van Dyke's Greatest Hits,* MCA DL 75346. Brenda Byers, *The Auctioneer,* MTA MTS 5013.
"Black Land Farmer." (Out of print.)
"Busted." Johnny Cash, *Blood Sweat And Tears,* Columbia CS 8730, CL 1930. Burl Ives, *Burl,* Decca DL 74361.
"Cotton Mill Colic." Dave McCarn, *Singers of the Piedmont,* Folk Variety Records.
" 'Leven Cent Cotton, Forty Cent Meat." J. E. Mainer, *The Legendary J. E. Mainer With Red Smiley and the Blue Grass Cutups,* Rural Rhythm RR JE 198.
"Louisiana Man." Doug Kershaw, *The Cajun Way,* Warner Brothers WS 1820. Jerry Lee Lewis, *She Still Comes Around (To Love What's Left Of Me),* Smash SMA SRS 67112.
"Mississippi Delta Land." Johnny Cash, *The Johnny Cash Show,* Columbia KC 30100.
"Mule Skinner Blues." Jimmie Rodgers, *My Rough And Rowdy Ways,* RCA LPM 2112. Bill Monroe, *Bill Monroe's Greatest Hits,* MCA 17.
"Nine Pound Hammer." Bill Monroe, *Bluegrass Ramble,* Decca 74266. Johnny Cash, *Blood, Sweat And Tears,* Columbia CS 8730, CL 1930.
"Oney." Johnny Cash, *Any Old Wind That Blows,* Columbia KC 32091.
"Roughneck Blues." (Out of print.)
"Six Days On The Road." Dave Dudley, *The Best Of Dave Dudley,* Mercury SR 61268. Bud Brewer, *Big Bertha, The Truck Driving Queen,* RCA LSP 4746.
"Sixteen Tons." Tennessee Ernie Ford, *Country Hits Of The '50's,* Capitol ST 885. Jerry Reed, *Hot A' Mighty!,* RCA LSP 4838.
"These Hands." Jimmy Dean, *These Hands,* RCA LSP 4618. Hank Snow, *The Best Of Hank Snow, Vol. 2,* RCA LSP 4798.
"Truck Driver's Blues." (Out of print.)
"Weaveroom Blues." (Out of print.)

COWBOY SONGS

"Back In The Saddle Again." Gene Autry, *Gene Autry's Hall Of Fame Album,* Columbia CS 1035.

"Blood On The Saddle." Tex Ritter, *An American Legend,* Capitol SKC 11241.

"Carry Me Back To The Lone Prairie." Eddy Arnold, *Cattle Call,* RCA LSP 2578. Sons Of The Pioneers, *Lure Of The West,* RCA LSP 2356.

"Cattle Call." Eddy Arnold, *The Best Of Eddy Arnold,* RCA LSP 3565. Slim Whitman, *The Song Of The Old Waterwheel,* Imperial LP 12102.

"Cimarron." Johnny Bond, *The Best Of Johnny Bond,* Starday SLP 444. Bob Wills, *Bob Wills, The Living Legend,* Kapp KS 3587.

"Cool Water." Sons Of The Pioneers, *Cool Water,* RCA LSP 2118. Marty Robbins, *Gunfighter Ballads & Trail Songs,* Columbia CS 8158.

"Dusty Skies." Bob Wills/Tommy Duncan, *Legendary Masters,* United Artists 9962. Hank Thompson, *Hank Thompson Salutes Oklahoma,* Dot DLP 25971.

"I Want To Be A Cowboy's Sweetheart." Patsy Montana, *Patsy Montana,* Birch 1951.

"Last Roundup, The." Sons Of The Pioneers, *Cool Water,* RCA LSP 2118. Burl Ives, *Songs Of The West,* Decca 74179.

"Oklahoma Hills." Hank Thompson, *The Best Of Hank Thompson,* Capitol DT 1878. Jack Guthrie, *Country Hits Of The '40's,* Capitol ST 884.

"Strawberry Roan, The." Marty Robbins, *Gunfighter Ballads And Trail Songs,* Columbia CS 8158. Sons Of The Pioneers, *Legends Of The West,* RCA LSP 3351.

"Take Me Back To My Boots And Saddle." Gene Autry, *Gene Autry's Country Music Hall Of Fame Album,* Columbia CS 1035.

"Texas Plains." Stuart Hamblen, *A Man And His Music,* Lamb and Lion LLC 4001.

"Tumbling Tumbleweeds." Gene Autry, *Gene Autry's Greatest Hits,* Columbia CL 1575. Sons Of The Pioneers, *Cool Water,* RCA LSP 2118.

"When The Bloom Is On The Sage." Burl Ives, *Songs Of The West,* Decca 74179. Sons Of The Pioneers, *Lure Of The West,* RCA LSP 2356.

"When The Work Is Done Next Fall." Doc Watson, *Doc Watson On Stage,* Vanguard VSD 9/10. Richard Kraus, *Square Dances With And Without Calls,* RCA LE 3004.

TRAVELING SONGS

"Brakeman's Blues." Jimmie Rodgers, *This Is Jimmie Rodgers,* RCA UPS 6091.

"Bumming Around." Willis Brothers, *Bummin' Around With The Willis Brothers,* Starday SLP 442. T. Texas Tyler, *The Hits Of T. Texas Tyler,* Capitol ST 2344.

"City Of New Orleans." Hank Snow, *Grand Ole Opry Favorites,* RCA APL 10162. Mac Wiseman, *Concert Favorites,* RCA LSP 4845.

"Fireball Mail." Roy Acuff, *Roy Acuff And The Smoky Mountain Boys,* Capitol DT 1870. Osborne Brothers, *The Osborne Brothers Bobby & Sonny,* MCA DL 5356.

"Freight Train Blues." Elton Britt, *Sixteen Great Country Performances,* ABC Records S 744. Roy Acuff, *Roy Acuff's Greatest Hits,* Columbia CS 1034.

"Golden Rocket, The." Hank Snow, *Souvenirs,* RCA LSP 2285.

"Hobo Bill's Last Ride." Jimmie Rodgers, *Train Whistle Blues,* RCA LPM 1640. Hank Snow, *The Jimmie Rodgers Story,* RCA LSP 4708.

"Hobo's Meditation." Jimmie Rodgers, *The Short But Brilliant Life Of Jimmie Rodgers,* RCA LPM 2634. Hank Snow, *Hank Snow Sings Jimmie Rodgers,* RCA LSP 4306.

"I'm Movin' On." Hank Snow, *Souvenirs,* RCA LSP 2285. Hank Thompson, *Hank Thompson Sings The Gold Standards,* Dot 25864.

"Lost Highway." Hank Williams, *The Very Best Of Hank Williams, Volume 2,* MGM SE 4227. Sue Thompson, *This Is Sue Thompson Country,* Hickory LPS 148.

"Me And Bobby McGee." Roger Miller, *The Best Of Roger Miller,* Mercury SR 61361. Bobby Bare, *I Need Some Good News Bad,* Mercury SR 61342.

"Night Train To Memphis." Roy Acuff, *All-Time Greatest Hits,* Hickory LPS 109. Grandpa Jones, *Grandpa Jones Sings Hits From Hee Haw,* Monument 18131.

"Orange Blossom Special." Johnny Cash, *Johnny Cash At Folsom Prison,* CS 19639. The Rouse Brothers, *The Railroad In Folk Singing,* RCA Vintage LPV 532.

"The Poor Tramp Has To Live." Stoneman Family, *Stoneman's Country,* MGM E/SE 4453.

"Streamlined Cannon Ball." Roy Acuff, *Great Train Songs,* Hickory 125. Hank Snow, *Lonesome Whistle,* RCA Camden CA S2513.

"Tennessee Central Number Nine." Roy Acuff, *Great Train Songs,* Hickory 125. Floyd Cramer, *Floyd Cramer Goes Honky Tonkin',* MGM 4666.

"Train Whistle Blues." Jimmie Rodgers, *Train Whistle Blues,* RCA LPM 1640.

"Wabash Cannon Ball." Roy Acuff, *Roy Acuff And The Smoky Mountain Boys,* Capitol 1870. Mother Maybelle, *Mother Maybelle Carter,* Columbia KG 32436.

"Waiting For A Train." Jimmie Rodgers, *Never No Mo' Blues,* RCA LPM 1232. Hank Snow, *The Jimmie Rodgers Story,* RCA LSP 4708.

"Way Out There." Sons Of The Pioneers, *Cool Water,* RCA LSP 2118.

"Wreck Of Number Nine, The." Doc Watson, *Ballads From Deep Gap,* Vanguard S 6576. Jim Reeves, *Tall Tales and Short Tempers,* RCA LSP 2284.

"Wreck Of The Old '97." Johnny Cash, *All Aboard The Blue Train,* Sun LP 1270.

STORY SONGS

"Ballad Of Forty Dollars." Tom T. Hall, *Tom T. Hall,* Mercury SR 61211. Osborne Brothers, *The Osborne Brothers Bobby & Sonny,* MCA DL 5356.

"Big Bad John." (Out of print.)

"Blizzard, The." Jim Reeves, *Jim Reeves On Stage,* RCA LSP 4062. Johnny Cash, *Mean As Hell,* Columbia CS 9246.

"Carroll County Accident." Porter Wagoner, *The Best Of Porter Wagoner Volume 2,* RCA LSP 4321.

"Coat Of Many Colors." Dolly Parton, *Coat Of Many Colors,* RCA LSP 4603. Norma Jean, *I Guess That Comes From Being Poor,* RCA LSP 4745.

"El Paso." Marty Robbins, *Marty Robbins' All Time Greatest Hits,* Columbia KG 31361. Tompall & The Glaser Brothers, *Great Hits From Two Decades,* MGM SE 4888.

"Kaw-liga." Hank Williams, *The Very Best Of Hank Williams,* MGM SE 4168.

"Leona." Stonewall Jackson, *The World Of Stonewall Jackson,* Columbia KG 31411. Mel And The Statesiders, *Thank You For Being You,* MGM S 4907.

"Long Black Limousine." Jody Miller, *The Best Of Jody Miller,* Capitol ST 11169. Dottie West, *Makin' Memories,* RCA LSP 4276.

"Long Black Veil, The." Lefty Frizzell, *Lefty Frizzell's Greatest Hits,* Columbia CS 9288.

"May I Sleep In Your Barn Tonight, Mister?" Charlie Pool, *Charlie Pool And The North Carolina Ramblers,* Vol. II, County 509. Wilf Carter, *Walls Of Memory,* RCA Camden CASX 2490.

"Mother, The Queen Of My Heart." Jimmie Rodgers, *Jimmie The Kid,* RCA LPM 2213. Stonewall Jackson, *The Great Old Songs,* Columbia CS 9708.

"Mother Was A Lady." Jimmie Rodgers, *My Time Ain't Long,* RCA LPM 2865.

"Ode To Billy Joe." Bobbie Gentry, *Ode To Billie Joe,* Capitol ST 2830. Tammy Wynette, *The First Songs Of The First Lady,* Epic KEG 30358.

"Philadelphia Lawyer." Wilma Lee And Stoney Cooper, *Family Favorites,* Hickory LPM 106. Tennessee Ernie Ford, *Sixteen Tons,* Capitol DT 1380.

"Saginaw, Michigan." Lefty Frizzell, *Lefty Frizzell's Greatest Hits,* Columbia CS 9288.

"Son Of Hickory Holler's Tramp, The." Johnny Darrell, *Giant Country,* United Artists 6745.

"Streets Of Baltimore." Charley Pride, *Charley Pride In Person,* RCA LSP 4094. Tompall & The Glaser Brothers, *Great Hits From Two Decades,* MGM SE 4888.

"Tennessee Stud." Eddy Arnold, *Thereby Hangs A Tale,* RCA LSP 2036. Osborne Brothers, *Osborne Brothers,* Decca 75271.

"Year That Clayton Delaney Died, The." Tom T. Hall, *Tom T. Hall's Greatest Hits,* Mercury SR 61369. Sonny James, *Sonny James Sings The Great Country Hits Of 1972,* Columbia KC 32028.

Index of Songs